ALSO BY DANNIKA DARK:

THE MAGERI SERIES

Sterling

Twist

Impulse

Gravity

Shine

The Gift

MAGERI WORLD

Risk

NOVELLAS

Closer

THE SEVEN SERIES

Seven Years

Six Months

Five Weeks

Four Days

Three Hours

Two Minutes

One Second

Winter Moon

Seven Series Companion: An Insider's Guide

SEVEN WORLD

Charming

THE CROSSBREED SERIES

Keystone

Ravenheart

Deathtrap

Gaslight

Blackout

Nevermore

Moonstruck

Spellbound

Heartless

Afterlife

Quicksilver

Evildoer

Forevermore

Crossbreed Series Companion: An Insider's Guide

THE BLACK ARROWHEAD SERIES

The Vow

The Alpha

THE CROSSBREED SERIES COMPANION: AN INSIDER'S GUIDE

DANNIKA DARK

First Print Edition 2023
ISBN: 9798374725278

Edited & proofread by Victory Editing.
Cover design by Dannika Dark. All stock purchased.

www.dannikadark.net

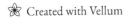 Created with Vellum

THE CROSSBREED SERIES COMPANION:
AN INSIDER'S GUIDE

USA TODAY BESTSELLING AUTHOR
DANNIKA DARK

CONTENTS

DEAR READER,

This is the official series companion for the *USA Today* bestselling Crossbreed Series by Dannika Dark. Contained within are spoilers to the series. This special insider's guide includes detailed character bios, author notes, quotes, a glossary, Breed facts, two new bonus short stories, and more!

A lot of love went into this series. I began working on it when the Seven series success was peaking. I had recognized the ending of that series was coming and really wanted to get my hands dirty with writing a gritty urban fantasy. Raven was a street-smart girl with survival skills and misdirected talents. Crossbreed allowed me to explore more Breeds in an exciting new way by featuring a cast who represented different Breeds and talents.

These characters will always remain close to my heart. I watched them evolve, and their voices and thoughts are always tumbling around in my head. This insider's guide offers an exclusive look at everything that went into the process of designing the covers, creating the characters, and Easter eggs you might have missed.

Enjoy!

PREFACE

The heart of the Crossbreed series has always been good versus evil, and this goes deeper than the plots.

Raven is a lost soul who kills nefarious criminals and enjoys it. She is angry and disgusted by the world of Breed after it chewed her up and spit her out. Her justice is swift and without mercy. She's especially protective of humans, and though she is no longer one of them, she can't relate to the Breed world. Unable to return to her old life, Raven is at the end of her rope. She sees herself as a monster, far removed from the human she once was. Even after joining Keystone, Raven struggles with whether she's fundamentally good or bad. The lines are blurred, and with each case, it becomes more difficult to tell where everyone belongs. Especially when Houdini, her Vampire maker, reappears in her life.

Fletcher (Raven's Mage Creator) is easy to place over on the dark side. We learn his motives, and we understand that he is evil to the core of his being. Throughout the series, Houdini proves more difficult to assess. While he has done wicked things, he justifies his actions with plausible reasoning, including Raven's creation. He wants to convince her that good and evil don't exist, that there's only action, reaction, and chaos.

Raven knows she's on the right side of the law. She's taking out criminals and preventing others from becoming victims. The trouble is, she enjoys it far too much. She's also reluctant to accept her Vampire nature. She associates it with evil and darkness, part of that stemming from her maker's apathy to the pain he's wrought on her.

It's easy to write a series where immortals kill with relish, but what happens when you give them a conscience? What does a new immortal struggle with, and how—if at all—do they overcome these inner conflicts? In Crossbreed, they're not just battling foes but also their personal demons.

While this is Raven's journey, let me make it very clear that each of them influences the other. They all have room to improve even if that means trusting more or opening up. At some point, all of them grapple with the choices they've made. They question themselves. What do they stand for? What are they willing to sacrifice?

There are people in our lives who are guiding forces—good and bad. Without them, we may never be capable of learning, growing, and becoming. So this was a journey for all of Keystone, including Switch, Kira, and even Crush.

Each member of Keystone is an outcast. Viktor found people who had nothing to lose and gave them a purpose in life. Left to their own devices, there's no telling where they might have wound up. He gives them structure and directs their misplaced talents and/or aggression toward something good. He helps them recognize that they can make thoughtful choices that don't just serve themselves. Part of that is getting them involved in charity donations, transporting kids to safe locations, and rescuing victims. This tremendous opportunity had a healing effect as all of them had endured a painful past that stole away their dreams. Forging a bond with a group of people who accepted them when no one else would, allowed each member to open themselves up to love, friendship, and happiness.

The Crossbreed series enabled me to add many complex layers to this dark world. Immortality isn't glorified. Breed are not more or less civilized than humans. They've spent centuries warring with one another. They fear power and shun those who are different. Crime is rampant since they don't have the ability to build prisons without exposing their world to humans. While there is wonder and magic, there is also darkness that stems from greed, jealousy, and power. That imbalance inspires some to make their world better.

Why have I chosen to keep their world secret?

Long ago, some humans knew about Breed. Fearing that power, they sought to kill them. For Breed, it was hard enough having to fear attacks among their own kind. Humans also found ways to use and exploit their powers.

While there are many distinct types of Breed, they are fundamentally different from humans. They created lies surrounding their limitations and abilities to confuse humans and even to frighten them. Eventually, especially with elders and Councils beginning to form, they retreated. It made survival possible.

In the modern world, they have to create jobs and work hard to remain in the shadows. Most see the absolute necessity since humans would never embrace them if they knew what they were capable of. No one wants war if it means bringing ruin to their businesses, family, and everything they've worked hard for.

But a few factions desire war. They're tired of hiding and want to create chaos because that might also mean dismantling Breed authority and all the institutions that currently hold them back from rising to power or committing crimes more freely. For this reason, the higher authority and all forms of Breed law consider deliberate attempts to expose their world treasonous.

The Crossbreed series is not about the Keystone members finding a normal life again. They have chosen the path less traveled. But they can find their own version of happiness along the way.

Note: Some Breeds, such as Gemini, are still a mystery. It was also mentioned in the Crossbreed series that a number of less common supernaturals exist. While this book contains a detailed breakdown, I have focused on the primary Breeds introduced in my world to date. Should there be any expansion in my world for new and existing Breeds, it will be in future books to come.

Dannika Dark owns the intellectual property rights of all unique creations within the Mageriverse.

Once upon a midnight dreary...

PART I

THE BOOKS

The Crossbreed series is a continuing storyline. While each book has its own separate plot, there are story arcs that span the series, so they must be read in order.

Crossbreed series reading order:

- Book 1: *Keystone*
- Book 2: *Ravenheart*
- Book 3: *Deathtrap*
- Book 4: *Gaslight*
- Book 5: *Blackout*
- Book 6: *Nevermore*
- Book 7: *Moonstruck*
- Book 8: *Spellbound*
- Book 9: *Heartless*
- Book 10: *Afterlife*

- Book 11: *Quicksilver*
- Book 12: *Evildoer*
- Book 13: *Forevermore*

If you're looking for the suggested chronological reading order of *all* the books in my universe, head over to my website.

KEYSTONE

BOOK 1

Word count: 99,794
Published: January, 2017
First chapter line: "Mmm, just like my mom used to make," I said, choking on my disgust as I unlatched my mouth from the whiskery neck of a Mage.
Last line: "Starlight, star bright..."

Epigraph:
Once upon a midnight dreary...
— *Edgar Allan Poe*

Summary: Raven Black hunts evildoers for fun, but her vigilante justice isn't the only reason she's hiding from the law. Half-Vampire, half-Mage, she's spent years living as a rogue to stay alive. When a Russian Shifter offers her a job in his covert organization hunting outlaws, dignity and a respectable career are finally within her grasp. The catch? Her new partner is Christian Poe—a smug, handsome Vampire whom she'd rather stake than go on a stakeout with.

They're hot on the trail of a human killer who will stop at nothing to get what he wants. One misstep during her probationary period could jeopardize Raven's chance at redemption, and her partner would love nothing more than to see her fail. Will Raven find the courage to succeed, or will she give in to her dark nature?

AUTHOR'S NOTE:

I wrote *Keystone* immediately after the Mageri series back in 2010. This was prior to publishing anything. I wanted to write a completely different protagonist while exploring what happened to Christian Poe after he left the Mageri crew. The first draft collected dust for many years until I pulled it out six years later to see if there was anything worth pursuing. Not all written work is meant to be published.

After reading the first draft, I decided there was enough there to pull together an interesting series. But it would require a huge rewrite. I had the bare bones of a story but lacked an overall series arc, which I had to develop. I also needed to do more than just flesh out the characters—some of them were ultimately deleted from existence. I got rid of a Vampire who didn't add to the story, and I also didn't want too many Vampires in the same house. Gem was originally a male, but I didn't like the character, so I did a complete rewrite and kept the name. There were too many males and not enough talented ladies, so in walked Blue.

When it comes to characters, I'm always fascinated by the outliers. The defects. The lost souls. Raven is a crossbreed that's unheard of—part Vampire and part Mage. Instead of giving her both gifts equally, I created limitations. The all-powerful angle didn't fit the story or serve the character. Often in life, we learn to make do with what we have. Some of her gifts are subdued, some are absent. She also has unique abilities, such as her immunity to impalement wood, Chitah venom, and stunners.

In the first book, it's unclear if Raven will fit in with this organization. She's a rogue who doesn't trust anyone, especially Breed, and she's never had to work with a partner, let alone a team. But her unpolished skills are exactly what Viktor's looking for.

Raven views nefarious criminals as menaces that deserve no mercy. While she was hired for her specific talents, many criminals are handed over for trial, and that's a hard pill for Raven to swallow. Niko points out that some people have the potential to change their ways. After all, each member of Keystone has a dark past.

The only way she's going to acclimate to this new way of life is to train with Niko and Christian so she can understand her limitations and abilities. It's important to remember that Learners and younglings live with their respective makers for a reason: figuring out how to use Breed gifts takes practice and a good teacher, something she's lacked this whole time.

Before Viktor came along, Raven lived on autopilot as a rogue. Her death was faked, and she couldn't return to the human world as Breed. Even going back to her father was impossible since it would put him in danger, but she also didn't want him to see her as a monster. She didn't think he could possibly understand. In the last years of her human life, their relationship was strained.

With no place to go and no knowledge of how to get a job in the Breed world without giving up her secrets, this posed an interesting question of how one might survive. Raven was reduced to living like a feral animal—abandoned, alone, and isolated. She lived under constant fear that the Breed authorities would discover her and end her life since her very existence was an abomination. She built a wall around herself. During those years of struggle, she never let go of her anger, and it manifested into something dark. That's the impression I wanted readers to have of Raven from the very first paragraph.

The real turning point in *Keystone* is the scene when she draws sunlight through her fingertips for the first time and heals herself. It was an awakening for Raven. She held on to so much fear and uncertainty about her place in the world and her future, but the moment she healed herself, another healing took place. It's the first time she truly accepts her life as an immortal instead of cursing it. Raven glimpses a light at the end of the tunnel, but her journey is far from over. While this wasn't the life she had imagined for herself, it was no longer bleak. If she can learn to let go of the rage and resentment for what happened to her, she might be able to move forward down a new path.

Nothing comes easy. You can't expect an untrusting person who has been deceived to suddenly obey without question. You can't expect a person who has experienced trauma to change the way it influenced their personality, choices, and way of thinking. Pain is invasive, and sometimes it's not easy to recognize all the different areas of our life that it's affecting.

This is what makes Viktor a special guy. He knows how to recognize the potential in someone. He expects a lot from his team, but he's also willing to listen. Over time, his rigid ways become more flexible, but not at the expense of his integrity. These lost souls must all learn to work together cohesively—each a teacher, each a student.

That's how I saw the natural progression of this series. A lot of self-analyzing and growth.

RAVENHEART

BOOK 2

Word count: 104,898
Published: May, 2017
First chapter line: "Either that's snow falling, or Wyatt's fed me one of his magic mushrooms again."
Last line: "Aye, Precious. I'll stay for as long as you want."

Epigraph:
Oh, what a tangled web we weave,
When first we practice to deceive!
— *Walter Scott*

Summary: Two weeks after joining Keystone, Raven Black is ready to take on the world as a criminal hunter for hire. If only her partner wasn't a bloodsucking Vampire with a penchant for getting under her skin. Despite her lavish surroundings, Raven misses the freedom of life without rules. And Keystone's next assignment is about to test her self-control in more ways than one.

Dead bodies are popping up in the human district, and all signs point to a Breed serial killer. In order to catch him, Raven and Christian embark on a mission that takes their partnership into uncharted waters. Lives are at stake. Can Raven trust her instincts, or will she fall into a web spun from lies and deceit?

Time is running out in this pulse-pounding tale of dark secrets, murder, and forbidden desires.

AUTHOR'S NOTE:

Every Crossbreed book features a different villain and plot, and *Ravenheart* has the team tracking down a serial killer. Not all of them are scary dudes who live in the shadows. Some are model citizens who are highly intelligent, hold good jobs, and may also have an active social life. That was the type of villain who interested me for this story—the one you would least suspect.

First off, let's talk about the shopping trip at the department store. I feel like the best balance in a good action book, particularly one that has a lot of deep and troublesome topics, is to throw in some crazy-ass high jinks. Because most Breeds live and work around their own kind, nothing highlights just how different they are from us like throwing them into a human environment. One perk of not leaving my story in the hands of a publisher: I don't have to cut out every scene that doesn't further the plot. Moments like these are great opportunities to get to know the characters, to see them in a different light. It was also the perfect way to highlight how Raven related to humans in the beginning, and by the end of the series, we see how much she's changed. I tried to put one of those scenes in every book, whether it's at a mall or grocery store. I love imagining Shepherd roaming the aisles with a cigarette hanging out of his mouth while store clerks explain why he can't cook the popcorn in the store.

You gotta love him.

In *Ravenheart*, we go relic hunting with the team. Part of their job involves scouring Breed resale shops for illegal weapons and collectibles. Raven finds an interesting puzzle box with the inscription THE DEVIL LIES WITHIN written in another language. Inside is a key that becomes important to her Vampire maker, whom we officially meet in a later book. There were a lot of moving parts that I had to keep track of in this series. I knew where I wanted to go with the key story, so I kept my notes continually updated as I added more information. It was tedious but worth it.

Raven is used to going after a certain criminal type, so she never saw this villain coming. Not until after he asks her out on a date, which is hilarious.

Great. I finally meet a nice guy, and he turns out to be a serial killer.

We also learn what happens when Raven drinks Vampire blood. I didn't want Raven to know everything about her gifts out of the gate. While she's been on her own for several years, she hasn't explored all her abilities and limitations as a crossbreed. Part of that was her reluctance to accept her Vampire half.

The side story involved a ghost witness who helps them out. Wyatt interacts with this specter, who makes a deal with him. He'll get rid of all the spooks in the house if they'll let him help solve their case. You see, this ghost is different. He wants to help—he knows he can be useful. Wyatt wouldn't normally rely on a ghost, but since he was around the crime scene, it seems like a win-win.

Mageri fans: You can read more in the *Spoilers* section under *The Goodie Bag* about this ghost, but holy shit. This was one of those beautiful moments where I tied up a loose end from a previous series. I never thought of it as a loose end, but this book gave me an opportunity to dig deeper into that story and give it the closure it deserved.

Even for readers who don't know John the ghost's true identity, he allowed us to see another side of things, and that was really special.

We've heard about Wyatt's abilities as a Gravewalker, but John revealed what it was like on the other side as a lost soul. We also see what Gravewalkers have to deal with and how the other side lives. Or doesn't live.

Most of us have a collection, whether it's figurines, rocks, coins, plants, cars, or books. Raven has been acquiring souvenirs from some of her cases. One is a diary that belonged to a victim of the killer they're hunting. It was important to me to not put all the focus on the killer. I wanted to humanize the victims, and Penny's diary and Raven's connection to it was a great way to do that. Raven became obsessed with reading about Penny's life and her one true love, so her death felt personal. These were all people, not just a name or number on a list. Thanks to Penny documenting everything important in her life, we also learn about her killer.

What made me hate the villain even more was knowing that Penny just wanted to find love again. All of us just want to go about our lives and pursue happiness, but there are always those who want to rip that away and leave a path of destruction. Penny had a lasting impact on Raven. Even in the final scene of the book, Raven wonders if she'll ever have anything remotely close to what Penny and Lachlan shared. Even though her story met a tragic ending, Penny experienced a love that Raven suddenly envied.

DEATHTRAP

BOOK 3

Word count: 104,220
Published: September, 2017
First chapter line: "So this is the place you keep raving about?" Christian asked, running his dark gaze over the diner and giving it a judgmental stare.
Last line: "Then I'll catch you."

Epigraph:
We are each our own devil, and we make this world our hell.
— *Oscar Wilde*

Summary: For Raven Black, hunting criminals is second nature. So is denial. It's not easy moving forward with one foot stuck in the past. But a new case offers her a much-needed distraction when Keystone accepts their toughest assignment yet—to track down an elusive criminal who's selling children on the black market.

Their investigation leads them deep into the underbelly of the Breed world, a place both treacherous and enticing. With no room for mistakes, Raven makes a tough decision to lock the door to her past before it interferes with her job. The only trouble? Christian holds the key.

The stakes are high, and a shocking twist turns everything on its head. Will they catch this criminal before more lives are lost? Find out in the latest edge-of-your-seat installment of the Crossbreed series.

USA Today Bestseller

AUTHOR'S NOTE:

Every book I've written brings back memories. *Deathtrap* is action-packed, and I remember writing a lot of intense scenes. The ticking bomb, Raven and Christian chasing a Mage on foot, the infamous car-surfing scene with Raven holding on to the roof rails, exploring the underground tunnels and secret world beneath the Bricks, Christian getting shot in the ass with impalement wood, and I loved the scene with them jumping off the bridge. Raven can't swim, so there's that moment of trust with Christian. This one has all the fun, nail-biting scenes I love to write, but it's also when Raven and Christian's relationship takes a serious turn.

Shepherd is also at the forefront of this story when he starts working with Patrick Bane, a member of the higher authority. Since Shepherd did him a good turn, Patrick is helping him get information on a Mage. But Shepherd's life flips upside down after Patrick's boy, who always wears a mask, takes an accidental selfie. Shepherd knows it has to be his son. All this time, Shepherd assumed his baby died along with his woman.

We also learned an important detail in *Deathtrap*: Christian saved Raven's life as a child. This knowledge created the emotional shift in their relationship that was needed. Sharing one's soul can be far more intimate than anything physical. This also showed Christian how his one act of kindness had a ripple effect, and the realization has a profound impact on him.

Raven also shares a memory about a guy she had a crush on as a teenager. Part of that story involves her father, and imagining how those scenes played out only furthered my desire to work Crush into the series. There was no way in hell a guy like that was going to slip by without introducing himself, and this seemed like the perfect book to make that happen. Raven wants to accept her life, but she can't move on without seeing her father one last time. She never got a chance to say goodbye or end things the way other people did before becoming immortal. Since her father thinks she's dead, Christian will have to scrub his memory of the entire conversation. I could have let it go that way and ended Crush's storyline right then and there.

Didn't seem right.

Crush knowing about Breed made sense. He's been around, runs with a wild crowd, and served in the military. He forms strong bonds and is a loyal friend, so I could easily see how he might have forged a friendship with a Shifter or two. That's why he didn't flip out when Raven told him what she was. I decided when Raven left the trailer, Christian and Crush could work things out privately, leaving our protagonist in the dark. Crush wants to keep his memory of Raven. Believing she had died nearly killed him, and he can't live like that. He won't. Knowing his baby girl is alive means the world, and he won't let any man take that away. Yet there was nothing Crush could have offered Christian to change his mind—nothing except revealing that he's a trusted human.

With everything happening in this book, the MoonPie scene was the most fun to write. Humor mixed in with a good action scene is always a favorite combination.

GASLIGHT

BOOK 4

Word count: 118,224
Published: February, 2018
First chapter line: When people harbor dark secrets, they close off their emotions.
Last line: "If that be the truth, then ruin me, Precious. *Ruin me.*"

Epigraph:

He who fights with monsters might take care lest he thereby become a monster. And if you gaze for long into an abyss, the abyss gazes also into you.
— *Friedrich Nietzsche*

Summary: Vampire trafficking is a sinister business, and nobody knows that better than Keystone. After Raven discovers hidden clues in a cold case, the group sets a trap in hopes of catching an elusive criminal. But when the plan backfires, Raven's world is thrown into chaos, and Christian's loyalty is put to the ultimate test.

Buried secrets come to light, and the only thing keeping Raven grounded is her insatiable thirst for vengeance. The stakes are high as they travel to a place where the landscapes are as treacherous as the immortals who live there. This time, there's no room for mistakes.

Will Raven have the courage to tame the violence in her heart before it swallows her whole?

USA Today Bestseller

AUTHOR'S NOTE:

Gaslight was a tough one to write. The key to understanding why Raven became the person she did after her making lay with both her Creator and maker. Showing is always better than telling even if it took us to some dark places. How would Raven cope when confronted with her past, looking at it without all the naivety of a human?

Keystone gets their first staff member. Kira arriving in a crate— there are just no words. Traveling by crate was once commonplace among Shifters in order to travel safely. With her never having been on a plane, there was no way to predict if Kira would get scared and shift. Being confined in a crate makes Shifters feel safe, and their animal is less likely to come out.

The first time Kira meets Shepherd, she's not afraid of him. They have several unremarkable interactions. It's not until the moment he walks into the kitchen shirtless after a workout that Kira freezes up. It appears that she's intimidated by his muscles or the scars all over his body, but when Shepherd touches a pan she drops, he feels her fear. After that, he makes a concerted effort to be nice to her. I love when I know how a story will unfold far in advance. It allows me to leave breadcrumbs throughout the books. Some readers pick up on them, some don't. But I always have a little side story unfolding.

In *Gaslight*, they're searching for a mysterious Vampire who's trafficking younglings. Unfortunately, their plan to capture him backfires. Raven has no idea until it's too late that Houdini is actually the one setting the trap. When he restores her memory, Raven realizes they've met many times before. With each encounter, he scrubs her memory afterward. Finding out that Houdini has been playing with her mind not only reveals a lot about his character, it also illustrates why so many in the Breed world don't trust Vampires.

I named this book *Gaslight* to show how Houdini can easily get in Raven's head. It's one of his many talents. Gaslighting is psychological manipulation. It's not always easy for victims to recognize when they're being gaslighted. They question their sanity, their memory, and their perception of the world around them. Even if they suspect someone is doing it to them, they might still question whether it's really happening. Their perception of the truth has been altered, and that's what happened to Raven. She was never allowed to build her opinion of Houdini because he made her forget everything. She couldn't even remember his face. It's easy to see how he could have talked her into being immortal in the first place—how he could have made it sound perfectly reasonable to not only fake her death but to go to the morgue.

We also meet Fletcher and get the full picture of what Raven endured after her creation. When Raven meets a woman who gained Fletcher's trust, she sees what her fate might have been had she never escaped. What can fear do to a person, and how far will one go in order to make their suffering stop?

The real kicker was when Houdini restored her memories of every time they met. Raven remembered how affable he was—how well they got along. It made her question what evil looks like. Is he a villain or just crazy? Houdini doesn't believe his intentions are malicious, and that adds a layer of fuckery to their relationship.

Before Raven leaves him, Houdini once again steals some of her memories away.

But this time not ones of him.

Raven losing memories of Christian was never meant to be permanent. While it's upsetting, this is Houdini we're talking about. *Of course* he would have seized the opportunity to meddle and see what happens.

The story moves to Newfoundland, and it's always fun when I can get Keystone out of the city and into a new environment. From the thrilling plane jump to meeting Crazy Joe, I really enjoyed writing those scenes. With the heavy material early in the book, I saw a chance to insert more humorous moments and bring some of that tension back down.

This is also the first book where Christian and Raven are intimate. Some readers wonder why I waited so long, but slow burns are worth it. They needed to build that trust between them naturally. That enabled them to not only share their bodies but their emotions. Some of my favorite conversations between them come *after* the steamy stuff.

BLACKOUT

BOOK 5

Word count: 108,784
Published: August, 2018
First chapter line: I dug my knee into the Sensor's neck, pinning his unshaven face even harder against the concrete.
Last line: "I knew you'd come home, Cookie."

Epigraph:
These violent delights have violent ends.
— *William Shakespeare*

Summary: The fate of millions rests on Keystone when they embark on their most important assignment of all...

After what was supposed to be a simple job, Raven and Christian uncover a sinister plot against the higher authority, and the stakes are as high as the body count. The assassins are merciless, with anyone who stands in their way becoming collateral damage. Meanwhile, Raven is still struggling to make sense of her feelings for Christian following a memory wipe.

During a blackout, the city erupts into chaos. With Breed on the brink of war, Keystone has only twenty-four hours to complete a secret mission. Raven seeks help from the most unlikely of places, but at what cost?

It's a race against time to save lives in this explosive installment of the Crossbreed series.

USA Today Bestseller

AUTHOR'S NOTE:

Christian Poe in a cassock. After that visual, most of us needed to take a long bath in holy water. I thought posing as a priest would be something he would have fun with, like when he found himself listening to people's confessions.

Christian and Raven take a step forward in their relationship by going on a real date. When they show up at the restaurant, things don't go as planned.

Do they ever?

After management snubs them, Christian gives her a memorable evening on a rooftop. That's the tone I wanted to set between these two. They have an unconventional relationship, and it works best when they're true to who they are.

So back to the plot. Someone is targeting politicians, and Keystone is in charge of protecting them. The location moves to a church, and there are questions as to who might be behind the murders. Sometimes I make the villain obvious from the start, and other times I like my characters to uncover the truth. In this case, they never see it coming. Immortals recognize the danger that would befall them if they expose themselves to the human world. The modern century isn't ready to learn that Breeds with immense powers live among them. Men like Patrick Bane want humans gone, and the first step toward achieving that goal is to eliminate those who support human rights. Who does he hire to help? Niko's enemies.

And the plot thickens.

This was also a tragic ending for Hooper. While his relationship with Gem wasn't honest, his death underlines the risk they take in forming friendships or relationships. The Keystone team is constantly creating new enemies, and because of that, they bring danger to anyone they care about.

Christian and Houdini finally confront each other. Houdini stole some of Raven's most meaningful memories of Christian and every intimate conversation that they'd had. Vampires can selectively remove and change memories, many of which are the fabric of who we are. It's hard to know what or who we would be without our memories.

Let's talk about Houdini stirring the pot by telling Raven how Christian originally bought that ruby necklace for another woman. This segues into secrets that Christian has kept about her father. She's understandably upset when she finds out. Can she ever trust him? All relationships are tested, and theirs hits a roadblock at the end—especially with some of Raven's memories gone. They need to work out their issues and find out what matters in order to see where they stand. That's why the next book, *Nevermore*, is more reflective as Raven takes a break to examine their relationship.

We also meet the infamous Lenore in the epilogue. I don't think of this as a cliff-hanger since there is no action scene that requires resolution. It's merely a teaser of what's to come. Raven can't be the only one battling ghosts from her past.

NEVERMORE

BOOK 6

Word Count: 106,192
Published: January, 2019
First chapter line: Nobody gave hugs like Crush.
Last line: "It's enough, Christian. It's enough."

Epigraph:

No man chooses evil because it is evil; he only mistakes it for happiness, the good he seeks.
— *Mary Wollstonecraft*

Summary: Raven returns to her childhood home to rebuild her severed relationship with her father. After a long year of capturing violent criminals and thwarting assassination plots, she could use a vacation.

But trouble is brewing on the home front. When Raven discovers her father is in financial peril, she's determined to set things right even if it means sacrificing her heart in the process. Meanwhile, her relationship with Christian is on shaky ground when a skeleton falls out of his closet. Will they be able to leave the past behind, or is the trust between them dead and buried?

When the bonds of love are put to the test, only the courageous will prevail.

USA Today Bestseller

AUTHOR'S NOTE:

While *Nevermore* is full of action and drama, the primary focus is between Raven and her father. Raven is prepared to live without going back to her old life, but when she discovers that Christian and Crush are keeping a big secret, all bets are off. So she takes a break from both Christian and Keystone to figure things out and decide what matters in her life.

I loved exploring her origins. Not just her childhood home but the man who raised her. The heartfelt scenes between her and Crush are among my favorites. Now that Raven's an adult, she realizes her father needs her just as much as she needs him, if not more. He's not in the greatest health or living his best life. They're both dysfunctional, but the love is there.

Backstory is important. We learn about characters through their memories or conversations, but here we get the chance to step into Raven's life and understand how she got from point A to point B. Through their relationship, we see a softer side of Raven. The cruelty she endured in her early years of immortality hardened her, but the true source of her relationship hang-ups goes back to her childhood. Mind you, she lived in a house filled with love, but there's a lot to unpack here. Because of the mistakes she and her father made in the past, they're trying to figure out a new normal.

We also learn more about Christian and Lenore's past relationship. Honestly, I enjoyed every moment of building her character into one that goes from questionable to downright loathsome.

Nevermore wasn't about throwing Christian and Raven's relationship in peril. It was about her reconciling with her past. In her eyes, if she couldn't fix what was wrong between her and her father, every future relationship was doomed to fail. What mattered most was mending fences... *and* saving Crush's ass from a psychotic loan shark.

While there wasn't a case to solve, there's plenty of suspense and danger. Crush was doing just fine getting himself into mortal danger without Raven's help. Despite their imperfect relationship, she loves him fiercely and will do anything to protect him. Love is more important than money, material things, or even one's pride. What she's willing to do for someone she loves goes above and beyond and reveals her true character. Life will test us, and only then do we know what matters.

We see more of Lenore here as a woman who not only helps Raven out but tries to give her advice. It's an important storyline because it shows how immortals sometimes have to put away any personal feelings in order to gain favor with others. Favor trading is important, and you can't burn every bridge. I also took the opportunity to show readers how clever Lenore is in manipulating people and planting ideas in their heads. It's important to see this in action so we better understand how Christian was able to fall under her spell so many decades ago. And despite how he feels about her, he knows that you have to play along with people like that so they don't feel threatened and cornered. That's when a wild animal is most dangerous.

There was also a pivotal moment when Christian and Raven came clean with Viktor regarding their relationship. Well, Christian revealed it in the form of a big tattoo that will forever mark him. If you read the Mageri series, you know why that scene was a tremendous declaration of his love. Christian has always had opinions regarding tattoos, and it showed how influential Crush was. Even if the two were constantly quarreling, Christian paid attention to something Crush said about Raven and tattoos.

This was the book that not only moved their relationship forward but also her life.

MOONSTRUCK

BOOK 7

Word Count: 115,894
Published: June 2019
First chapter line: Of all the pawnshops in Cognito, Pawn of the
Dead sold some of the rarest antiquities I'd ever seen.
Last line: "You're my home, Precious. Always will be."

Epigraph:
The most sublime act is to set another before you.
– *William Blake*

Summary: Transporting goods is part of the job, but when Keystone
accepts the daunting task of moving precious cargo, the team splits up.
Raven has orders to follow, but Christian's seductive ways draw out her
violent soul. Their journey is dangerous, their enemies ruthless, and
one misstep could prove fatal.

When one team member mysteriously vanishes, the rest must
choose between cutting their losses in the face of chaos or seeing it

through to the bitter end. Will Keystone have the fortitude to complete the mission, or will they fall like dominoes?

United they stand, divided they fall.

USA Today Bestseller

━━━━━

AUTHOR'S NOTE:

Moonstruck not only takes us away from Cognito but also separates the team. I wanted the group to be out of their element on a different type of assignment. We're used to seeing them take down criminals, but there are many other aspects to their job. This story introduces Potentials in the series and provides details on how some of those orphans are protected. Most people don't know about Potentials or believe that they exist, yet there's been an underground movement set in place to ensure they're kept safe.

This book gave me an opportunity to work on Niko's story. I'd already introduced his archenemies early on, which have remained a constant threat to the Keystone team. Niko has always been a powerful figure, but everyone has a story. We learn about the control they once held over him, and it breaks my heart to think about the humiliation he suffered long ago simply because he had no other options. The plan was to split the book so Niko could also face his enemies, but afterward I realized I needed to wrap things up in a separate book to give Niko and Gem the extra time they deserved. They are a positive influence on each other, and we still hadn't learned everything about Gem.

You see, the characters joined Keystone so they could forget their past. Viktor offered them a clean slate without any obligation to divulge the details of their history—not unless they chose to. In time, each character opens up to someone. While they all had partners, that wasn't necessarily the person they could confide in. Every single one has several moments in the series where we learn more about them. They each made a connection with someone and, because of that, were able to reveal more about themselves to the reader. In *Moonstruck*, we see a bond forming between Niko and Gem.

As for Shepherd, this is the first time he's had to leave his son home alone. Shepherd is faced with the uncertainty of whether he can offer constant protection with such an unpredictable job. This is where I was able to work Switch in. He stays at Keystone on a trial period, but I think Shepherd needed more to feel good about the decision. So placing Switch in a dangerous situation allowed him to prove that he can not only serve as a tutor but also as a protector. Even though we don't have a lot of deep moments with Switch, he still plays an important role in the series. He's a friend to Raven, a teacher to Hunter, and a guardian to all. Working for Keystone is a step toward rebuilding trust within his community.

I didn't plan on Matteo, but some characters just hop into a scene and remind me that I'm not always the one driving the car. I wasn't quite sure what his purpose was, but after his intimate kiss with Blue, I knew it wouldn't be the last time we'd see his face. Blue had a story yet to be told, and Matteo would be the one to pull it out in a future book.

While I love the strangeness and diversity of Cognito, it's equally thrilling to spend time in new cities and locations. I researched the regions, looking at maps and videos in order to accurately stage each scene. The train they took was fictional, but the highways, tunnels, and towns were not.

As for the children they were transporting, one of them was a defiant teenager who didn't want to be shielded from life. She was in love and insisted on choosing her own path. How readily would orphaned Potentials accept their fate to live in an isolated location even if it was for their own protection? As for the sanctuary, I didn't want it to feel like a prison. These children would grow up as trusted humans, regardless of what fate they would one day choose for themselves.

Because of that, it was important that their first experience in the Breed world be a positive one. A place where they can flourish and learn—a home that encourages hard work, creativity, and play. These kids have no one but each other, so if the protectors didn't build an environment where the Potentials could find happiness and feel safe, there would be too many runaways. After all, the kids are sacrificing their freedom. With the right guidance, once they turn eighteen, they'll be better prepared for the life ahead of them.

I love that it's not just Raven's story with a supporting cast; they all have their own personal stuff to deal with. Blue becomes permanently scarred, and Niko's fate is in question. They all face important choices and sacrifices, including the secondary characters.

Moonstruck also had one of the most dangerous sex scenes. I have zero regrets.

SPELLBOUND

BOOK 8

Word Count: 54,734
Published: November 2019
First chapter line: The wind howled against Gem's bedroom windows, and a flash of lightning illuminated the darkened room.
Last line: "For the first time in my life, I finally can."

Epigraph:
Mastering others is strength.
Mastering yourself is true power.
– Lao Tzu

Summary: Niko is caught in a powerful spell that was cast from the very book he sought to protect. Trapped between life and death, his chances of returning look grim.

Gem is determined to set things right. Armed only with her innate knowledge of language, she begins her daunting quest to break the diabolical spell... no matter the cost. When an irreversible action unleashes a new threat, Keystone scrambles into action. Lives are at stake as the team scours the city in search of an elusive foe.

A bond forged in secrets. A courageous sacrifice. Will Gem succeed at her daring attempt, or will she inadvertently destroy them all?

USA Today Bestseller

AUTHOR'S NOTE:

Spellbound was initially planned to be a novella (standard word count is usually 17,500 to 40,000 words), but when the writing began, it grew large enough to qualify as a short novel. There was a lot that happened in *Moonstruck* with Niko and Gem's storyline that I couldn't resolve in that book alone, so the story continues in *Spellbound*. Packing it into one of Raven's books would have pulled readers out of her story.

While Niko is a central part of *Spellbound*, this is also Gem's moment to shine. She takes extreme action to save Niko, but when it throws him under a spell, she's forced to confront what she's done.

To be clear, I was never going to kill Niko. That's not a story arc that ever changed. I know readers were holding their breath throughout the series, wondering who might be my target. After all, Keystone lives dangerously. Yet, despite the obstacles each has faced, they're committed to sticking around. What separates them from the herd is that they've chosen a hard life. They could easily walk away, but they don't.

For Gem, this was her finest hour. She's a sharp Relic who chose to become a Mage, and yet she's afraid of her own power. Because she doesn't know how to control it, *everyone* is afraid of her gifts. When she decides to destroy the spellbook, her courage and loyalty are put to the ultimate test. Only she has the power to do it, but everyone doubts her. She accepts the sacrifice, which I found touching, given her back-story. Gem values her life, but she's willing to give it up if it means saving Niko or anyone else who might become a victim of the spellbook.

Gem also meets Mary, a Relic who specializes in energy disorders. Even though Mary doesn't appear again in later books, she plays a vital role in Gem's development. Gem was never able to master her power as a Wielder. Destroying the spellbook was a first step, but she realized later how someone like Mary can help her work through her issues. Not every immortal is perfect. Some have defects, and others were never taught how to use their gifts properly. Why shouldn't there be group therapy for Breed? Since Relics each have different knowledge, this was a unique chance to show how one woman is helping others with her professional insight.

With Niko's archenemy still out there, I was able to split up the team. Niko and Gem could have more alone time to forge their new friendship. The experience bonded them, and they revealed things about themselves that they hadn't confided to anyone else.

While action and romance are fun, I love digging into the meat of a character and facilitating their personal growth.

HEARTLESS

BOOK 9

Word Count: 129,674
Published: June, 2020
First chapter line: Ruby's Diner was one of those old-fashioned joints that stood frozen in time, and tonight it was lit up like a pinball machine.
Last line: "There's hope for me after all."

Epigraph:

We often give our enemies the means of our own destruction.
– Aesop

Summary: Despite the spoils of a solid relationship and an idyllic life at Keystone, Raven is itching for the thrill of another big case. Things begin to heat up when a dangerous assignment falls in her lap.

Searching for the mastermind behind an illegal fighting ring is no easy feat, but as the weeks roll by, Raven's undercover job begins to take an unexpected emotional toll. It's a deadly mission, and if she's not careful, she could lose everything.

AUTHOR'S NOTE:

I'd wanted to do an undercover assignment for some time. Little did I know how tough this one would be. Dirty politicians, cage fights, and then throw Chaos into the mix.

On occasion, I've fallen in love with tertiary characters. Usually I have to restrain myself from making their role even larger than it needs to be so it doesn't detract from the story. But sometimes that guy or gal will give me a wink, sparking curiosity to know more about their life. That's how I felt about Raven's coworkers, Simone and Flynn. They were wildly interesting, and in another world, they might be the protagonist in their own story. Even Pablo hooked me in more than the primary villain, but that had to do with his backstory surrounding one of the dead girls. Despite how that storyline played out, I had no sympathy for the man.

He made his bed, and he had to lie in it.

Let's talk about cage fighting since it's something I've mentioned in the Seven series. It's definitely a dark aspect of the Breed world, one steeped in a lot of Shifter history. *Heartless* allowed me to show how a modern-day operation works. Especially from the perspective of voluntary fighters and those who recruit them.

Even though Fletcher isn't in the picture, it's not always realistic to have characters bounce back from trauma as if nothing happened. Sometimes the past grips you when you least expect it. For Raven, seeing the BDSM around her was unexpectedly triggering, so she started drinking to get through the night. Houdini took notice and decided to teach her a lesson by spiking the bottle with sensory magic. His little chaos experiment made a bad situation worse.

Meanwhile, Viktor and Lenore are getting chummier. Remember when she said a little bird told her something about the fights being more than just a money venture but also a way to have politicians in their pocket? That little bird was Houdini. Those were the bread-crumbs I left that weren't obvious, but how else would she have gotten inside information? Lenore saw the bust as an opportunity to knock officials out of their seats and replace them with trusted allies. It was all part of her long-term plan to secure her rise to power.

Most of the villains up to this point have been male or a powerful Breed. Audrey is a Sensor whose customers are exclusively rich men and politicians. She's very business savvy and discovered that servicing those who cared about their good name would offer her more protec-tion. Every villain needs a motive, and for Audrey, she had disdain for Shifters. Many in the Breed world share her views—especially the older ones. Having Shifters tear each other apart in cage fights wasn't good enough, so she took it a step further. Audrey catered to a specific crowd who didn't want to see Shifters fighting each other; they wanted to see Shifters dominated by another Breed.

Villains are fascinating because no two are alike. Revealing their thought process or even backstory isn't about creating sympathy but offering insight to their actions so that they're more dimensional. Some are driven by hate, fear, jealousy, money, or revenge. Other characters are weak and get swept up in a crime after affiliating themselves with the wrong person. In *Heartless*, there are varying levels of villains at play.

Speaking of villains...

Lenore finally steps into the spotlight and makes her intentions known. Burying people seems to be her signature move, and it makes you wonder how many other people she's put in the ground. Christian was the only person she ever trusted to do her bidding and commit murders on her behalf. He had given her what no one else had: uncon-ditional loyalty. Lenore believes she can control him again, only this time without all the emotional attachments he once had. While her servants carry out her orders, they aren't killers, let alone fighters. You can't buy absolute loyalty. She needs Christian, and only Raven stands in the way. Lenore would prefer to do away with Raven permanently, but she doesn't have anyone she can trust with that task. Burials aren't technically murder, so that's her best option. She believes that once Raven is out of the picture, she'll have Christian within reach.

And that, my friends, is why Lenore earned the title of this book.

AFTERLIFE

BOOK 10

Word Count: 110,709
Published: May, 2021
First chapter line: "Who wants cake?"
Last line: For now.

Epigraph:
The difficulty in life is the choice.
– *George Moore*

Summary: Only a week after solving their last case, Raven is itching for a new assignment. In her downtime, she's focusing on the two most important men in her life: her father and Christian. But there's no rest for the wicked.

When an old friend seeks Raven's expertise on a delicate matter, Viktor reluctantly accepts the case. But without evidence of a crime, they might have no choice but to walk away, even if that means countless bodies filling the graveyard. Dark secrets, evil forces, and an unexpected visitor will keep you on the edge of your seat.

If only the dead could talk.

AUTHOR'S NOTE:

Shifters are the target in *Afterlife*. It takes some digging before Keystone figures out what the victims have in common. The villain is portrayed as the least likely to be a villain. After all, he's a primary contact who's helping out with the case. But what makes a guy like that tick?

Emotional baggage. Graham developed serious issues with Shifters after extreme bullying he suffered as a kid. You'd never know it to look at him, especially since he works with Shifters. One particular incident took away his ability to have children. Most villains tend to be either powerful, rich, or dangerous. I enjoyed writing a weasel like Graham into the story. Relics possess the gift of knowledge, so they're not the first person we single out as the bad guy. Most immortals don't fear them since they have no special abilities that are physical threats. They're more likely to be involved in secret lab experiments than random murders. When I create a villain, I need to understand what drives them. Were they always evil, or was it a gradual process? Do they see their actions as evil? Without that information, their role makes no sense. And because Raven's journey of finding her place in a world of good and evil was pivotal to her story arc, it was an angle I couldn't ignore. She gains more understanding in seeing the wrong choices others have made and how some were ruled by their emotions.

An unexpected courtship unfolds in this story. Not just between Viktor and Lenore. Matteo (the Chitah we met in *Moonstruck*) shows up with the sole intention of winning Blue as a mate.

Well, Blue's not having it.

Both Matteo and Blue have suffered a similar loss, but Blue chose a different path in life. Matteo's presence allowed me to reveal Blue's story, and it was a doozy. I ache for this woman and the unimaginable pain she carries. Her tough, somewhat aloof personality should now make more sense to readers. Blue keeps people at arm's length for a reason, and it's not a weakness or a flaw. It's simply self-preservation. Not just from the trauma of losing the most cherished people in her life but also from being deceived by two men she trusted.

While I could have had her confide in Viktor or one of the team members, the storyline with Matteo felt more organic. Oftentimes it's easier to reveal our secrets to a stranger than someone we know. Their story also ended with no hard feelings. Matteo had to learn that not everyone has the same life goals. His actions were premature even for his own path in life. While his heart was in the right place, his reason for courting her wasn't going to heal his soul.

But Blue isn't the only character experiencing growth in this story.

One thing I'll say about Wyatt Blessing is that he reveals his story piece by piece. By the end of the series, we know everything we need to about him. Not just about his past but his thoughts on relationships and kids. In *Afterlife*, Wyatt has a near-death scare. This moment is gripping not just because he almost died but also because Wyatt has always tried to avoid death and danger.

And then comes this beautiful scene where he risks his life to save a child—one he doesn't even know. Moments like those reveal a person's true character, and Wyatt is more compassionate than we give him credit for.

Regarding our villain: Graham had no remorse for the lives he'd taken. He was so driven by his own pain and anger that he didn't give any thought to the pain he caused others. Though we don't get to know much about all the victims, Blue's backstory allows us to connect with their loved ones, who have to cope with the unexpected loss, pain, devastation, and anger. Losing someone we care about changes us, especially when it's sudden or they're a victim of violence. Even Blue admits that she didn't truly understand the purpose of her life until she almost died herself.

The word *afterlife* has a couple of meanings. One is life after death. Another is the latter part of someone's life. I approached this book as one that puts more focus on the survivors—how everyone manages their pain differently when dealing with loss. For Graham, he chose to use his pain as a reason to inflict more in the world. For the members of Keystone, they chose a different path—one where they could save those children and make a difference in their lives. Everyone has suffered in some way, but it's what we do with that pain that matters most.

QUICKSILVER

BOOK 11

Word Count: 134,563
Published: March, 2022
First chapter line: A gala invitation should have been thrilling, but the immortals in our social circle didn't throw raucous celebrations with rock music, cheap beer, and delicious barbecue.
Last line: "And you're my king."

Epigraph:
He who does not punish evil, commands it to be done.
– *Leonardo da Vinci*

Summary: In the world of crime fighting, Raven has learned that formal affairs are a necessary evil. So when Keystone receives an invitation to a winter ball, she tries to make the best of it. The most powerful elites in Cognito are attending—a perfect opportunity to network and have a few drinks. But when a guest hijacks the party in a violent display of dark power, chaos ensues.

It's a race against time as Raven searches for a way to thwart his diabolical plan. Will Keystone find the fortitude to prevent the downfall of civilization? Or will they bow to a new king to save their souls?

"And a terrible curse befell the winter ball."

AUTHOR'S NOTE:

Quicksilver took time to write. Like many people, I was still recovering from the aftermath of 2020. Even though it's a time when people need artists more than ever, stressful and emotional phenomena like that can impact the creative process. It was also important to get the story right, so I didn't concern myself with how long it took to complete. When I started the first draft, I wasn't certain if this would be the final book. But once I established the plot, I quickly realized that another book was needed to wrap up everything with Lenore, Houdini, and Fletcher in a way that wasn't rushed. By the end of *Quicksilver*, I'm certain most readers had had enough with Lenore getting away with everything.

Quicksilver gave me access to explore more magic within the Mageriverse. I've always left just enough wiggle room to expand in new ways. Here we meet a Mage who has acquired more power than should be permitted. Sparrow's not only a Unique but also a Stealer *and* Infuser. The clear abuse of his gifts is a shining example of why immortals once hunted their own kind. Breed are afraid of those who have power that few understand. It's another reason most aren't willing to disclose what their rare gifts are to others. Anything that might be too rare or a powerful combination could make them a target.

We kick off the story with a bang. In some of the books, I've built up to the main conflict. But in *Quicksilver*, I wanted all the cards on the table from the first chapter.

When the team and many prominent immortals are cursed, they're initially in a state of shock and disbelief. It's a common reaction when something happens so quickly that you haven't had a chance to fully process the ramifications. They now exist in a realm between the living and the dead, and while they have some new abilities, they're also losing something far more valuable. It isn't until later that Raven realizes what it would mean if she's no longer visible to humans: she would lose her father. Lose their conversations, their hugs, their kisses, their time. Bringing those two back together in the series had a tremendous impact on her life, and I wanted readers to feel her desperation and fear at the prospect of losing him.

This curse could also mean the end of the Keystone organization. They chose not to join Sparrow, which means they could be cursed forever. Better that than be called traitors. But not everyone will make the same choice; fear drives people to do desperate things. Others from the party are already giving Sparrow their fealty so they can live again. No one knows how the curse will evolve over time, and Shepherd is growing nervous at the idea of losing Hunter.

After I developed the central plot, I had to set the book aside and come up with a list that I fondly refer to as the "dead rules." So much was unfolding about this shadow realm, and I knew if I created rules as I went along, it might force me to go back and do massive rewrites. Therefore, I created a list of their abilities and limitations in the realm that would be known by the end of the book. Obviously Houdini will dwell in this realm for potentially the rest of his immortal life, so we won't know anything beyond Raven's experience. Because they still had physical form, I didn't want them to have the same experience as specters—unseen by all. Sparrow used his power to create an existence between the living in the dead, so it required its own set of rules. I briefly considered making them invisible to everyone except one another, but that would dissolve the conflict if they could simply walk through the front doors of Keystone undetected. I also didn't want to separate Raven and Christian more than necessary.

After defeating Sparrow, Raven finds herself in a quandary when she's tempted with the opportunity of acquiring infinite power.

Permanently.

The all-powerful protagonist is a common trope in fantasy. Even when I created my Breed world, I made sure that each Breed had flaws or limitations. What would that level of power mean to Raven? Well, it would disrupt her life in a big way. People often believe more money and more power solves problems when, in fact, it creates more. She would always have a target on her back and so would Keystone for as long as she remained with them. The Mageri might not even permit someone like her to exist when they got wind of it. Especially given her background and the fact she could have let Sparrow's power go.

While others could offer their two cents, it was a decision only Raven could make. She had to weigh the pros and cons and think ahead. The fact she took time to think it out shows how much she's changed. Raven used to be ruled by her emotions, and desire is a pretty strong one. More power wouldn't give her an easier life. In fact, given how young she is as a Mage, it could corrupt her.

We also saw glimpses of Raven's potential. When we first met her, she was a diamond in the rough. While she was fearless, determined, ferocious, and intelligent, she was about as unpolished as they come. She didn't even understand her own power. Now she's weighing decisions carefully and thinking about how every action shapes her future. In the many years to come, as the world changes, I see her rising to power.

For now, she just wants to enjoy what she has, learn more about her natural abilities, and forge a path as a crossbreed. She's not settling; she's taking the time to grow, and I think that's admirable.

EVILDOER

BOOK 12

Word Count: 126,496
Published: November, 2022
First chapter line: I never thought the dead would drive me out of my own home.
Last line: "My heart will always be yours, Precious. Forevermore."

Epigraph:
The woods are lovely, dark and deep,
But I have promises to keep,
And miles to go before I sleep,
And miles to go before I sleep.
– *Robert Frost*

Summary: Raven has come a long way since joining Keystone. She embraced her Vampire side, learned to work with others, and even fell in love. But how far is she willing to go for the greater good?

When Viktor receives an anonymous tip regarding the whereabouts of the most notorious oligarchs in the Breed world, Keystone's courage is put to the test. The stakes are high—one wrong move could have catastrophic consequences. In a shocking turn of events, Christian's recent disappearance reveals secrets that could ruin him. The past is finally catching up, and Raven is faced with her greatest decision yet —one that could seal her fate forever.

Will Keystone deliver the justice these men deserve, or will the cost be greater than the reward? Find out in this powerful conclusion to the Crossbreed series.

The hardest demons to conquer are often our own.

AUTHOR'S NOTE:

Deception. Now we finally know what secret Christian's been hiding. When Raven discovers Christian's dirty little secret that he's kept chained in the woods, her world spins off its axis. This storyline was many books in the making. We've often seen Christian as a man of control. Holding Fletcher hostage is a prime example of how he reverted to his old ways of fixating on revenge. I'm sure it started out as a great plan, but as time went on, Raven began to move on and get in a better place.

That left Christian holding the bag. Initially he wanted to wait until he felt like she could understand his actions of hiding Fletcher from her. Deep down, he knew that the longer the game went on, the more he would feel like a monster. He needed Raven to validate his actions by exacting her revenge. In some ways, Christian wants Raven to come to his level. But part of his growth has been through Raven. Even though he has more experience in the Breed world, he doesn't always make the most well-thought-out choices. When it comes to Christian and Raven, there is no one power player in the relationship. I wanted them to be equals in that both are flawed and both have something to teach the other.

Raven is initially upset with Christian. *Upset* is an understatement. She's pissed. They had agreed not to keep secrets. Christian spent months upon months torturing this man, and when Raven found out, he wasn't sure if she would understand or see him as a monster. He needed her to validate his actions through violence.

By the end of this series, I wanted Raven to be the one pulling Christian into the light. At the start of their journey, Christian is a guide. He helps her become not only stronger but more knowledgeable about the way their world operates. Raven has struggled with her own darkness throughout the series, all while Christian encouraged her to embrace it. Christian has lived in the shadows for all his immortal life, associating his wicked deeds with his Vampire nature. In walks this woman who not only accepts him for who he is but inspires him to be a better man. She gets him to think about his choices and how they might impact their future together. She makes him realize he doesn't have to choose between light and dark; he can choose both. Being a kind man doesn't make him less of a Vampire, nor does it make him weak.

I never wanted to write a normal romance between these two. What they have is complicated and doesn't follow the same rules as everyone else. Their job makes it impossible to have anything conventional. Aside from that, how they choose to love is largely based on their own personal experience (or inexperience) with navigating relationships.

The most important ingredient when developing a romance is staying true to the characters. I've done this with every couple I've written. Some have conventional happy endings and some don't. Compromises are sometimes made. I do what's best for the characters based on a number of factors. Love is the main ingredient, but the recipe is different every time.

Since book one, Raven has struggled with figuring out if she's good or evil. In her old life, it was easy to distinguish right from wrong. But in the Breed world, there are a whole lot of grey areas. After escaping her abusive Creator, she became a vigilante. She killed nefarious men for sport. Always Breed. She didn't feel a part of this new world, so that's how she dealt with her rage. Then she gets a job working for an organization that essentially does the same thing, only they get paid. Isn't murder still murder? Does enjoying the act make it wrong? In *Evildoer*, Raven is led in different directions and forced to choose a path. Through all the villains in the series, we see how readily a person can go down the wrong road. In *Evildoer*, the title could have easily been about her. It shows how much influence Viktor and Keystone has had on her.

A perfect storm is brewing in this series finale, and the primary archenemies are coming to the fore.

Finally.

And we're not talking about the oligarchs. That storyline had Keystone accepting a deadly case—one that tested their loyalty. But it also led them straight to Lenore.

I realize many readers wanted her to burn in a lake of fire. I get it. She was always meddling and getting away with everything. Lenore had rough beginnings, living in times when women didn't hold power, and power is the only form of protection. She created a social network and found a safe harbor with the rich and powerful. But her resentment for men polluted her motives. When she opened herself up to love, it nearly killed her. In fact, it changed her. She completely closed off her heart so that people were either a stepping stone, an obstacle, or a puppet.

There are moments in the series when she relates to Raven, and these are honest moments. Lenore sees herself in Raven, and that scares her. Raven isn't someone she can easily control, though she tries. Lenore sees everyone as a tool, and when she no longer has use for them, she throws them away. Like she did with Viktor. In the previous book, she even had plans to eventually do away with Godfrey. *Quicksilver* revealed her true thirst for power in a desperate moment. It tempted her so much that she finally crossed a line in *Evildoer* by organizing a plan to steal an obscene amount of money that would guarantee her all the power she desires.

In the end, Lenore got what she deserved.

Then there's the other character that loomed over most of the series. Houdini. He was always a grey character. You don't truly know his motives. Is he evil? Is he capable of redemption? Does he want it? Truth be told, Houdini doesn't see himself as either. He doesn't form emotional connections with people the way we do, and that makes him dangerous. Houdini views life abstractly and only does things to serve himself or feed his curiosity. In the end, I wanted him to do something that was both ruthless and yet selfless. The idea of staking Lenore and passing her over appealed to his curious nature. What might his progeny do if given the very gift she wished for?

This wasn't a moment of redemption for Houdini. He's done unforgivable things, and more importantly, he did them to Raven. You can't trust his motives. Did he hand over Lenore because she betrayed him, or did he do it because he wanted to make things right with Raven? Maybe he just wanted to see what would happen, because that is so Houdini.

His giving her land would further add to her confusion, and that's what he enjoys. Raven is left to wonder if it was an apology or just another way to link them. You could spend a lifetime trying to understand a man like him and never come close. But I do think he wants her to succeed in life. He mentored Lenore, invested in her success. While this angle was never mentioned, I think Houdini played a vital role in Lenore's mindset. While she was already on a path to power, I have no doubt that Houdini used his influence on her. You saw him doing that throughout the series with Raven. I'm sure he enjoyed watching Lenore surreptitiously wreak havoc in everyone's lives. He taught her well.

Until she made the mistake of targeting Raven.

Houdini is possessive of his things, and he knows Lenore won't stop until she gets what she wants. If she's made enemies with Raven, it's only a matter of time—something immortals have an abundance of. Even if Raven hadn't made that wish outside the Mexican restaurant, Houdini would have done away with Lenore. He had no intention of letting the monster he created destroy something that belonged to him. While he could have asked her to stay away from Raven, that would have been a favor trade, and Houdini doesn't like to be in anyone's pocket.

While Houdini has created a number of Vampires, Raven fascinates him because she's like him—a crossbreed. She held a mirror up to his face and challenged his views. Not because she cared, but to see if it was possible for him to change. She needed to believe that at least one of her makers wasn't a complete lunatic.

Raven has battled demons throughout the series, so the choice she faces in the end will live with her forever. Killing her Creator and Lenore could have far-reaching consequences because of the Breed's rigid laws. It's hard to keep secrets in the Breed world, especially when Vampires can pick your brain. I'm proud of our girl. The villains got what they deserved, and now Christian and Raven can walk away with a clear conscience.

Raven was a very dark character at the beginning of the series. She was living on the streets, begging for scraps, and killing at will. The way she was brought into the Breed world was cruel and filled her with resentment. Her isolation became a black hole. That isn't who she always was—it's who she became through circumstance. All those layers are peeled away through Viktor, Keystone, reuniting with her father, and falling in love. At the end of the series, she lets go of the hostility and fear, allowing her to fully embrace her power. The key to her strength and understanding isn't hardening her heart but opening it, even if that makes her vulnerable. And all that is put to the test when Raven has to pull herself together after Christian is staked and winds up on the operating room table.

I almost wrote that scene from Christian's point of view, but I didn't want to get graphic. We already knew how traumatic the event was without explicit details, visuals, and especially the horror of experiencing it. This was Raven's moment to show her steadfast love and unwavering devotion. She made decisions on his behalf and stood by his side. She gave her blood and ordered Shepherd to remove his memory of pain.

Villains were a central theme in *Evildoer*. New and old. What makes a person become a villain? Most that we've seen in the series were incapable of love or suffered trauma. At some point they made a conscious decision to hurt others for their own gain.

Raven almost went down that path. Hers was a journey to understanding how her choices can positively or negatively impact herself and others. Often in ways not imagined. In the end, she's no longer ruled by her emotions. She's able to make thoughtful decisions. The Breed world can be dark and full of wickedness, but Raven finally realizes she doesn't have to choose between living in the dark or the light. She can walk through darkness, allowing her wisdom and courage to light the way.

FOREVERMORE

BOOK 12.5

Word Count: 36,642
Published: May 2023
First chapter line: After straightening the white tulle on my dress, I emerged from the dressing room.
Last line: "Home. Let's go home."

Epigraph:
Love is composed of a single soul inhabiting two bodies.
— Aristotle

Summary: Keystone's planning an unforgettable wedding, but there's only one problem: the groom is missing. To top that off, the father of the bride is out of town, leaving Raven to wonder if destiny has screwed her over once again. Despite the setbacks, she's full steam ahead—even if that means showing up at the altar alone.

Hilarious antics ensue as readers catch up with their favorite characters. A high-octane chase, a tattoo gone wrong, and a stunning surprise. Will Christian pledge his eternal love, or has the twice-burned Vampire gotten cold feet?

The series ending you've been waiting for.

AUTHOR'S NOTE:

I adored writing this novella. Readers may ask why I didn't include the wedding in *Evildoer*. For starters, it didn't flow with the storyline. It would have also been a distraction many chapters after the main plot ends. When I write the last novel in a series, it's important that the series arc is complete. I want readers to walk away with a clear understanding of the hero's journey and the story arc.

But ask yourself: did you really think I would offer up the prospect of a wedding without delivering?

I was dying to write it!

Forevermore has no villains. Unless you count Flash, but he's more of an obstacle. I pack everything we love about the characters into novellas. They are the cherry on top, so I want them to be sweet. Each one I've written serves an important role in the story and also allows me to wrap up a few loose ends. This one is no different. It was a wonderful peek at the Keystone crew and a completion of the love story that blossomed between Raven and Christian.

First of all, I hope no one is left with the feeling that Kira's story is unresolved. It's not. She has chosen to remain with Keystone for protection, and it's also in her best interest to keep her secret. Now that we know the history of phoenixes, we understand that her fear is justified. Even though she's socially cut off from the team, she loves her job. She loves Hunter. She has Viktor to talk to and Shepherd to confide in. Perhaps their friendship will grow stronger over time. Kira is safe, happy, and enjoying a life of privacy. I didn't want to end the series without giving her someone she could trust and bond with. Otherwise, we would be left with a feeling of her being ostracized from the group. Shepherd stood up for her and convinced Viktor to start paying her a salary. Now that she's not an indentured servant, she has options. But for now, Keystone is where she needs to be.

Same with Switch. Hell, same for all of them. They found more than just a job with Viktor's group—they found a second chance.

My favorite part was creating a wedding that was perfect for this particular couple. Anything too traditional wouldn't work. Raven didn't even want a big ceremony to begin with. That's why everything became a last-minute effort. Raven is a brave and fearless woman, so I enjoyed showing the terror she was feeling. It makes her more relatable because tough or not, we all experience similar anxieties, doubts, and that little annoying voice in our head that never seems to shut the hell up.

I didn't need to write an outline for this book, but I had several ideas I wanted to include. One of them was my favorite: the infamous car-chase cake scene. Shepherd has a short fuse and is known to go ballistic. So when he catches sight of the guy who made off with his wedding gift, he gets tunnel vision, completely forgetting about the cake in the back of the van.

While it ruined a beautiful wedding cake, those little disasters make life memorable. Sometimes you just have to roll with it and have a good laugh, so I think Raven appreciated the substitute cake even more.

Remember the graveyard scene where Wyatt is off in the distance, sitting by a gravestone and talking? I revealed his backstory in previous books regarding a human he once loved. When she died, her spirit stayed behind and slowly went mad. While I don't provide details about whether her spirit was actually there or if Wyatt was just speaking to her headstone, that's what that scene was about. Wyatt was visiting someone he loved, probably reminded of her more than ever after the wedding ceremony.

Initially my plan was to have Raven buy a new house for Crush. Crush doesn't ask for much. He's happy, especially now that he has his daughter back and a beloved dog. But I wanted him to have something special by the end of the series. He's a blue-collar worker who has busted his ass, overcome addiction, served in combat, suffered loss, and frankly deserves something life changing.

After Raven got the tattoo, it was clear that Christian had nothing to give back with sentimental value. She's not materialistic, so he had his work cut out for him. Why not have him build a home on her property? For one thing, it would be difficult to pull that off next door without her knowing. But I don't think Christian would take away her involvement in designing and building their home. So I flipped the idea of Raven giving Crush a gift to make it Christian's gift to both of them.

Because he was busy and didn't want to raise any suspicion, he fell out of touch. That created a little tension with Raven wondering if he might have cold feet. His disappearance was also important in underlining the trust between them. While Raven is having the usual wedding jitters, she never once doubts Christian's faithfulness and love. Their job requires a level of trust since they might be out of touch for long periods or have to work undercover. Her only concern is whether they rushed into this union too fast.

One thing Christian had to consider was Crush's wishes. He wasn't the kind of guy who would appreciate an insincere gesture. It was important for Crush to remain close to not only his job but also his friends. Uprooting him to a new location wouldn't make him happy, so an upgrade was the best solution. Even though Crush is an older man, it doesn't mean he can't have new things to look forward to. He has a tendency to cling to the past. His furniture is a prime example of that. I wanted to give him a better living environment that would not only be safe but also a place he could look forward to coming home to. Crush deserved an HEA, just not in the way of a female companion. Now he has more room, comfortable living, a fenced-in yard for Harley, and one hell of a son-in-law.

Christian put thought into the design. He also made sure absolutely nothing was thrown out, including a pair of dirty socks on the floor. Building this house wasn't an attempt to buy Crush's love; it was a chance for Christian to win his trust.

I'll be honest—I didn't know what to do with Crush midseries. At one point, I considered killing him off. Not because I didn't love him to pieces, but I wanted to figure out his value to the story. Sometimes a character's death helps facilitate character growth with someone else. It didn't take long before I realized he was essential in Raven's growth and healing, which was an ongoing work in progress. Killing his character would have been a massive setback for her.

Crush isn't the easiest guy to relate to, but he's genuine. He's overcome a lot, including the belief that his daughter had died. I wanted Raven and Crush to start over as adults. They had a lot to work through. We see how protective he is. While Christian has done a lot for Raven, Crush wants to make sure this is the best guy for her. Just because you love someone doesn't mean you're the best choice for them. He learned that from his own failed relationship, and he didn't want to see his only daughter settle for less. It takes some effort on Christian's part, but Crush soon realizes his daughter is in good hands.

We can't look back on the series without talking about Hunter Moon, our brave little man. He experienced a traumatic beginning, and we don't know the full extent of the conditions he lived under while staying with Patrick. That's often the reality for many adoptive parents. I wanted to focus less on his past and more on how he's coping in his new environment. How he's working hard every day, learning, and yet still dealing with separation anxiety from Shepherd. Sometimes he has nightmares. Shepherd is still figuring out how to navigate through all this. He doesn't make Hunter go to bed alone if he's upset. He doesn't tell him to stop crying. Most importantly, he's not trying to fix him. Total acceptance is critical in Hunter's recovery.

Hunter requires a lot of structure because that often provides a sense of security. He's also learned that while there are rules, he doesn't have to fear punishment. The team makes him feel useful, like when they're fixing things and Hunter gets to hold the tools. They still need to guide him through his emotions, but otherwise, Hunter is free to be who he wants to be. If he wants to wear pink socks or butterflies on his shoes, Shepherd is going to make it happen. This kid never had a real childhood. He grew up fast and learned how to wield his gifts much sooner than most Sensor kids his age.

Hunter also has selective mutism. He's been known to whisper in people's ears, but he chooses not to use his voice. That's all he's known. Likely he was once punished for speaking loudly or out of turn. Switch decided that teaching him (and everyone in the house) sign language was the best approach. Once Hunter learns to write better, he'll be able to communicate in whichever way makes him comfortable. That will help him build better relationships. Hunter's a smart little guy, so it seemed natural that he would want to teach others how to sign. I never wanted him to speak, especially at the end of the series. That doesn't signal a happy ending, but accepting people for who they are is. If he ever chooses to talk, it'll be in his own time. But if not, he'll continue with sign language and writing. Speech is not the only means of communicating. This is his journey to take.

Speaking of journeys... Y'all, I love Harley. I've always had cats as pets in my books, and this was the first dog. Harley has his own unique personality. He's loyal, loves kids, and any scene where he's chasing after Christian is pure gold. Whenever I think of Crush, I will always think about him riding down the road on his bike, Harley in the sidecar with goggles on.

Now to Gem and Niko. The scene at the club could have gone another way, but it would've been forced. It's important as a writer that I not project my own wishes onto a character. I have to honor who they are and the journey they're on. Readers would also want more of their story, and I think those two have decades if not centuries to build on. They are exactly where they want to be in their friendship. I respect how Niko sees her as a woman who needs time to figure out who she is.

After all, time and experience changed him, and he knows it will also change her. I think what they have is beautiful just as it is.

This novella had all the feels, the laughs, and the tears.

If I can say just one more thing about Christian and Raven, it's that I loved writing their banter. I've heard from many readers who said that was their most favorite thing about them. Most of the books have a scene where they're discussing what the other would do if they died some horrible way. In *Forevermore*, they joke about lions eating them on their honeymoon. I'm not exactly sure how I built a romance around two people with a twisted sense of humor, but somehow it worked.

For that reason, they will always remain one of my favorite couples.

PART II

THE MAIN CHARACTERS

Part of crafting a memorable character is going deeper than just their looks or backstory. It's diving into their personality, the way they speak, mannerisms and habits, what they like and dislike.

With every new character, I create a basic outline. It's usually not until the second draft that I've figured out what needs to change. Characters have a way of painting their own picture that occasionally goes against my initial plan. In a series, I get to unravel more about them with each book.

The bios listed in this insider's guide contain most of what's in my series bible, but not every detail. For one, backstories are best enjoyed during the read. Characters also have specific habits, like eye rolling or fidgeting, but those aren't listed as they're more intrinsic to a person's behavior in a nonessential way. I have compiled a list in this book of the most essential facts about each character, including the main foods they like or dislike, but I don't list every single thing they've ever eaten. Are you asking if I keep track of that? Read on...

There are two documents I always have open while writing a series: my series notes and the character bios. It's important to remain consistent as even authors can forget the little things, especially when there are numerous characters and details. For instance, the writer might have their characters enjoying a meal where one is eating a burger with pickles and onions. They might have forgotten that five books ago, that character mentioned how they hate onions. Each book in a series will often have more information to add to character bios. Mine were continually updated until the final novella.

Facts that aren't known are not listed. For example, we don't know everyone's original name. Niko, like almost every other Mage, received a name from his Creator. His true name was never specified. Nor was Gem's. We do know what Shepherd's first name was before he changed it for personal reasons.

Let's talk about vocabulary. Every person has their own way of speaking. Language is a form of expression, and besides accents and dialect, we adopt a lot of phrases. Not everyone speaks grammatically correctly (Viktor, for instance, often drops certain words), and some use words incorrectly. It's all about carving out their personality through speech and being consistent. Believe it or not (and believe it), I have a spreadsheet of words and phrases unique to each character. A catchphrase or two is fun, but I want readers to know which character is speaking even if there aren't any dialogue tags. This is largely dependent on the vocabulary I've built for them.

Christian alone has over a hundred words and phrases in his toolbox. Something to keep in mind is that he's old Irish, so he may often speak or use words that modern Irish people don't. He's also lived in America for a long time. There is more flexibility with immortals due to their age and travel history. It's not uncommon for people to pick up or lose an accent, adopt modern slang, or stick with old-fashioned phrases. Since my spreadsheet is ridiculously long, I only included the most well-known catchphrases in this guide.

Part of a character's personality shines through in how they communicate.

Gem has a lyrical and expressive way of speaking. When she's upset, you'll know it.

Shepherd is less chatty, gruff, and cusses a lot. Hunter forced him out of his shell, and as a result, he's gotten better at communicating.

Niko is calm, intelligent, and thoughtful. But he also has occasional fun with idioms or phrases.

Blue is matter-of-fact. She's very much one of the guys with her bluntness and serious tone, but she's always respectful where Viktor's concerned.

When Viktor gets upset or tired, he'll start thinking in Russian and struggle with his English. He only learned English recently after centuries of speaking his native tongue, and that's why he continued using some Russian words that came natural to him that everyone understood, like *da* and *nyet*.

Claude is well-spoken, and I always saw him coming from a family that was upper-class. He's educated and patient, but he also has a sexy and confident way of speaking that many Chitahs have.

And let's not forget Wyatt's "abuse" of air quotes. I had a blast creating unique catchphrases with him, like "hold your ponies" instead of "hold your horses." He's an original, and that came through in his vocabulary.

I also take into consideration their age, where they lived, and how they grew up. Wyatt's been around for a while, and I imagined him having left home as a young man. He's obviously a guy who adapts to his environment, so I dropped his Southern accent. Christian, on the other hand, is Irish through and through. It wasn't uncommon for immigrants in the early 1900s to live and work in the same community. He held on to his roots as part of his identity.

Fun fact: When writing and editing dialogue scenes, I always read them aloud in each character's accent. I speak the way they would deliver the line. It's the only way I can make sure it sounds authentic, and it also helps me understand what emotion they would put into their words. Every author has their own method. This is mine.

Gifts: To read more about the Breed gifts referenced for each character, locate the corresponding Breed section in this guide and refer to *Gifts* listed under that Breed.

CHRISTIAN & RAVEN

From the very first time they met, these two were pure magic on the page. They share the same dark humor and strange pillow talk. Writing intimate dialogue is the air that I breathe. Those moments are revealing, like when Raven opens up about her mother's death. Because she took the chance in making herself vulnerable, it led to a shocking discovery that Christian and Raven had met once before.

When it came to their romance, I had to think outside the box.

Christian isn't the guy who makes women swoon, and Raven is far too abrasive for most men. When Christian offered Raven a live heart, that's the only way I could have written that scene. Their love colors outside the lines, and I didn't want to change it. Christian finds his own path to romance even if it means chaining up her enemy.

RAVEN IMOGEN (GRAVES) BLACK

Breed: Crossbreed (Vampire/Mage)
Rare Mage gift(s): Stealer
Mage Creator: Fletcher Black
Vampire maker: Houdini
Creator's mark location: Behind left ear
Age: 30 when the series begins. Turned when she was 25.
Height: 5'8"
Hair: Midnight-black hair, past the shoulders
Eye color: Right eye blue like a husky, left eye copper brown
Physical: Although her forever age is 25, she looks older. Her body is strong because she works out and isn't lazy by nature. Her legs are her best asset, especially since she uses them to strangle her victims. Not much on wearing makeup, but when she does, she likes burgundy lipstick. Fingernails are on the short side.
Scars/Marks: Scar on right hip below belly button from a Chitah bite. Covered some of it with the Keystone tattoo, which is over an inch in size. Large gemstone heart tattoo on her left thigh in front. Surrounded by Victorian-style ornaments and baroque flourishes that are black and grey. Above it is written the word: FOREVERMORE.

Clothing: Prefers broken-in, ripped jeans. In summer, her style is comfy shirts or tank tops. In winter, oversized sweaters. Usually dark colors but not always. Owns several leather jackets and a trench coat. Black boots are a favorite and sometimes sneakers. She likes fingerless gloves because they allow her to grip weapons better. Often paints her nails black. Likes to conceal small daggers in her belt buckle, boot heel, or inside her coat. Wears them either strapped to her leg or on her belt loop. She feels naked if she's not armed. Also wears a 32-carat heart-shaped Burmese ruby pendant on an unbreakable chain. Prefers to be braless around the house.

Occupation: Works for Keystone

Keystone partner: Christian

Nicknames: Precious (by Christian), Cookie (by Crush), Butterfly (by Houdini). Crush also calls her *baby girl* as a term of endearment.

Family: Crush Graves (Father)

Personality: Confident, blunt, sarcastic, and not overly sensitive. Not easily ruffled, but she loves pushing other people's buttons when she spots a weakness. Has difficulty relating to other women. She's tough but also vulnerable. Doesn't like people seeing her cry. Compassionate when it comes to humans.

Loves: Hanging out on rooftops, sleeping beneath the stars, her father's laugh, the color red, the noisy city, newspapers, dogs, being on a motorcycle, reading the obituaries, bantering with Christian

Hates: Drinking blood, lemon bars, exposing her weaknesses, people pointing out her eye color, bondage, pistachio ice cream

Flaws: Can't swim, cynical, doesn't trust easily

Food/Drink: Angus burgers with extra cheese, apple pie with vanilla ice cream, onion rings, tequila, black coffee, cocoa with three tiny marshmallows, bacon, grilled cheese

Car: 1974 blue Ford pickup truck. Decal on the back that says: Outlaw.

Property: Owns the land next door to Keystone. There is a small underground dwelling.

Weapon of choice: Push daggers
Catchphrase(s): "Disastrous." / "I know a thing or two about a thing or two." / "This wasn't in the brochure." / "Lights out." / "Once again, destiny screws me over."

More about Raven's unique gifts/limitations:

- Vampire hearing: No
- Vampire strength: No
- Vampire shadow walking: No
- Vampire vision: Somewhat but not 100 percent
- Vampire fangs: Yes
- Charming/scrubbing ability: No
- Can be charmed/scrubbed: Yes
- Reading information in blood: Yes
- Impervious to temperature: No
- Mage flashing: Yes
- Mage common gifts: Yes

Her Vampire traits: Raven doesn't have flawless Vampire skin or black eyes. She dislikes the taste of blood except for Christian's and possibly Shifters in animal form. When she consumes Vampire blood, it temporarily increases her hearing and sight and gives her Vampire strength. Vampire blood will heal her, but human blood will not. Vampire blood also doesn't influence her the way it does some. She is still learning how to read blood. Because she is part Vampire, she doesn't require as much food or sleep as the average person, but unlike a true Vampire, she still needs both. Doesn't have a personal scent.

Her Mage traits: Most of her common Mage abilities are intact. Flashing uses up more of her power than typical but not by an extreme amount. She's sensitive to Mage energy, and when she consumes dark light, it makes her sick. The same happens with blood consumption of evil people. She can use Mage light to heal but prefers sunlight.

Immunities: Chitah venom, stunners, and impalement wood have no effect on her.

AUTHOR'S NOTE:

Raven was a complicated gal to write. She's a dark character with extra baggage and a conflicted soul. In the first book, Raven is tough, confident, and doesn't trust anyone—especially the Mageri. She's afraid they'll execute her. Forced to live on the streets, Raven is bitter about her struggles and lonely life, so she takes it out on the criminal element. She doesn't feel connected to the Breed world, so she targets them.

Viktor is looking for someone with her skills, and when he tracks her down, he offers her a chance at a better life. Raven's biggest obstacle is learning to work with others since she's still in a pattern of self-destructive behavior.

You can't flip the switch overnight.

Character growth is usually a process of two steps forward, one step back. They have to make mistakes and take chances in order to better themselves. With every challenge Raven faced, she learned something about herself.

When we first meet Raven, she's taking a man down without any remorse. She targets Breed, hates Vampires, and prefers keeping company with humans—the people she understands. Christian was instrumental in helping her deal with her hatred for Vampires. Partners have to trust each other, and their bond grows as he teaches her about her gifts.

As the series progresses, Raven builds new relationships. She isn't looking at the Breed world from the outside anymore. As a result, she's learning to trust people and embrace her gifts. You have to remember that neither Houdini nor Fletcher educated her on Breed history, customs, or gifts. She had to learn things on her own, and some of it she got wrong. Eventually she no longer feels like an interloper in their world. It's nothing like the human world she grew up in, but she gains an appreciation for it. She sees not only the bad but also the good.

By the end of the series, we see how much she's changed. Raven's human interactions become more awkward, just like the rest of the Keystone team whenever they go out to a human establishment. Now that Raven is comfortable in her own skin, she is less comfortable around humans.

Since pairing her with Christian was always the goal, she had to be a person who wasn't easily rattled. They had to be compatible without too much personality conflict. While Christian can get under some people's skin, Raven isn't intimidated. Never did I want theirs to be a mentor/student relationship where he spends half the book berating her abilities and intelligence. He wants to guide her and offer advice, but she has a lot to teach him as well. Neither of them is better than the other, but they both become better by learning from each other.

I admire the woman Raven became—who she is still becoming. Once she released the pain of her past, she was able to find happiness. Her friends and family only make her stronger in her convictions. She stopped questioning her morality. Raven is a soldier, putting her life on the line to make the world a safer place. It's been an arduous journey, but one that has only just begun.

Maybe someday she *will* be a great leader.

CHRISTIAN POE

Breed: Vampire
Maker: Ronan
Age: Born late 1800s. Turned at age 31.
Height: 6′ thereabouts
Hair: Dark brown and a couple of inches long on top
Eye color: Black (human eyes were blue)
Physical: Scruffy beard. Whiskers below jaw and a little on his neck. Skin tone is a natural beige with warm undertones and flawless like a Vampire. Average build, commanding posture with straight shoulders. Sometimes has a crooked smile. He can easily blend into a crowd. Blood type is O positive.
Scars/Marks: Keystone tattoo on his groin, dead center beneath the pubic hair. Tattoo of a raven on his right pec and arm. One wing spreads over his chest and the other wing around to his back. The tips of the feathers are red, and the right eye is pale blue.
Clothing: Trench coat, Henley shirts (buttons undone), V-neck shirts, and dark trousers or jeans. Most of his sweaters have holes or the threads are loose. Doesn't like flashy clothes since he prefers blending into a crowd. Sometimes wears dark sunglasses in the daytime. Boxer-

brief guy. His lace-up boots are worn out. He'll dress in leathers if he feels like it. Wears a silver ring on his middle left finger with intricate designs on the band and an oval onyx stone. The ring was a gift from Raven.

Occupation: Works for Keystone. Also an experienced guard.

Keystone partner: Raven

Nicknames: Chrissy (by Lenore), Peckerhead (by Crush), Poe or Mr. Poe (by Raven)

Family: Father, brothers, and younger blind sister (Cassie) are all deceased

Personality: Cocky. His tone is low and serious, and his humor is dry and dark. He's suave with women. Won't suffer fools. When he's upset, he likes to deliver creative threats that will make people's skin crawl. Has an air of superiority as if everyone is wasting his time. He's blunt and doesn't have a filter, saying whatever is on his mind without regard.

Loves: Animals and facts about them, Raven licking his arteries, going to old cemeteries to clear his mind, creative threats, telling people what he really thinks of them. When it comes to sex, he's occasionally into exhibitionism and also likes it rough. Sometimes just dirty talk about someone watching them is enough to satisfy.

Hates: Litterbugs, eating too much, champagne, technology and people's dependency on it

Flaws: His insults can be cutting. Doesn't easily let people love him. Doesn't censor himself and speaks his mind even when it's not appropriate. Holds grudges and becomes fixated on revenge.

Food/Drink: Watermelon, hard candy (butterscotch, peppermints, flat suckers), lemon bars, pecan pie

Vehicles: Ducati Scrambler motorcycle, black Honda

Property: Small, windowless structure in the middle of the woods. One single room with only a mattress and table. Raven dubbed it Château Cinderblock.

Weapon of choice: Thunder & Lightning (his fists)

Accent: Irish
Catchphrase(s): "Jaysus wept." / "One more word and I'll drain you." / "Over my rotting corpse." / "What you know about _____ could fill a thimble." / "For feck's sake."

AUTHOR'S NOTE:

Jaysus wept. Where to begin?

Christian Poe first appeared in the Mageri series as the absolute fanghole that he is. When those books were released, most readers hated him. They couldn't stand the way he talked to Silver. But he did have a small fan club. I originally wrote the Mageri series in early 2010, along with sixteen other novels (including Keystone) before I ventured into publishing. I only wrote one Crossbreed novel before moving on to other projects, partly because I wasn't entirely satisfied with the original story. When I revisited the book years later, I saw the potential. That said, I knew it would be risky to create a series with Christian as one of the leads. He was never entirely despicable, but I wasn't sure if my Mageri fans would trust me enough to venture into a series where he's the romantic lead.

I never wanted to change Christian. Hell, I don't even think that's possible. Life hardened him, and he didn't want to be vulnerable again. That's why he's so extra prickly. A woman he devoted himself to put him in a pine box, and other relationships never ended well.

In order to figure Christian out, we had to dive into his backstory. Christian Poe was the son of a poor farmer who worked hard but never owned land. Though he was quite attached to his younger sister, he and his brothers fled Ireland in search of opportunity. There were lots of rumors about land in America, but when he arrived, he couldn't find decent work being that he was Irish. He picked pockets, suffered humiliation at the hands of a wealthy woman, and endured hardships. After a Vampire chose him as his progeny, things were looking better.

Until he crossed paths with Lenore Parrish.

Christian devoted himself to her completely. Though he obsessed over her, part of that was blood manipulation. The things he did on her behalf made him her monster. She broke his spirit. Not just through rejection, but burying him, where he remained underground for a decade. And not because he betrayed her or even challenged her but because he *wouldn't* betray her. She wanted to match him up with someone in a power play, so he finally confessed his true feelings for her. Giving himself completely to a woman brought him unimaginable suffering.

Knowing all of that is the key to understanding Christian Poe.

When he meets Raven, she's the polar opposite of Lenore. She's uncouth, fierce, and says what she means. He can also relate to her struggles of living on the streets. She seems to speak his language, and that's why they had great banter. There were never tears or hurt feelings over something said. But that wasn't enough to establish a connection that would flourish.

The more he got to know her, the more he saw something he no longer saw in himself: her humanity. Partnering up forced them to trust and confide in each other. It created a foundation they could build on. They each have trust issues, so their partnership sped things up. Raven has a tendency of closing herself off, whereas Christian is inclined to go too far to protect the people he's loyal to. Sometimes he doesn't make the best choices. He has a history of ruining friendships, and Raven helps him see that good intentions can lead to ruin.

There will never be anyone quite like Christian Poe. I'm not exaggerating when I tell you that his vocabulary chart has at least one hundred words and phrases, but I only included the gems in his bio. He's not the noble gentleman who waxes poetic. Christian is direct, condescending, and has no regard for what people think of his thoughts or behavior. That's why Raven would often turn to him and say, "Do I know you?"

The best characters are ones who grow and become better versions of themselves while still remaining authentic. He hasn't changed but only became a better version of himself.

I'm going to miss that fanghole. If anyone deserved a happy ending, it was him.

VIKTOR KAZAN

Breed: Shifter wolf
Animal description: Grey coat
Shifter craving: Unspecified
Age: At least 400
Height: 6′0″
Hair: Silver hair in loose waves combed back. Dark grey mixed in.
Eye color: Steel grey
Physical: Robust man who appears in his late forties or early fifties. Grecian nose. Defined abs but not an overly muscular build. He keeps his beard trimmed short, the goatee around his mouth and chin a little longer. Has lines on his forehead and around his eyes.
Scars/Marks: Keystone tattoo on his left pec, about five inches or so in size
Clothing: Around the house, he'll dress in a cozy dark brown cardigan or knit sweaters. He is a sophisticated dresser who always chooses the right attire for the occasion. Also wears dress shirts (with the sleeves rolled up) and chinos. Viktor likes either leather dress shoes or loafers —never sneakers. Long grey winter coat with a high collar. Silk pajama

pants for sleepwear. He always considers the image he projects with his attire, especially at parties.

Occupation: Leader of Keystone. Former bounty hunter.

Nicknames: N/A

Family: Last living member of his family. Viktor's alpha brother was named Yarik.

Personality: Cuts to the chase. He sees himself as a professional, so every social event is an opportunity for him to make business connections instead of friends. He carries the weight of the world on his shoulders. Dry humor. He doesn't have an ego. If Gem corrects his speech, he appreciates her desire to help him learn or correctly get his thoughts across.

Loves: Structure, his team, cracking open a bottle of wine and telling stories about his childhood home. Jogging on the property, playing violin or guitar in private. Can fly a plane.

Hates: Deceit

Flaws: Can sometimes be abrasive when speaking to people. Reverts back to speaking Russian when he's tired, drunk, or upset. Can be overly strict. He's cheap and would rather not run electricity throughout his house even if it would make his team more comfortable.

Food/Drink: Vodka, wine, espresso, meals that remind him of home, and Blue's scrambled eggs

Car: Black van

Property: Keystone estate

Weapon of choice: His wolf

Accent: Russian

Catchphrase(s): "Let's not be dramatic." / "What would I do without my Blue?"

AUTHOR'S NOTE:

Viktor was a tough nut to crack. Some characters show me who they are out of the gate and others don't. I knew some of his backstory before readers were privy to it, so I always understood why he was so aloof. Why protecting his team and his home meant everything. Why he would sometimes be hard on them.

For years, Viktor felt responsible for the death of his family. As the leader of Keystone, all he wants to do is protect his people and his organization. They are all he has. He chose others who, like him, had lost everything and were willing to sacrifice their lives for a greater cause. He carefully selected and planned their cases, making sure to never accept a job they couldn't complete or one that would compromise his values. Viktor is hard on them because he has to be. Their lives are in his hands as well as the lives of innocents who might be impacted by the case. He knows firsthand the sacrifices required. He once was part of a resistance who fought in times of war, he carried out assassinations, and he worked as a bounty hunter.

This guy is made of steel.

As the series went on, the Keystone fighters were developing close friendships and bonds. Each time I wrote him in a scene with them, his loneliness was palpable. He believed in socializing with them as a group, but he couldn't go beyond that.

He also didn't want them to see his vulnerability. A leader has to project strength so that others will follow. Respect is sacred to him. Without anyone to confide in about confidential work stress, it was only natural that he thought Lenore would be a good match for him. Not a love match, but he could finally have a companion. Whatever feelings Viktor had for Lenore were manipulated and amplified, but he no longer felt alone.

It wasn't until the team started coming together as a family that he realized he wanted to be a part of that connection. One reason he always kept his distance also had to do with the fear of losing them. But even Raven learns in the end that you have to accept loss if you want love.

Viktor's journey was letting his walls down and building genuine relationships with people who already loved him.

NIKO (NIKODEMOS)

Breed: Mage
Rare Mage gift(s): Thermal, Healer
Unique abilities to him: Has the ability to see energy
Creator: Artemon
Creator's mark location: Left pec
Age: Over 1,500 years old. His human age when he was made is unspecified.
Height: 6'0"
Hair: Long, wispy black hair. Several inches past shoulders. Sometimes he'll wear it in a topknot or braid, especially when he's working out. Occasionally lets Gem add a few thin braids.
Eye color: Crystal blue, almost colorless. Eye color may be genetic or a medical condition related to his blindness. Because of his age, no one knows.
Physical: Niko was born blind and grew up in ancient Japan. His father's heritage is unknown but may account for his height. Almond-shaped eyes, thick eyebrows, carved cheekbones, light brown skin. While he is on the lean side of an athletic build, his muscles are toned and strong from the strength training he does.

Scars/Marks: Keystone tattoo behind his right knee
Clothing: Always wears black so he never has to think about coordinating his wardrobe. Prefers hoods on his shirts and jackets. Also has a black cloak that he often wears to conceal his katanas in public. Around the house or late at night, he wears Hakama or drop-crotch pants. There are two shirts in his wardrobe that his team placed in there as a joke: a rainbow shirt and a pink shirt with the Pink Panther's face. He marked the tags to make them easy to find and enjoys wearing them when he wants to rouse a chuckle.
Occupation: Works for Keystone
Keystone partner: Blue
Nicknames: N/A
Family: Parents and sister are long dead. Never married or had children in his human life.
Personality: Soft-spoken, observant, and patient. Calm demeanor and always has words of wisdom. He enjoys mentoring others. Niko is loyal, considerate, and highly intelligent. Has a warm laugh but sometimes laughs when it's not appropriate and abruptly stops before offending someone. He's a good listener. Believes that it's bad luck to take something without paying or trading for it. Very perceptive of his surroundings. Niko is a virgin who believes in spiritual purity.
Loves: Beating everyone at darts, origami, Gem's innocent way of looking at the world, strength training, motivating others, reading in braille
Hates: Stealing, drinking too much alcohol in public, crossing the street because of all the cars
Flaws: Who? Niko? If he has one, it's probably concealing his emotions. He is also uncomfortable with the dating scene.
Food/Drink: Traditional hot tea, cheeseburgers. Enjoys hard liquor but only at home.
Car: Doesn't drive but jokes about it
Weapon of choice: Katanas
Catchphrase(s): "As you wish." / "Apologies."

Niko had a group of Mage brothers who all shared the same Creator, who was Greek. His Creator made a number of men, so these are not all of them, only the ones he escaped with who made him their servant.

MAGE BROTHERS:

- Cyrus (leader)
- Kallisto
- Arcadius
- Lykos
- Plato

MORE ABOUT NIKO'S GIFT OF SIGHT

Niko grew up in darkness. It wasn't until he received his first spark that he developed an unexpected ability. It took him a long time to understand it. Because no one else sees the same way as he does, his ability to describe it is limited. The energy he sees has visible differences, one he can only attribute to color, texture, and behavior. His description of red or blue may not be the color we actually see since he has never seen those colors before. But it was important for him to give everything a name. It's also possible that Niko sees colors beyond the spectrum or is able to detect nuances that we have never perceived.

Everyone has a personal light. The color, size, brightness, texture, pattern, and behavior makes it unique to them—like a fingerprint. Because emotions affect energy, it can take Niko some time to learn someone's personal light. Once he does, he's better able to interpret their emotions. Most emotions have the same color and pattern for everyone. An individual's personal light rarely changes unless something permanently changes them. Because he can see a person's emotions even when they hide them from everyone else, he's more compassionate and is always there to lend an ear to anyone who might need it.

According to Niko, almost all living things give off some degree of energy. When people touch objects, they might leave behind residual energy. He can see faint trails where people recently walked. Mage light differs from other Breeds, so he can tell by looking at a recently deceased body if they were a Mage. Niko can often tell gender through energy. However, like every other Mage, he can't sense a Vampire's energy. His unique gift of sight doesn't allow him to see their energy either, but he can sometimes see a Vampire's strong emotions.

Niko can see the sun because of its energy, but it's so bright that it washes everything out when he looks right at it. He can't see small creatures such as insects. The ones he can see might just appear as a tiny sparkle. Trees absorb sunlight, so he can sometimes see trees at night from the residual energy. His limitations are seeing inanimate, man-made objects. They might give off faint energy, but only if someone touched it. That's why it can be difficult for him to walk in unfamiliar places.

How Niko sees everyone's personal energy (that's mentioned):

Gem: Deep amethyst and silver. Her light is like a perfect ribbon that leaves traces of itself behind her.
Shepherd: Leaves behind flecks that crackle and burn out
Claude: Smooth sage color
Raven: As of *Gaslight*, he sees pulses of ruby-red and silver mixed in with her light. He doesn't mention the primary color, but he did say that her light permanently changed after she fell in love with Christian.
Blue: Red, like the color he sees in fire
Crush: Silver
Wyatt: Smoky blue. When he gets riled up, his light funnels in a circular motion like a tornado.

Emotional light indicators:

- Black and red crackling indicates someone is lying or being deceitful
- Bright flashing in someone's light signals anger
- Deep blue flutters show fear
- Dark green usually means confusion

AUTHOR'S NOTE:

I never had any hesitation when creating a blind character as a hero. Disabilities don't hold people back from doing great things. One aspect I had to consider was how he would get around. Niko's situation is unique since he was born over 1,500 years ago. He's had centuries learning how to adapt by using his other senses—especially his unique ability to see energy. He had no choice but to learn how to disappear in a crowd. Showing any sign of weakness could have put a target on his back. It's easy to imagine that he might have gotten away with using a walking stick since sighted people use those. But in the modern world, using a white cane or other walking stick would draw negative attention, making his job difficult if not impossible. So he still relies on step counting, using his hands, and memorizing his surroundings. Blue is especially helpful by giving him all the information he needs to navigate in a new location.

Understanding how Niko got from point A to point B was crucial. A blind man doesn't just acquire mad skills with a sword. Niko's early years as a slave were brutal, and even after he and his Mage brothers fled, he was completely dependent on them for everything. While his first spark created an ability to "see" energy, he couldn't comprehend what he was experiencing for a very long time. Imagine what life was like in the Middle Ages. Even as a free man, he lived in servitude for hundreds of years. When he escaped his brothers, his life began.

Niko was taken in by a Mage who became his mentor. Sato-Sensei taught him everything he knows, including how to pass for a sighted person. He learned how to survive independently, which was crucial in a time long before modern conveniences and inventions that help the blind. He harnessed his ability to use his other senses and learned how to fight.

Most importantly, he discovered how to interpret light. When a Mage is given their first spark, they acquire the common gifts as well as rare ones. How that first spark affects everyone is different, and I wanted to give Niko an ability that no one else has. Perhaps his Creator's light found a way to compensate for his blindness. With guidance, Niko was able to identify connections between different energy sources and understand their meanings.

While there was a lot to consider with writing a blind character, I never wanted his disability to be the primary focus. Because of his Mage gift, Niko can often read a room better than the people in it. He's observant, quiet, and possesses inner strength that's unparalleled. Because he had such a wonderful mentor, he often shows interest in being that guide for others.

Regarding Niko's personal life, when Niko reveals he's a virgin, it's not a moment of shame or vulnerability. It's not a fact he intentionally hides from others; he's simply a private person. It was something his Mage brothers rubbed in his face while they went to brothels. For a while, he felt ashamed. But most of his feelings really had to do with the fact he was completely dependent on others. With no family or skills, he had no way to earn a living wage. He couldn't even be a proper thief. Niko's prospects for marriage were nonexistent. It wasn't until his sensei taught him about spiritual purity that he started reshaping his thoughts and seeing it as a gift. That only reinforced his desire to guard his virginity. It will always remain his choice, and we have to respect the choices that others make for themselves. He's fully embraced it, and his purity is now a part of him.

With all the high energy in the house, Niko was a calming influence. He guided others to seek their full potential and to push themselves. He gave good advice, listened, and mentored others. And seeing someone's true feelings made it easier to know when to step up and back that person.

The friendship Niko forged with Gem isn't surprising. While they couldn't be more opposite, she has reawakened his curiosity about life and helped him lower his guard. Gem reminds him to smile and try new experiences. She shows him things he's never seen. In return, Niko helps her realize her true potential. She suddenly wants to try harder to challenge herself and learn to use her gifts. He has someone to confide in with absolute trust, and the love he feels for his friend is unwavering. They complement each other, and Niko has finally found a slice of happiness that he's always been searching for.

Love transcends the physical.

— SPELLBOUND

BLUE

Breed: Shifter falcon
Animal description: Peregrine falcon. Steel-grey feathers on head and wings. Underbelly is white with dark, horizontal stripes. Breast feathers on neck are soft and white. Yellow beak that slopes down to a dark hook. Blue eyes. She is awake during her entire shift.
Shifter craving: Green olives
Age: 85
Height: 5'10"
Hair: Long, dark brown hair
Eye color: Blue, which is a trait shared by everyone in her tribe
Physical: Native American Shifter. Olive complexion, long legs, beautiful facial features that aren't overly feminine. Voluptuous breasts, narrow waist, lush lips, thick eyebrows.
Scars/Marks: Keystone tattoo on lower back. A lion attacked her and raked its claws across her chest from her left shoulder diagonally down to her right hip. Four white claw marks are highly visible and didn't heal. The scars are across her shoulder, breast, between the breasts, abdomen, lower belly, and hip.
Clothing: Uses feathers her falcon loses during a shift and makes

earrings out of them. It requires her piercing her ears each time, but she doesn't mind since she doesn't shift every single day. Likes tall black boots over dark jeans. Otherwise, she'll pair combat boots with cargo pants with lots of pockets. Blue prefers tank tops or sleeveless shirts. Like Niko, she often conceals her face in Breed places and even has short-sleeved hoodies. Winter coat is a soft brown leather jacket with a cloth hood. Around the house at night, she wears a Medieval-style cotton dress that is long with wide sleeves and a hood. Also owns cloaks. Sometimes wears a stunner spike around her neck or in her pocket. When she first received her scars, she would cover them up and felt like less of a woman. But once she embraced them, she went back to wearing her low-collar shirts or tank tops around the house.

Occupation: Works for Keystone primarily as a scout, but she is also a fierce warrior

Keystone partner: Niko

Nicknames: N/A

Family: Estranged from her family and tribe. Her two young sons (Chen, for short, and Nayati) were murdered.

Personality: Serious, tough demeanor. Never runs from a fight. Walks with a strut, likes to be one of the guys, and is unflappable in all situations. Despite that, she is graceful in her own way. Reserved (not shy), down to earth, and follows the rules. Because of her past trauma, respecting leadership is important above all else. She's private about her past and doesn't share it with the people closest to her. Blue doesn't care about her natural beauty and has always seen it as a curse, but she uses it when needed on the job. She isn't sentimental about kissing and has no desire to mate.

Loves: Rock climbing, picking locks, architecture, heights, noble men, the statues in the house, and decorating with flowers picked from outside. Enjoys feeling useful and thrives under structure and order. Enjoys cutting her own hair to annoy Claude.

Hates: Men noticing her for her looks, Vampires, being left out of a job, her singing voice

Flaws: Her falcon is considered a weaker Shifter animal. Makes terrible stew.

Food/Drink: Pizza, breakfast burritos, hot dogs, plain soda, baked beans

Car: Electric-blue Mustang (newer model)

Weapon of choice: Tomahawk that's a foot long. Usually wears it on her belt loop. It has a wooden handle bound in leather at the grip. The quick-draw sheath is plastic and conceals the blade. It's a bottom with-draw, allowing her to pull the weapon out fast.

Catchphrase(s): "Is that so?" / "Serves you right." / "Don't be ridiculous." / "File a complaint."

AUTHOR'S NOTE:

Of all the characters in the series, Blue was the hardest to get to know. Sometimes characters let me see their cards early on, and other times they hold them close. I don't always like having a full outline about a character's backstory. Sometimes events happen in the natural progression of the series that bring out something unexpected.

Blue is the name she chose for herself, not her given name. Like Shepherd, she wanted to dissociate herself from her past as well as the ones who betrayed her. Viktor needed a scout, and Blue was an ideal candidate since she also had no qualms about fighting or doing anything else required of her. Many immortals struggle to be more than just the gifts they were given, so she's eager to prove to Viktor that he can count on her for anything. While her falcon fills an essential role, Blue's a strong woman willing to run into battle without hesitation.

And a woman like that has a story to tell.

It wasn't until several books in that I realized her full backstory. In my earlier notes, I considered having an estranged husband return to reclaim his mate. That storyline didn't make sense, so I allowed her to take the lead and tell me in her own time.

Blue never experienced genuine love until she gave birth. Let me explain. Her father was a prominent leader, and while she respected him, I never got the feeling there was love. After all, he used her as a means to gain a treaty. Blue wanted to please her father, but more importantly, an arranged marriage was good for the tribe. So she sacrificed her idea of love to unite two enemies. Her mate was a provider and a father. It wasn't until her children came along that she understood unwavering love. They were her world. Watching them grow into young men brought her joy, and watching them leave this world killed a piece of her soul.

Writing her story gutted me. After that revelation, I really got her. I understood why she was holding back from me. Why she wasn't leaping into relationships or looking for her old tribe. I understood the pain she still carries—pain that never fully leaves a parent who has lost a child, especially to violence. I understood the importance of the second chance that Viktor had given her. She had finally found someone she could believe in—someone who wouldn't break her trust. Someone who stood firm in his convictions and was a man of integrity. Given the leaders in her past who had failed her, that was critical in her healing.

The one thread I wanted to weave through this series was the different types of love people can experience—all equally fulfilling. The love of a father, a friend, a child, a lover, and even a makeshift family. Even love of self. As these individuals move through life, finding a mate isn't their only path to happiness.

While Blue isn't the most outgoing or the easiest person to get to know, she's a woman you can trust. A woman with courage who has dedicated her life to making her world a better place.

And that's a woman I'd want to know.

SHEPHERD MOON

Breed: Sensor
Gifts: Standard Sensor gifts, but he's skilled at picking up trace emotions on objects
Age: Unknown
Height: 6'2"
Hair: Dark brown. Buzz cut that's nicely shaped.
Eye color: Brown
Physical: Dark eyebrows. Over two hundred pounds of hard muscle. Does a lot of pull-ups and works out daily. Strong bone structure in the face with a square jaw. Two lines etched in his forehead. Nice tan. Sometimes stubble on his face. Stern expression makes him look like he's ready to fight.
Scars/Marks: Fifty-three scars total from a knife attack. His left hand is worse than the right. Most of them are defensive wounds on his arms and hands, but he also suffered stabbings on his chest. Large compass tattoo with Hunter's name above north, located on left inside forearm. Black phoenix inked on his upper right arm as a sleeve that spreads across his chest and back. Celtic tattoo of a lover's knot on the back of his neck. Keystone tattoo, location unspecified.

Clothing: Jeans, black T-shirt kind of guy. Boxer briefs. Also wears a black leather jacket, black boots, and muscle shirts. Works out shirtless in track pants or sweatpants. On some jobs, he carries a black medical bag since he's the official team medic.

Occupation: Works for Keystone

Keystone partner: Wyatt

Nicknames: Shep (mostly by Wyatt)

Family: Hunter (son). His former love, Maggie, is dead.

Personality: Quiet. Gruff and closed off from people. Comes across as having a negative personality. Doesn't open up to people easily, including his own partner. Rarely smiles. He enjoys tormenting Wyatt and keeps good company with Christian. Likes to work out alone as he is the more reclusive of the bunch.

Loves: Routine and order. Likes sharpening his knives on a whetstone, meditating, working out alone, a good cigarette, and hard liquor. Shepherd loves his kid more than life itself.

Hates: People who disturb him when he's working out. Men who ogle or sexualize women in front of him. Can't stand rats. Dislikes it when Wyatt has conversations with the dead and ignores the living.

Flaws: Smoking, swearing, cursing

Food/Drink: Beer, whiskey, coffee. Enjoys food that sticks to his ribs like steak, sausages, bacon, ribs. Enjoys almost anything Kira serves.

Car: Metallic grey Jeep Wrangler. Special edition hardtop, extra big with tinted windows.

Weapon of choice: Guns, knives, anything

Catchphrase(s): "This looks like something we'll have to deny later." / "Nobody's got time for that." / "Clusterfuck." / "Button it up." / "We're in a tight spot."

AUTHOR'S NOTE:

Shepherd's one of my favorite characters in terms of growth. He's a severely scarred man, inside and out, who lost everything. Even the name he uses is one he gave himself to start a new life (his first name was once Samuel). Shepherd formerly worked for the Sensor Council in the evidence room, pulling emotions from crime scene weapons. When he was reassigned to a hospital, he fell in love with a pathologist. She got pregnant, and shortly after came a brutal attack that left his family in ruins.

I didn't know how things would evolve with his character, but when the idea of him having a son struck me, I knew it would be the one plot twist that would challenge him to the core. Could a man so broken and closed off from everyone raise a child? Would he give Hunter up so his son could have a better life? That was always a question mark in the beginning. Even I wasn't sure how it would work out —if a child could live in such an unpredictable environment.

Shep is the guy who slides up to the bar, has a few crazy stories, but carries a distant look in his eyes. Without Hunter coming into his life, he would have remained that guy. I wondered how having his child back would change him. Would he leave Keystone with his son? Would he screw up and decide he's not cut out for fatherhood?

Those fears were valid.

While Kira and Switch didn't have large roles, they were important in contributing to Shepherd and Hunter's success story. Without them, there might not have been a happy ending. Reuniting father and son doesn't solve everything. There was a lot to work through, and he couldn't do it alone. He might have given up, afraid they didn't have a stable enough environment. Kira gave Hunter the mothering he needed, and Switch gave him the education and mentorship.

Another part of Shepherd's journey was figuring out how to love and feel deserving of love. More importantly, he had to accept that he couldn't do this alone. He needed to depend on others. Love isn't always enough, and it's important to know when to ask for and accept help from others.

There were parallel stories between Shepherd and Crush. Both were men who weren't prepared for fatherhood. Neither had the tools needed to navigate it, nor did they have a partner to share in those responsibilities. Crush did, but only for a few years of Raven's life. They're both making mistakes but trying the best they can to be better fathers.

Despite the dangers of living with Keystone, Hunter has protection and love. He has a future and people to watch over him. Shepherd realizes that while he can't do everything himself, that's okay. I liked that moment in the game room when Crush was informing Wyatt that everyone in the house plays a role in Hunter's upbringing. Shepherd doesn't have to do it alone. It takes a village to raise a child. All you have to do is find your tribe.

WYATT BLESSING

Breed: Gravewalker
Gifts: Typical gifts of seeing the dead
Age: Born in 1803. Looks in his mid to late twenties.
Height: 5′11″
Hair: Light brown and unkempt. His hair doesn't play by the rules and is kind of wavy, which is why he puts it under a hat.
Eye color: Olive green
Physical: Handsome features with a kind face. When he smiles, it carves a line in one cheek. Whiskers grow patchily on his face and are soft. Slender but fit. He doesn't work out, but he burns off all the calories he consumes by running around the mansion. He has a youthful appearance like a guy just out of college.
Scars/Marks: Letter tattoos on his fingers between the base and middle knuckles that spell LOST SOUL. Keystone tattoo on his inside left heel.
Clothing: Because his hair is wavy and wild, he covers it with a slouchy beanie, which also keeps it out of his eyes. Always wears an old pair of black cowboy boots beneath his jeans. Likes novelty T-shirts that either poke fun at ghosts or reflect his personality. Wyatt owns a few skull belt

buckles—one of them has ruby eyes. Winter coat is a green Army jacket.

Occupation: Works for Keystone as their main computer geek. Hacks computer systems, performs research, obtains video footage, monitors dark web, and handles any aspect of the job related to technology. He was not hired for his abilities as a Gravewalker but his skills as a computer genius.

Keystone partner: Shepherd

Nicknames: Spooky (by all). Shepherd sometimes calls him Spooks.

Family: Parents and nine older sisters have passed on

Personality: Wyatt has a carefree personality and loves to laugh. He's animated, extroverted, easygoing, intelligent, and loves playing jokes on people. He walks with a swagger in public as if he's a fashion model. Big flirt. Proud to be a Gravewalker but is also shunned by his own kind since he chose a different line of work that has nothing to do with the dead. Sometimes ends his laugh with a snort. He isn't the type to hold a grudge or be spiteful.

Loves: Computers, computer games (especially old-school games like Pac-Man), and getting his snack on. His music taste is primarily 70s or 80s soft rock, especially groups like Air Supply, ELO, Pink Floyd, and REO Speedwagon. But he also listens to early punk rock. His favorite vacation stops are visiting food factories around the United States. Wyatt collects gargoyles and cat figurines, both of which are supposed to ward off ghosts. He enjoys magic mushrooms and marijuana recreationally. When he learns a new word from a crossword puzzle, he tries to use it in conversation as his "word of the day." Since he works late hours, he likes sleeping in.

Hates: Ghosts, especially when they live in his home. Also dislikes locations that have a larger ghost population, such as hospitals, funeral homes, and newer cemeteries. Not a fan of relic hunting in resale shops. Hates zombie movies because they always get it wrong. Afraid of butterflies. Dislikes being taken advantage of, such as people eating up his snacks or using his things without permission. While he may complain about it, Wyatt is also a problem solver and comes up with solutions.

Flaws: Uses air quotes incorrectly, messy snacker. Because he's a Grave-walker, he doesn't see death as a touchy subject, so he often makes inappropriate or insensitive remarks about it.

Food/Drink: French fries, with or without cheese. Loves drumsticks, chips, cinnamon buns, candy like Raisinets and Whoppers, frozen burritos, shrimp, beer, and soda. Is a huge snacker since he spends a lot of time at the computer.

Car: 1971 red Austin Mini Cooper S. Steering wheel is on the right side. Two-door with a stick shift, loud engine, three-spoke wheel, and blue driver's side door. Black leather bucket seats in front and leather bench in back. Rear windows aren't the kind that roll down but instead crack open at the side.

Weapon of choice: Computer. He's a lover, not a fighter.

Accent: None. But he can easily slip into a drawl if he wants to since he's originally from Tennessee.

Catchphrase(s): "Holy Toledo!" / "Son of a ghost!" / "I'm all booked up on crazy." / "That's a therapy session I ain't got time for." / "Out of sight." / "Blast!" / "You scared the crazy (or ghost) out of me." / "Hold your ponies." / "Now that's a twist I didn't see coming." / "Buttercup."

<u>Wyatt's memorable T-shirt collection:</u>

- THE FUCK I GAVE WENT THAT WAY (*with an arrow*)
- YOU'RE DEAD TO ME
- I WOULD CUDDLE YOU SO HARD
- KILTED FOR HER PLEASURE
- NO BONES ABOUT IT (*with skull and crossbones*)
- EAT RIGHT. EXERCISE. DIE ANYWAY.
- I HAVE A HEART-ON
- HAVE A NICE AFTERLIFE

- GIVE UP ON THE GHOST (*skeleton hand giving the finger*)
- I FOUND THIS HUMERUS (*image of a long bone*)
- DEJA BOO (*with a ghost*)
- PAC-MAN (*his lucky tee*)
- TACO TANGO (*two tacos dancing*)
- I SEE DEAD PEOPLE (*cartoon eyes looking left*)

Wyatt's lingo for ghosts:

- Freshy/Freshies
- Ghosts/Ghosties
- Specters
- Spooks

Other:

- Eternity box (coffin)
- Fleshwalkers (the living, but not a Gravewalker)

See the *Gravewalker* section to learn more about ghosts.

AUTHOR'S NOTE:

Every group of friends has that one person who's a little eccentric, extroverted, and marches to the beat of his or her own drum. While every character in this series has their own brand of humor, Wyatt Blessing was off the rails.

Whenever there's a medium who talks to the dead, they're often portrayed as serious. While creating Wyatt's character, I wondered what it might be like to turn down the hall and run into a ghost with missing limbs. To be stalked by them or harassed. That could make a person jumpy. Nighttime can be especially creepy in a dark mansion, and he works late hours, often high on caffeine and sugar. So in the early books—before the house was spiritually cleaned—he's always racing around corners, easily spooked.

Wyatt is a Gravewalker who wants nothing to do with the dead. Now *that* was a fun angle to imagine. Most Breeds gravitate toward professions where they can use their gifts, but he doesn't want anything to do with spooks even if that makes his life more difficult. Because ghosts don't like being around too much electricity since it confuses them, Wyatt spent a lot of time in arcades and around computers in the early days. As a result, he discovered his passion and built a career on it. His technical skills are what Viktor hired him for, so naturally he's less than thrilled whenever he has to do something involving the dead.

Gravewalkers have a different perspective on life. They don't question whether there's life after death—they see it every day. Ghosts are a constant reminder to enjoy life. Because they see the dead wherever they go, they aren't as sensitive about the topic as others. So when a Keystone member comes close to death, Wyatt is the least affected or emotionally moved. He knows death isn't the end. And his message has always remained the same: Don't linger. Move on.

I always knew Wyatt had a story; it just took me a few books to figure it out. He got mixed up in the wrong kind of work and, as a result, lost everything. And I mean everything.

Wyatt never liked being around ghosts, so he hung out in places with lots of electricity, lights, and energy. Places like arcades, concerts, clubs—all which would have attracted lots of humans. So it's no surprise that he would have befriended humans and even fallen in love with one.

Wyatt's nostalgic about those days even though they were the best of times and the worst of times. Whenever he locks himself away in his room, listening to Air Supply and getting stoned, he's thinking about the best of times. Especially when his mind goes to dark places. He's thinking about that beautiful girl, so full of light, who captured his heart. But it's hard to think about someone you loved when there wasn't a happy ending.

Losing Dawn was devastating, so just imagine how Wyatt suffered in watching his best girl stay trapped in the afterlife. She didn't move on; she stayed behind for him. So he slowly watched her lose pieces of herself, in much the same way loved ones do with an Alzheimer's patient. Only for him, there's no closure. Sometime ghosts don't get a second chance to move on to the next life and they linger behind forever.

That's why he doesn't have any interest in pursuing serious relationships, let alone having children. He doesn't like his abilities and knows how mentally taxing it can be to have to see and deal with the dead on a constant basis, so he doesn't want kids to pass that along to. Wyatt's perfectly fine with the family name dying with him.

I loved writing a Gravewalker who would rather be a computer geek. Wyatt's quirky personality and quips made every scene with him enjoyable. A lot of immortals close off their emotions as a defense mechanism, and as a result, they can come across as wooden and cold. Not Wyatt. He's living in his own reality, and part of that is not caring what people think. He sullied his reputation years ago, so he doesn't see a point in trying to be a people pleaser.

And based on Wyatt's T-shirt collection and kilt scene, we all know that being self-conscious is a therapy session he ain't got time for.

As for the tattoo on his fingers, once you know his backstory, it doesn't need explanation. Wyatt felt like a lost soul for years. Even though he's one of the liveliest characters, he still suffers bouts of depression. It's one reason he self-medicates with drugs. We see glimpses of it in the books when he locks himself away or is suddenly down when a certain topic is brought up. Extended lives are often glamorized, but I've always wanted to show the realness of it—of what it would truly be like for an individual to live for centuries or more. The continual loss they would endure, the tragedies they would witness, the loneliness they would feel. That's why I placed value on the friendships even more than love.

Though Shepherd gives Wyatt a hard time, they've formed a bond from their partnership. I don't think they fully realized it until Wyatt almost died in *Afterlife*:

> *Shepherd kept holding the handkerchief against Wyatt's head to stanch the bleeding. "You gotta wake up, man. Don't do this to me."*

Wyatt is unapologetically himself. He doesn't hold grudges or maliciously lash out at people. Instead, he'll find solutions to problems. Why argue with the team about stealing his snacks when he can just install a vending machine?

Wyatt is a problem solver extraordinaire.

GEM LAROUX

Breed: Crossbreed. Born a Relic, became a Mage.
Relic gifts: Knowledge of ancient and obsolete languages in both the Breed and human world, whether written or spoken. Fluently speaks sixteen languages, including Russian, English, Spanish, Mandarin, and Arabic. She can still absorb knowledge into her DNA, but since she's a Mage, she can't have children to pass it on to.
Rare Mage gift(s): Blocker, Wielder
Creator: Margaret Laroux (deceased)
Creator's mark location: Unspecified
Age: About 50. Turned when she was 23.
Height: Under 5′4″
Hair: Dyed violet. Slightly wavy and just barely past her shoulders. When wearing it down, she parts it off-center. Often she'll wear it up in two cute buns. Natural hair color is almost white, and she hates it.
Eye color: Pale violet like an amethyst stone, the irises rimmed in black. Eyes are wide and expressive.
Physical: Fair-complected, heart-shaped face, beauty mark below outer corner of left eye. Full lips but almost no Cupid's bow. Keeps her nails short but paints them. Gem is petite with a slim frame. Enjoys wearing

makeup and sometimes fake eyelashes. She prefers glitter or bold eyeshadow to match her outfits.

Scars/Marks: Keystone tattoo on sole of her right foot along the arch

Clothing: Always wears her favorite raw quartz crystal pendant. She prefers above-the-knee skirts or short dresses to make her appear taller. Loves heels—the higher the better. Most of her shoes are platforms, high heels, chunky boots, or stacked sneakers. Owns several pairs of roller skates but only uses them around the house. Has a colorful wardrobe that includes floral leggings, shorts, rompers, and polka-dot pajamas. Her fun personality shines through in rhinestone sunglasses or a pink puffy coat. When she floats in the pool, she usually has on an old loose nightgown and takes a blue kimono robe with her. Gem is very expressive in her style and loves color. When she attends costume balls, she goes all out. Instead of sexy gowns, she picks outfits because of their uniqueness. Around the mansion it can feel chilly, so you'll often see her in a long thin duster sweater over her shirt.

Occupation: Works for Keystone, primarily translating books and papers, researching artifacts, and locating information on people through history books

Keystone partner: Claude

Nicknames: Rollergirl (by Wyatt), braveheart or little flower (by Niko)

Family: Unknown. Was sold on the black market as a child.

Personality: Upbeat, positive disposition. She's friendly with everyone, playful, and vivacious. If there's a party invitation, she'll be the first to accept. She loves the magic and sparkle of social gatherings. Gem is asexual. She's passionate about forming close friendships and the most affectionate in the house with hugs. Nosy by nature. Believes that a sense of belonging is more valuable than money.

Loves: Etymology, dancing, costume parties, gemstone jewelry, collecting crystals and rocks, musicals, the Spice Girls, roller-skating, racing people, floating on her back in the pool at night, daffodils. She loves children and babies but is awkward with them. Gives good massages using stones.

Hates: Alcohol, dead bodies, flaring in public, alcohol, men who judge her for her height or appearance

Flaws: Impulsive. Blindly trusts. Doesn't have good coping skills when it comes to rejection or loss. Her naivety can be easily preyed upon. Can't always tell when she's crossed a line pranking someone. Gem didn't grow up around people or with television, so she struggles with social cues. No one taught her how to deal with her emotions, so when she gets upset because she's done something wrong, she'll sometimes hit herself in the head or call herself stupid.

Food/Drink: Spreading jelly on her bacon. Likes sandwiches, hot tea, fruit juice, strawberry shakes, and waffles. Only drinks her coffee with cream. Avoids alcohol entirely.

Car: None

Weapon of choice: Energy balls, her intelligence

Catchphrase(s): "Alas." / "Behold!" / "Moi?" / "Jiminy Christmas!" / "Don't be a grump." / "Bingo." / "Heebie-jeebies."

AUTHOR'S NOTE:

Every member of Keystone provides a valuable contribution. Viktor didn't need a team composed entirely of warriors. In fact, Keystone started with Gem. She had a tragic childhood, lost her Creator, and then got into illegal work. Gem was a lost soul with so much potential but no one who believed in her. Eventually she stopped believing in herself until Viktor came along and gave her a second chance.

Gem was always a bright spot on the page, so bubbly and colorful. While she's over fifty, she's childlike. That's how her personality developed. As a child, she had no identity and no exposure to the outside world. She didn't have a TV, let alone friends. So once she gained her freedom, everything became a first-time experience. I wanted an explanation for her innocence and excitement since these aren't common personality traits for someone her age. Gem was manipulated as a child for her Relic abilities. When she gained her freedom, she absorbed American culture. Fashion, music, style—all of this breathed life into her.

We learn a lot more about Gem in *Spellbound*—shocking facts that reveal how she ended up with Keystone and why she struggles with relationships. For a sweet girl like Gem to end up working for Viktor, she had to have a lot going on to put her in the position of having no other options. Theirs is dangerous work, and sometimes all of them are expected to go on deadly missions.

Why would a gifted girl like Gem have no other options? Developing her backstory was crucial, from childhood all the way until her darkest days. It helps to not only understand her motives but also her personality traits—why she has difficulty making mistakes and processing negative emotions.

With that information, I was able to shape certain scenes that connected to her insecurities. There's a scene when they rescue a baby in *Deathtrap*. Gem is very emotional and empathetic, and yet she doesn't always understand emotions or how to process them. When she holds the baby, he starts crying. Gem thinks it has something to do with her, so she quickly passes him off. But she has a childlike response to this—as if it means something is wrong with her. Gem was raised without learning how to deal with frustration, grief, or fear. She takes rejection to heart. This scene is also revealing in another way: did you notice how natural calming a baby came to Blue? And how reluctant she was to get attached? Those little breadcrumbs to a character's backstory can often make rereading a series enjoyable. With more knowledge, you see things you didn't see the first time around.

With a large cast of characters, it was important to have balance. Not all heroes have to be warriors. Gem showed us bravery as a Wielder, but her contributions as a Relic are invaluable. Because she grew up in isolation, she thrives on the company of others. She was one of the first to reach out to Raven to build a friendship. Gem gives everyone the hugs they may not have realized they needed.

Of all the characters, Gem is purest of heart. I never wanted her to "grow up and act her age" since she's against that concept. There's room for all different kinds of people in this world. Gem is a constant reminder that life is beautiful. Savor each moment, especially with roller skates on.

CLAUDE VALENTINE

Breed: Chitah
Age: Says he is centuries old. While not specified, he was born and raised in Williamsport, Pennsylvania. Based on the date the city was founded and his mentioning that he didn't fight in Gettysburg due to them recording names, his birth is likely in the early 1800s.
Height: 6'6"
Hair: Dark golden hair with beautiful large, soft curls instead of tight ones. His hair covers his ears and his nape, styled a little messily, but he looks like he could be a model.
Eye color: Pale gold rimmed in black
Physical: Deep-set hooded eyes. Claude is extremely handsome with broad shoulders and a V-shaped torso. Has a strong brow and sensual lips with a Cupid's bow. Complexion is a light golden shade. Sometimes has a light dusting of whiskers on the face, but he mostly shaves. Athletic body. His arms and shoulders are powerfully strong. Large hands.
Scars/Marks: Keystone tattoo (location unspecified)
Clothing: Likes white tank tops. Often walks around the house shirtless in grey sweatpants. Prefers sneakers over dress shoes since he's a

Chitah and it helps with running. Winter coat is a leather jacket. His work attire is a black tank top with the salon logo on the front. Claude likes drawing attention to his shoulders and arms.

Occupation: Works for Keystone. He also owns a hair salon called Razor Sharp. Having rich and powerful clients enables him to listen in on conversations so he's always in the know. He pays attention to anything that might lead to a case or signal changes happening within certain circles.

Keystone partner: Gem

Nickname: Pretty boy (occasionally by Shep)

Family: Parents and sister (Yvette) are deceased. His kindred spirit (Josie) also died, though they were never a couple.

Personality: Very sensual mannerisms. Almost predatory due to his Chitah behavior. Cool, collected and walks gracefully with slow intent. He'll often stare at people, growl, purr, or exhibit other characteristics attributed to Chitahs. Flirts with women but not in a lewd way. He admires the power and sexuality of women and never objectifies them. Claude is sweet and has a soft spot for Gem, who is like a sister to him. When he's close to someone, he'll protect them, comfort them, and look after them the way that comes natural to Chitahs.

Loves: Kids, leather furniture in his bedroom, working on projects with Hunter, rope climbing, cuddling with Gem, and the movie *A River Runs through It*. Says he has "magic fingers" since he cuts great hair and gives amazing massages.

Hates: Anyone who would hurt or neglect a female or child

Flaws: Snores. Also gets hot when he sleeps.

Food/Drink: Red licorice, powdered donuts, beignets

Car: Red two-door Porsche. Automatic, two-seater.

Weapon of choice: His fangs and his bare hands

Catchphrase(s): "You slay me." / "Sounds delightful." / "Challenge accepted."

AUTHOR'S NOTE:

If this series ever makes it to the big or small screen, I will demand we get the scene with Claude in those infamous gold shorts, covered in body glitter.

Claude Valentine initially seems like the least likely to join an outfit like Keystone. He's outgoing, likable, and a talented hairdresser. But like everyone else on the team, Claude suffered a tragic loss. Afterward, he went on a murderous rampage that eventually led him to cage fighting. Keystone was his last stop.

How every person deals with tragedy differs. Claude has to cope with the loneliness of knowing he'll never have another kindred spirit. Even if she hadn't died, it wouldn't have worked out. Josie had chosen a different path, sacrificing a normal life so she could fight for women's rights. Claude never got answers about her murder no matter how many people he killed. Life doesn't always give us answers, and he'll have to live with that.

Claude brings valuable skills to Keystone as a tracker. He's an experienced fighter and obviously has no qualms about killing when necessary. He could have just provided those contributions, but I thought it was important to give him something that would prevent him from going down a dark path. Claude always had skills doing hair, so a side job running a salon created a perfect opportunity for collecting intel. Everyone needs their hair done, and while they might not confide their darkest secrets to their hairdresser, people love to gossip and talk business in Breed establishments. And who wouldn't go to a salon where a sexy guy like Claude is the eye candy who will give them personal attention? Additionally, it might also open doors for a different line of work should he ever leave Keystone.

In *Moonstruck*, we learn more about why Claude can be a sweetheart. He once had a human sister with Down syndrome and was very protective of her. It was a different time when people didn't accept those with special needs. He styled her hair just like the ladies on the streets and always made sure she knew how precious she was.

Most Chitahs give up their human babies for adoption to protect them from the dangers of the Breed world. Yvette was special, and children like her have been treated inhumanely throughout history. So the family kept her since only they could provide her with the love she deserved.

Claude reveals his true character through recounting his memories of his human sister. He's compassionate, loyal, fiercely protective, and loving. Claude often exhibits the same brotherly protection with Gem, his partner. Their relationship has always felt more like siblings, which makes them a compatible team. I also liked pairing them because of the height difference.

In one conversation, Claude briefly mentions why he didn't join the Army during the Civil War. It had to do with records and his name and information being documented, which most Breeds avoid. But given he lived in a city that played a role in the Underground Railroad, I could easily imagine his involvement in ensuring the safe travels of humans escaping slavery.

I know some readers were hoping Claude would find love, but this wasn't a romance series even though a romance flourished with the primary characters.

Claude finally found the home where he belongs. He's on the path to healing and seeks comfort in the important work he does. That's his happily-ever-after. It's always important to remember that when the series ends, the characters live on. They have long lives ahead of them and many journeys to take.

Learn more about Chitahs in the Mageri series.

EUGENE "CRUSH" GRAVES

Breed: Human
Age: In *Heartless*, he's 58. Crush is well on his way to retirement age.
Height: Unspecified. Slightly taller than Raven, who is 5′8″.
Hair: Salt-and-pepper hair that's a little long and usually tied back
Eye color: Blue. Close to Raven's eye color but a smidge darker.
Physical: Grey mustache and goatee. Has a big nose, silver tooth, weathered face, rough hands, and a little bit of a belly if he lets himself get out of shape. Sometimes ties his goatee in a rubber band. His hands often have grease and oil stains in the cuticles and calluses.
Tattoos mentioned include (but are not limited to):

- *Left biceps:* Skeleton riding a motorcycle with flames
- *Left outside forearm:* Dagger with a banner flying across with COOKIE written on it
- *Right biceps:* Bulldog with SEMPER FI written below it
- *Right forearm:* Skull with roses in the eyes on inside forearm. Wolf on outside forearm.

- *Chest:* Across his heart is a heart shape with flames on one side and a coy bluebird on the other. Banner across the heart has BONNIE written on it.
- *Right ankle:* Pink unicorn

Clothing: Wears skull rings. Prefers T-shirts that have skulls or biker emblems on them. He has quite a few outfits with Harley-Davidson logos. Usually wears dark jeans. Sometimes his shirts are too tight, but he doesn't care. Owns a black sweatshirt Raven gave him that says BIKER DAD on the back. Work attire is blue coveralls and steel-toe boots. Raven thinks his signature cologne smells awful.

Occupation: Owner of Graves Auto Repair

Nicknames: Crush (by everyone), Bulldog (by Raven)

Family: Raven (daughter). Love of his life, Bonnie, died in a fire.

Personality: Tough guy with a soft spot for his baby girl. Loyal, courageous, outspoken, loves a good laugh as much as he loves giving people a hard time, and is the first person to help out a friend in need. Lives by his own rules. Doesn't like talking about his emotions. Perceptive, straight shooter, man of honor, proud Marine, biker. Recovered alcoholic. Crush wants to right all the wrongs in his life, and there's one thing he can't stand seeing—Raven wallowing in self-pity or drinking. He raised her to be like him, but now he's afraid of what that might mean.

Loves: His daughter, his friends, the occasional cigar, watching TV (especially old Westerns and classic sitcoms), a good laugh, his beat-up recliner, Harley-Davidson, and working on bikes and cars. Loves spoiling his best boy Harley. Sings when he's happy.

Hates: Vampires (with the obvious exceptions), marshmallows, being interrupted during dinner, hospitals. Doesn't trust the systems of law and government. Hates his neighbor, Lou Johnson. Hell-bent on revenge against those who cross him.

Flaws: Cusses a lot. Has terrible eating habits. Never asks for help.

Food/Drink: Orange sodas, smoked turkey, barbecue, fried chicken, pistachio ice cream, extra cheese on his burgers. Never touches alcohol.

Vehicles: Harleys, including one with a sidecar. New red pickup truck with a decal on the front windshield that says BAD TO THE BONE.

Property: Lives in an upgraded home (formerly a single-wide) on a modest piece of land in a small trailer park

Weapon of choice: Shotgun or anything from his gun rack

Catchphrase(s): "All out of fucks to give/I ran out of fucks to give." / "You got that?" / "What's done is done." / "Don't give me your sass."

Friends mentioned: Ren, Wizard, Tank, and Tire

Employees mentioned: Red and Jimmy. Third employee name wasn't given.

Facts about Bonnie, Raven's mother: Crush called her Bonnie Bluebird. She had brown hair and eyes. Worked for an insurance company, though Crush helped her financially. Bonnie died in an apartment fire after falling through a hole where her floor caved in from the intense flames in the old building. She was buried in a blue dress, closed-casket funeral. Her grave has a raised headstone with Raven's grave next to it.

AUTHOR'S NOTE:

I'm not lying when I say that I could write scenes with Crush all day long. There's just something about him that reels you in even though he's abrasive. Every writer has characters who make it enjoyable every time you hit their scenes.

Crush was that guy.

Whether it was the heartfelt moments with Raven or the crazy-ass shit he got into, it was always a wild ride. Maybe part of what made it easy is I've known people with his personality traits. There are people in real life who are characters, and you never forget them. They make no apologies for who they are.

One of the most important factors in Raven's growth was mending the broken relationship with her father. Even after joining Keystone, she still feels lost—afraid of who she's become and unable to let go of the past. She secretly visits her father just to listen to him walking around the trailer and laughing at the TV. She never got closure.

And neither did he.

Portraying the father as the villain is a popular trope. I never wanted to go that route. Crush played a vital role in this series. Besides that, in every scene where he appears, I would get out the popcorn and soda because I knew we were about to have some fun or shed a few tears.

Crush isn't for everyone. I get it. While he's not always easy to understand, men like him exist. They're imperfect, overbearing, and stubborn. A perfect dad would have made zero sense in the grand scheme of why Raven is who she is and why she would have turned her back on her mortal life to become a Vampire.

Crush is a former alcoholic—one whose addiction was so out of control that he would black out. It's one of two main reasons the love of his life wouldn't marry him or share a home, but she never excluded him from his daughter's life. He just wasn't willing to quit, even after Bonnie died. He got full custody of Raven and wasn't prepared for it. His drinking habit continued, and when he almost lost custody of her, that was enough to make him quit.

It's been a long road ever since.

Even though Crush comes across as bossy and a handful of trouble, that doesn't make him a bad person. He's been through a lot and suffered loss. He's seen the worst in life, and as a result, he became an overprotective dad. Even more so after he got sober. As Raven got older, their relationship became a struggle until they were estranged. It happens. Sometimes nothing in particular instigates it.

When Crush got the call that Raven died, it wrecked his world. It changed him in a way that I didn't fully explore. Losing a child is hard enough, but all that regret he must have felt for the things unsaid and mistakes he made must have been soul crushing. It truly shows how strong he was not to turn back to the bottle, but something tells me he wanted to do right by Raven and Bonnie. He probably spent a lot of nights blaming himself. So when he found out she was alive, he suddenly had a second chance.

For both of them, rebuilding their relationship was a priority. Having a reunion was great, but that was just the start. There was a lot of work to be done. He needed to learn to give her the space she required to grow and find her own way in life while still being the over-protective dad. His worst fear is losing her again, so they're both trying to navigate uncharted waters. Her happiness means everything to him, and that's one reason he didn't tell her that he was in so much debt. Crush didn't want to be a burden. He didn't want to risk fracturing their relationship again.

Now let's talk about the boys...

One thing about Crush and Christian's unique relationship is that they are both authentically themselves. Neither is putting on airs. If you read the books again, you'll see just how similar they actually are.

Crush is a trusted human who knows all about Vampires and their bad reputation. So when his daughter falls for one, alarm bells go off. Vampires can charm and manipulate, so his concerns are valid. Crush wants the best for his daughter, but that doesn't mean he'll turn a blind eye to anything that might pose a danger to her. Maybe it's from being in the Marines, maybe it's just being a dad, or maybe over the years he picked up sacred pack beliefs from his Shifter friends. In any case, he has to find a balance between protecting her while letting her go. His journey is being the dad she needs while giving her the love and support she deserves.

It's a quality Christian admires. Christian also butts heads with Switch at times, but he truly appreciates how Raven has people in her life who are protective and willing to die for her. That's something he's never known. Not until he met her.

Toward the end, it was clear that Crush needed a buddy. Raven can't always be there, and if he's not going to take a wife, he might as well take a dog. Sometimes people don't realize they need a pet until they get one, and then that furbaby just changes everything. It's like Crush and Harley were made for each other. Harley was a rescue who was almost euthanized, so it seemed fitting he got a second chance like everyone else in this series. Despite his cantankerous personality, Crush is a softy. He's always helped out rogues and outliers who needed it the most, so there was no way he was sending that dog back.

Somewhere out there, I imagine Crush is sitting in his beat-up recliner, eating a Hungry-Man chicken dinner and watching a rerun of *Gunsmoke*. Harley's sitting on the floor next to him, smacking his lips and waiting for a bite of that corn that Crush is going to pass over for the brownie. Wind chimes are tinkling on his spacious front porch, and the sun is streaming through the much larger windows of his newer home. Raven's at the store, picking up groceries and a prescription medication. Crush puts the TV on mute to listen to the sound of water spraying outside. Christian offered to wash his truck, and Crush has an urge to go outside to make sure he's doing it right. But he lets that feeling go because he knows that Christian will do a good job.

He always does.

HUNTER MOON

Breed: Crossbreed (Relic/Sensor)

Relic gifts: Inherited knowledge about human genetics and pathogens

Sensor gifts: Has the usual Sensor gifts. Learned at an early age how to transfer emotions and read complex ones. It's unknown whether he has the immune system of a Relic or a Sensor. Relics are like humans and can catch viruses and develop diseases.

Age: Born on June 2. Around the time we meet him, he's five years old. By book ten, he is six. According to his mother, Hunter will have the lifespan of a Sensor.

Hair: Blackish-brown. Tousled and wild.

Eye color: Blue with black rims. White streaks that radiate from the center like electricity.

Scars/Marks: Prominent scar across his face. Starts at the corner of his left eye, curves across his cheek and to the center of his nose. Deep scar that won't fade with time since it never healed properly.

Clothing: Often wears Sensor gloves to protect himself from feeling residual emotions left on objects, particularly in public. Loves sneakers with butterflies or blinking lights on them. Always wears socks with pink in them.

Nicknames: little man (by Shepherd), little monkey (by Wyatt)

Family: Shepherd (father), Maggie (mother/deceased)

Personality: Shy, insecure (especially about his scar), and has separation anxiety. He's curious, explores his surroundings, brave, and giggles a lot. Hunter is a selective mute, though he will sometimes whisper in Shepherd's ear. Learning sign language. Because he was taught very young how to use his Sensor abilities, he's very attuned to people's emotions in the house. He's leery of strangers, but he's also eager to form friendships with children his age. Hunter is a bright kid who needs structure and rules. He's still getting over being raised by Patrick and then having to adjust to a new house and people. He's a heavy sleeper and sometimes has nightmares. When he's feeling scared or upset, he'll put a mask on, but he's doing that a lot less now.

Loves: Pink socks, the color green, dogs, cupcakes, pizza, mint chocolate chip ice cream, candy, mechanical horses, books, a teddy bear Shepherd gave him, exploring, climbing, drawing, watching TV. He likes playing with marbles, rubber balls, kites, dinosaur toys, and sometimes pretends he's an animal.

Hates: People who stare at his scar or say something about it, being separated from his daddy, mean people

---

AUTHOR'S NOTE:

My favorite little man.

I didn't plan on bringing a child into the series, but sometimes they sneak into a scene. Once he did, I knew how the storyline would tie in with Shepherd. The hardest part was getting him away from Patrick. But when I did, I was curious how he would adapt to his new life. The adjustment wouldn't be easy. He's too young to understand what's happening, and even though Patrick was a wicked man, Hunter's entire life was upended following his death.

When we first meet Hunter, he's an obedient but curious child. Patrick manipulated him by getting him to use his Sensor gifts to read people to give Patrick inside information. Hunter learned how to read complex emotions, and he whispered that information into Patrick's ear. He always dressed up as Zorro, wearing a mask to hide his scar. You can bet that was Patrick's idea. Hunter's scar became his insecurity, so it took time after moving in with Shepherd to stop wearing the mask and see that he was a beautiful boy.

I think about the scene when Shepherd first walked into Hunter's bedroom at Patrick's house. There were no toys, no colorful blankets or pictures. Going in public must have been a treat to the senses—all the foods, toys, and colorful window displays. I loved when Hunter sneaked away from Patrick to sit on the mechanical horse. When Shepherd saw him, he already knew at that point that Hunter was his son. He put a quarter in the ride and watched Hunter's eyes light up. You could see hints early on that Shepherd would make a good father.

After Hunter moved in with Keystone, every scene became a cautious step. You have to acknowledge and respect what a person's been through to understand their journey to healing. It wouldn't be natural for Hunter to start talking. Given his upbringing and his punishments, he would be naturally apprehensive, quiet, watchful, and fearful of making mistakes.

He didn't even have a name. Patrick called him "boy."

Even after he's given a name and learns that Shepherd is his father, Hunter displays pure terror when he accidentally breaks a glass. Telling a child they're safe isn't enough to make them *feel* safe. All he's ever known are rules and punishments. They could have hugged him and told him it was okay, but they all took a glass and broke it. He learned in that moment that his life going forward would be different. But it's unrealistic for a person (especially a child) who's been conditioned to behave a certain way to change overnight. There is an unlearning that needs to happen, and the burden doesn't all fall on Shepherd. The team had to reinforce that Hunter was in a safe environment, but even still, it didn't take long for Shepherd to realize he was in over his head.

Hunter is bright, and you can see how he wants to connect with others. He befriended a young girl who temporarily stayed with them, and he bonded with Crush's dog. He's not hiding under tables anymore. But Keystone is a dangerous organization, and his adjustment wasn't going to work without the right support. Kira sometimes kept an eye on him, but Hunter needed guidance.

Enter Switch. While his past may look checkered to some, it actually makes him the ideal candidate. Hunter needs a watchdog who can protect him, and Switch is instinctually protective of children. But he's also an excellent teacher. Because their home environment isn't entirely stable and their jobs can take them away unexpectedly, it was crucial for Hunter to have a daily routine—something he could count on. And that's what homeschooling offered.

Hunter is moving through life at his own speed. The series ends with him learning sign language, which will allow him to communicate with everyone in the mansion. Hunter's journey wasn't just about finding his father; it was learning that there are people in this world who will love and accept him for exactly who he is. There will always be challenges and there will always be bad guys, but there are also people he can count on. Hunter used to hide his scar because he thought it was ugly. Then he saw how scarred his daddy was—someone who makes him feel safe and chases away his nightmares. Learning what love is taught him that ugly comes from within.

Wherever Hunter goes in life, I bet he'll have his father's courage and his mother's heart. He'll march to the beat of his own drum, pink socks and all.

HARLEY

Breed: Red bullmastiff
Physical: Red coloring, black muzzle and ears. Muscular.
Clothing: Occasionally wears goggles when riding with Crush. You can bet Crush has bought him a leather vest and spiked collar.
Family: Crush
Personality: Rescued from a kill shelter, so he is grateful for his new home. Obedient, smart, fiercely protective, eager to please his daddy. Treats Crush like the alpha. Great with kids and can pee in a toilet. Tail wagger.
Loves: Being a good boy, riding in the motorcycle sidecar, and chasing Vampires. Smart boy who listens to commands and loves pleasing Crush.
Hates: Vampires, anyone who threatens his humans
Flaws: Slobbers, passes stinky farts
Food/Drink: Dill pickles, cheese, hot dogs
Car: Sidecar on Harley bike
Weapon of choice: Teeth
Catchphrase(s): "Woof."

AUTHOR'S NOTE:

Don't think for a second that I didn't have a section set aside for Harley in my character bios. When I first thought about Raven getting Crush a dog, I went to work searching for the right breed. I wanted a dog that would match his personality, be a fierce protector, and also be a comical sidekick. Whenever I wrote him in a scene, the page came alive. I could hear his toenails clicking against the steps, his heavy breaths, his snorts, and all his many vocalizations. For having such a small part, Harley had a larger-than-life presence. And an important role. He fills an empty void in Crush's life and has become his lifeline.

There was just one problem: all of Crush's friends are Shifters. And Shifters generally don't believe in owning pets. Once he broke the news to them, we got to sit back and enjoy watching Crush dress up his dog and parade him around in the sidecar he built.

Clearly he's all out of fucks to give.

As for Harley's name, Crush wasn't the only one who almost named him Pickles. That was all me. Names are important, and it has to feel right. I played with a few name ideas, and this one tickled me. But I had to get inside Crush's head and figure out what he would have named his dog. The man loves the Harley-Davidson brand, so it just made sense.

Not only do I love the pairing, it's nice to know that Crush has a buddy. One that will make him more active as well as give him years of laughter for chasing Christian across the yard.

SWITCH

Breed: Shifter wolf
Animal description: Chestnut-brown wolf with dark ears and dark fur around his neck. Like most Shifters, he loses control after a short period and blacks out when his wolf takes over.
Shifter craving: Green beans
Age: Unspecified. A few years older than Raven.
Height: Unspecified
Hair: Brown, long, just past his shoulders
Eye color: Brown
Physical: Circle beard around his mouth that is more whiskery than long. Pensive eyebrows that are wolfish. Prominent brow, which gives him an animalistic look. Full lips and broad mouth. Nice build.
Scars/Marks: Left upper arm is a tattoo of a large owl and a clock
Clothing: Jeans or grungy pants, cotton shirts. Wears heavy motorcycle boots with thick soles to give him extra height. A black helmet with a face shield when riding. Sometimes wears a bandana.
Occupation: Hunter's teacher. Also his watchdog during the times Shepherd is away. Former teacher and pack nanny.
Nickname: Switcharoo (by Raven)

Family: Father (living). No mention of other family.

Personality: Sexy, straightforward, masculine. He owns his power as a Shifter. Switch makes direct eye contact and gives you his undivided attention when you're speaking. Not much of a jokester, but not overly serious either. Somewhat mellow but knows when to get tough. Doesn't keep his feelings or intentions to himself but makes them known.

Loves: Reading, teaching, kids, Jimi Hendrix, quoting authors or people in history, riding his bike, rock climbing, playing pool

Hates: Anyone who hurts kids, liars

Flaws: He can be nosy, judgmental

Food/Drink: Pie, donuts, beer, bologna sandwiches, and sweet pickles. Only puts tomatoes on his burgers.

Vehicle: Black Yamaha Cruiser motorcycle

Weapon of choice: His wolf

Catchphrase(s): "News flash:" / "No worries."

AUTHOR'S NOTE:

From the moment Switch stepped on the scene, I knew he was going to stir the pot. Raven never considered him a love interest, but she had options. Growing up around Shifters, she became familiar with their mannerisms and way of life without even realizing it. Another reason she was easy with him is that they knew each other as kids.

Switch never loved Raven or had a crush on her as a child. But as a woman, she embodies the qualities he most admires. Switch is more than happy to explore their relationship, but this is a crossroads in Raven's life where she needs a friend. That was the role I wanted to give him going forward. Aside from her father, she has no one to tether her to the real world—the one outside her crazy job.

Switch had another important role to play as the perfect candidate for schooling Hunter. Kira's lovely with the boy, but she has a full-time job, and Hunter requires an education.

The thing about Switch is he's a good guy at heart. He just made an impulsive choice in the past that had a lasting impact on his future. While he was a talented teacher, and many knew he would be a good protector around their children, it was the Packmasters who didn't want him. They can't trust someone who might defy their authority. Pack always comes first, and they can't take chances on someone with a history of taking matters into his own hands instead of leaving it to the alpha.

While the Council forgave him, the Packmaster kicked him out. That tarnished his reputation with the local leaders. Yet it was that controversial action that made him the ideal candidate for becoming Hunter's watchdog and teacher. Working for Keystone under the watchful eye of a powerful Shifter will restore his reputation in time. Switch didn't follow protocol and acted on his feelings even if those feelings were justified. Viktor's guidance and high expectations will help Switch become a stronger man who will respect the authority demanded in a pack.

Switch may be a secondary character, but he plays an important part. Without him, Hunter wouldn't have a protector when Shepherd is away, a broad education, and someone who can help him communicate. Switch also keeps Kira company, provides friendship to Raven (which she desperately needs), and helps Keystone whenever they ask.

I also think Crush likes the idea of someone he knows looking out for Raven.

If anyone is curious about his tattoo, I chose an owl because it symbolizes wisdom and knowledge.

KIRA

Breed: Shifter phoenix
Animal description: Shifts into a phoenix that's as large as an ostrich. Beautiful feathers that are red and gold like fire. Massive wings and a long tail.
Gifts: Breathes concentrated fire that can incinerate a man to ashes. She can make it widespread or very precise. Phoenixes cannot die and come back to life (myth), but they are invincible to their own fire.
Shifter craving: Unknown
Age: Unknown
Height: 5'9"
Hair: Flaming red with an ombré effect where it gets lighter at the ends. It's long and wavy. Long bangs she wears off to the side. Sometimes pins it up in a messy knot or wears two loose braids.
Eye color: Copper
Physical: Heart-shaped face. Her light skin is peppered with moles and freckles. Feminine features but her hands less so since she does manual labor.
Scars/Marks: Trail of tattooed symbols from her nape to the base of

her spine. They're written in an archaic language that was her mother's tongue and are words of protection.

Clothing: Often wears a kerchief to keep her hair out of her eyes when she's working. Prefers dresses, especially ones that conceal and are suitable for working in. Sometimes wears shawls in the winter. Uses aprons while cooking. Flat, practical shoes.

Occupation: Works for Keystone, doing all the domestic work. These tasks include but are not limited to: cooking, cleaning, laundry, light yard work, and occasionally watching Hunter. Kira is also tasked with lighting the lanterns and candles in the most widely used rooms and hallways. That job also entails cleaning the wax from holders and snuffing out candles. Kira makes sure the house doesn't fall apart from neglect, and she takes pride in her work.

Family: Father (Valko) and her mother are deceased. Her father was an alpha wolf and her mother a phoenix.

Personality: Strong personality even though she stays quiet. When she does speak, you get a sense that she's not shy and is strong-willed. Intelligent and a fast learner. Hard worker and enjoys feeling useful. Protective of those she cares about. Untrusting of everyone because of her animal type and the history surrounding phoenixes and her own family.

Loves: Cooking, gardening, reading, keeping things tidy, children, certain fantasy movies, and healthy food

Hates: Messy people, having to live her life in hiding, the men who hunt her kind

Flaws: Won't trust even those closest to her

Food/Drink: None specified

Weapon of choice: Breathing fire

Accent: Bulgarian

AUTHOR'S NOTE:

The second Kira poked her head out of a shipping crate, I knew she had a story. She comes from an old way of life—one without modern conveniences. Kira was never exposed to the modern world until she traveled to Cognito. She lived in a small house with her father, and they farmed and hunted. She lived a sheltered life for her own protection, so when her father died, she was terrified of the world and what might happen to her. Keystone became her refuge in an uncertain time.

Here's the thing: Viktor needed help. Keystone Estate is massive. There are tons of rooms, hallways, windows, and endless chores the team doesn't always have time to do. As their job becomes more demanding and unpredictable, it makes all the domestic work increasingly difficult to manage. Viktor would never hire an outsider, especially not someone he didn't know. The team discusses sensitive information in open rooms, and he wants to protect his organization from deceit. It was important to work in someone trustworthy—a person who needed Viktor as much as he needed them. Viktor knew Kira's father, and he trusted him. He also felt a sense of obligation to help his friend's daughter.

But why would a young woman need protection?

I wanted to allude to what she was, but I wasn't yet sure if or how I wanted to reveal her secret. She never shifted around others, and no one was quite certain of her animal. Initially they assumed she was a wolf since her father was, but that also depended on what her mother's animal was. I didn't want to push her story, so I kept her in the background. But I knew from the beginning what she was; hence the reason she feared Shepherd's tattoo. Also the reason I gave her a fiery hair color.

When the opportunity presented itself, it let me reveal a Shifter animal not yet seen. Up until that point, all Shifters were based on real-life animals. The idea of phoenixes intrigued me since they're mythological, but what if they did exist? Just not in the way we imagined. Gem mentions prior to Kira's reveal how phoenix feathers were allegedly used to write spellbooks like the one Niko carried. I've always loved the idea that even among Breed, there are urban legends. That they too can be skeptical about the existence of other Breeds or gifts if they haven't seen it with their own eyes.

But the ones who *do* know—they're to be feared.

The reason men hunted phoenixes is that unusual gifts not understood are either coveted or feared by immortals—even ones of the same Breed. Many have speculated what power phoenix feathers, blood, and meat hold. There may be truth to some and myth to others. Kira's animal is seen as a rare and valuable commodity—the white whale for many hunters.

It was interesting writing a character who never speaks and yet always has something to say about the team's manners or requests. Kira's able to converse with Viktor in other languages, and it's likely they speak more often in private. She understands that his expectation is that she doesn't learn English or make an effort to communicate with the team. It's for their safety as well as hers. Kira spends more time with them than Switch does, so she's more likely to overhear something.

But isn't she clever? She notices how Gem pays attention and picks up on language, so she and Viktor converse in an ancient language that Gem doesn't understand, and only rarely in front of the group.

As time goes by, her role in the house will change. Earning money allows her more freedom and opportunities. Perhaps she might one day purchase her own plot of land.

Kira is a self-assured woman who, by no fault of her own, must conceal what she is. Given the history with hunters and her family, having a big reveal party at the end where she shows everyone her animal wouldn't honor her story. While it's unfortunate she can't tell everyone, it's not essential she does. The Keystone team is entitled to their secrets, and Kira is no different. She believes this is one that will not only protect herself but those closest to her.

It's clear from what we witnessed in *Quicksilver* that, despite her secrets, Kira will never let harm come to Keystone if she can help it.

HOUDINI

Breed: Crossbreed (Shifter/Vampire). Born a Potential.
Maker: François
Shifter animal: Various. Always white. Animals mentioned are panther, wolf, white owl, cat. There are likely more.
Shifter gifts: Unlike other Shifters, Houdini does not have a spirit animal living inside him. When he shifts, he is the animal he shifts into. He can choose what animal he wants, but within limits. He can only become an animal if he has slept with another Shifter of that animal type. Because he was a Potential and due to the way he was made, it activated something unique within him that allows him to do this.
Vampire gifts: Unlike Raven, he has all the typical Vampire traits with the exception of sight. It's better than average but not 100%, similar to Raven. Never experienced bloodlust and also doesn't like the taste of non-Vampire blood.
Other gifts: As of *Quicksilver*, he is now permanently half-dead, living in what they refer to as the Shadow Realm. *See below for more info.*
Age: Born in 1500s France
Height: Just over 6'0"
Hair: Naturally dark hair but bleaches it. Unkempt. Sometimes styled

in thick, spiked chunks that Raven thinks make him look like an anime character.

Eye color: Hazel. Can change his eyes to black at will when he's charming or scrubbing someone.

Physical: Deep-set eyes that are narrow like he's squinting. Dark eyebrows that slope down in the middle. Pretty eyelashes. Body type is on the leaner side like a man who doesn't work out. Pale. Looks young. Deep lines on face when he smiles. Broad mouth, friendly face, a few tiny moles. Has a regal look with a straight, narrow nose.

Scars/Marks: His Potential mark is on his scalp, hidden by hair. No tattoos or obvious scars observed.

Clothing: Black ear studs are his signature accessory. Owns dark dress shirts, faded jeans, and a grey sweater. Occasionally paints his fingernails black. Around his house, he wears tight pants that stop above the knee. Sleeps in a white tank top and grey cotton pants. Though he doesn't need a jacket for cold weather, he wears a long grey coat with the collar pulled up to shield some of his face. In the Shadow Realm, he now has permanent attire. *See below for more details.*

Occupation: Owns the White Owl club. Used to make money turning willing women into Vampires before selling them on the black market. His maker instilled in him the wisdom of how to build a fortune. Has no real purpose in life.

Nickname: Chaos (by Raven)

Family: None

Personality: Affable and laid-back. Has the ability to switch his personality and way of talking depending on whom he's speaking with or what his objective might be. Presents himself as a person with candor but is deceitful and secretive. Enjoys meaningful and philosophical conversations. Doesn't come across as insidious, cruel, or with evil intent. Mysterious—you never really know what his motivations are or what he's thinking. He's fascinated by people's reactions under duress.

Loves: The chaos theory, blues music, watching Raven, studying behavior. Sings old songs with lyrics relevant to the situation in order to drive his point home.

Hates: In-your-face sexuality, a party atmosphere, order and rules, people who aren't perceptive or intelligent, inane questions, arguing

Flaws: Narcissist. Doesn't care about humans, has no scruples about tampering with people's lives. Believes his way of thinking is the only way.

Food/Drink: Doesn't require food but sometimes enjoys coffee, pastries (beignets), and milk. In the Shadow Realm, he no longer has the ability to eat or taste food. *See below for more details.*

Car: Unspecified

Weapon of choice: Sharp wit, Vampire strength

Accent: None

Catchphrase(s): "I'll see you when I see you." / "All in good fun." / "I do love a good plot twist."

As of *Quicksilver*, Houdini now exists in a realm between the living and the dead. Here are his abilities and limitations living in the Shadow Realm:

- Sees ghosts
- Can't die
- Humans can't see or hear him
- Vampires can hear him speaking, but they're unable to hear him moving or walking, so he can slip by them easily.
- He discovered how to borrow energy from humans to make physical contact with them. Can also borrow energy from Breed but that's pointless since they can see and touch him.
- Stuck wearing the same clothes forever. Can't change them or remove them. *See below for his attire.*
- Unable to carry anything in his pockets or on his person— they will disappear. Items include jewelry, clothing,

accessories, shoulder bags, and even hair dye. But he *can* carry items in his hands and move them from one location to another. He can also drive a vehicle.

- Since he's part Vampire, Houdini never experienced hunger or required food. His new condition now prevents him from tasting food or drink, and while he can eat it, the food will reappear back on the plate. This has dulled the pleasure he enjoyed from certain foods and drink.
- He shifts back to human form fully clothed now
- Unable to have sex anymore due to the inability to remove his clothing

His "forever" look:

- Long coat jacket that is a deep red/burgundy with black cuffs. Gothic style with black lapels.
- Black ear studs
- Sword sheathed inside his long coat
- Black shirt and black pants
- Bleached hair that's a couple of inches long and spiked different ways. His hair will always bounce back to its original shape from when he was cursed, and it can't be cut or dyed.
- Blood, paint, mud, and anything that marks his body will disappear within several minutes. His clothing can't be altered, and he can't set his sword on a table without it reappearing inside his coat. He's able to use his sword as a weapon.

AUTHOR'S NOTE:

Houdini's character is a trickster. He's one of the greyest characters I've ever written. Technically the antagonist in the story and not a villain. Some love him, some hate him, and some aren't sure what to think about him. That's the feeling I wanted to create throughout the series up until the last page. There's no redemption story or grand unveiling of a hero inside.

Houdini never portrays himself as good or evil. He's not driven by greed, anger, lust, or fear. He believes in cause and effect—that negative actions can have positive reactions and vice versa. He's justified every act he's ever committed, including the younglings he made and sold. Houdini has psychopathic traits. He's a skilled actor who manipulates people for personal gain even if it's just for his own personal amusement. It's hard to ever really tell if he's experiencing an emotion or faking it. He's calculating, charming, and patient.

Houdini selling Raven showed just how asshat crazy he was. As much as I hated scenes in *Gaslight*, it was important for Raven to revisit that relationship. Both of them. While Raven wasn't forced into becoming a Vampire, she was deceived all the same. Houdini scrubbed her memory of his face and subsequent encounters they'd had over the years. When he restored her memories, she had to come to terms with the fact that she had always liked him. Between him and Fletcher, she always resented Houdini the most for not preparing her and abandoning her. Readers needed to see what he was capable of in real time.

I also wanted to show how good Houdini was at gaslighting. Raven continually questioned her beliefs, her memory, and her existence because of him.

Houdini wasn't just a Vampire who shirked his responsibilities by abandoning his youngling. He just doesn't care about anyone but himself. He's only interested in the end result since that's where he draws his entertainment.

We only learn about Houdini's past through his own account, but we get no sense of whether he changed over time. It's possible he was always unstable, even in his human life. Or perhaps he reflected much too often on his life choices and how each path could have led him in different directions until it became an obsession. We don't know everything about him because he will only reveal so much.

Houdini isn't his given name nor is it the one his maker gave him. His early beginnings in Paris and how he fled a marital life and financial comfort for personal freedom are somewhat revealing. He never had to claw and scrape his way out of poverty. Though he lived on the streets for a brief time, he knew he could always return home. He had that luxury that others didn't. His education also put him at an advantage.

Is he grateful for the opportunity he's shown at being a scholar's apprentice? No. He risked his job to practice debauchery right under his employer's nose. And that indulgence is what ultimately led to him becoming Breed. I'm sure that had him thinking for many years. What might have happened had he kept his pants zipped? Would he have ever been turned by François? Or was he merely a curiosity who would have lived the rest of his life as a human?

Leaving readers confused on how to feel about him accurately illustrates how Raven was so easily influenced by his opinions and yet equally hated him. Her conflicted feelings deserved to be explored, so Houdini had to manipulate the reader just as much as he did the protagonist.

Raven is the only one who ever held a mirror up to Houdini. Though he refuses to admit he's doing any wrong, there's a sense toward the end that something got through to him.

Or did it?

Even his actions with turning over Lenore and giving Raven property might have a different explanation or ulterior motive. Maybe he just wanted to see what might happen. In the end, there's no clear understanding of why Houdini is the way he is. No singular moment where we finally see his truc intentions.

Houdini will always be an enigma.

FLETCHER BLACK

Breed: Mage
Mage gift(s): Jumper
Age: Unknown
Height: Unspecified
Hair: Brown or auburn, but he shaves his head bald. The stubble on his head reveals a widow's peak, so it's possible he's insecure about natural hair loss prior to his first spark.
Eye color: Deep blue
Physical: Odd-shaped head that is noticeable since he shaves off his hair. Has a wiry beard that's auburn. His mustache covers his upper lip, and none of his facial hair is neatly trimmed. There are deep lines in his forehead, and his gaze is menacing. Physically strong, like a light-weight boxer. Not muscular but tough all the same. Looks like he's lived a hard life.
Scars/Marks: His body has lines and scars he got before becoming a Mage. Specific scars and their locations are unspecified.
Occupation: Previously worked for the Mageri, processing bodies in the morgue of a human hospital. His job was to identify any Breed and turn them over to the authorities so they wouldn't be discovered by

humans. Those bodies, living or dead, would be returned to their families. It's important to note that some Breeds experience paralysis when impaled with certain weapons, so they might only appear dead.

Nicknames: N/A

Personality: Short-tempered and easily provoked. He's a juicer with a serious light addiction. He also has control issues and enjoys brainwashing and dominating his victims, which he keeps as light slaves. Fletcher is mostly impotent but has certain sadistic triggers that get him going. Doesn't like anyone having the upper hand. He wants what he wants.

Loves: Having complete control over a woman where she does whatever he says, Mage light

Hates: People laughing at him, feeling like he's not in control, insolence

Flaws: Bad breath, short-tempered, insecure, lowest life-form

Food/Drink: Lamb shanks

Car: Unspecified

Weapon of choice: Mage powers

Accent: British (London/cockney sound)

Catchphrase(s): "All in good fun." / "My little pet." / "wakey-wakey" or other word repeats, like "nicey-nicey"

AUTHOR'S NOTE:

Sometimes I write villains that make me want to burn sage around my laptop. If I had to create a list of villains I wanted to throw under a steamroller, Fletcher would be near the top.

Humans glorify immortality. When I created Breed, I saw it as a rose garden filled with weeds and thorns. There are power plays, addiction, and battles waging. Fletcher is a light addict, but he's not a rogue who hangs out on street corners. He collects unguarded and inexperienced women. He breaks them down until they're too mentally and physically weak to fight back. Regardless of why he terrorized his victims, Fletcher was absolute scum.

The series had three primary villains. One belonged to Christian, and the other two belonged to Raven. Lenore made enemies of all, but she was the demon that Christian needed to bury. Raven hated her Vampire side because of Fletcher. But why? Fletcher was a Mage.

While it might seem more likely that Fletcher's cruelty would have driven Raven to hate her Mage side more, not everyone blames their abuser. Every victim processes their pain differently, and some redirect their anger and resentment toward enablers. In Raven's mind, had she never met Houdini, she would have never suffered. She would still have her old life. But he left her at the morgue and never came back. When he broke his promise, Raven fell into the hands of a monster.

So Fletcher became the man she feared, and Houdini the man she despised.

As we reached the end of the series, Raven needed to face her demons. Christian couldn't be the one to kill Fletcher as that would rob her of closure. Throwing him in jail wouldn't be enough. Raven had a conflicted soul throughout the series, and her emotions have ruled her decisions. When she faces her ultimate fear and temptations, she realizes the only way to make the right choice is to put aside her emotions.

I wasn't about to let Fletcher slip through the cracks of justice. Hints were left early on regarding Christian's late-night disappearances or conversations when he would ask Raven offhanded questions about Fletcher. In the end, Fletcher got exactly what he deserved.

Though I might have personally added five hundred fire ants in the coffin for good measure. I'm sure Christian would have appreciated the suggestion. Then again, who's to say he didn't sneak back in there later on to do it himself?

Sleep tight, Fletcher.

LENORE PARRISH

Breed: Vampire
Gifts: Typical Vampire gifts
Age: At least 1,000 years old
Height: 5'11"
Hair: Long, silky blond hair. Sometimes wears it up with a few wispy strands hanging loose. Also likes intricate braiding around her head.
Eye color: Black
Physical: Lithe and graceful with straight shoulders and a narrow nose. Though she has small breasts, they seem large on her narrow, skinny frame. Not much of an hourglass shape. Slender fingers, always manicured. Graceful and feminine. Flawless Vampire skin.
Scars/Marks: None
Clothing: Elegant dresses that are usually thin and formfitting. Occasionally wears slacks. Always dresses feminine in a way to draw men's attention.
Occupation: Higher authority official
Nickname: None (The one you might be thinking of was never her nickname.)
Family: None

Personality: Persnickety, judgmental, calculated. She's stoic and rarely loses control of her emotions. She will insult people with a smile and do it with such finesse they don't always recognize it as an insult. Has other people do her dirty work. Masterful manipulator and can make people believe that her idea was theirs. Doesn't like making enemies because they're difficult to deal with. Not shy about her body. Has never made another Vampire. Lenore isn't her real name; she changed it to fit the times.

Loves: The color purple, roses, statues of people, flaunting her wealth, finding out a person's insecurity and picking at it. Enjoys basking in a sunroom filled with plants. Likes flowers or things with flowers on them, such as her bone china tea set.

Hates: Crass people, those who don't go along with her plans, idiots, men in power, city noise, people who can't keep their mouths shut

Flaws: Greedy for power, highly paranoid

Food/Drink: Tea, absinthe

Car: Classic white Rolls-Royce. Has a chauffeur.

Weapon of choice: Her Vampire strength

Accent: None

Catchphrase(s): "Dear oh dear." / "No hard feelings?" / "This will not do."

AUTHOR'S NOTE:

If ever there was a villain in my series most hated...

Lenore was our connection to Christian's past. Through their shared history, we finally gained insight to why she buried Christian and why his opinion of love became negative. He got too close to the fire, and he got burned.

What sets Lenore apart from other villains I've written is how charming she is—how affable. There are moments when she pulls

Raven under her wing and gives valuable advice. It's hard to tell if she might consider mentoring Raven the way she did with Christian. We know all about her past, but people change.

Lenore is a woman from humble beginnings. She clawed her way through life. It's suggested that her family came from poverty, and while we don't hear many details about her past, she once mentioned how she fought off a pack of wolves as a young Vampire. Lenore entertained Viktor with tales of ancient Greece. Even if she's not originally from there, we know she's well traveled.

Lenore depended on men for her survival. They held the lion's share of power in the Breed world. Female Vampires were kept as bloodslaves in earlier times. While the details of her struggles aren't known, it's clear she's a survivor. Vampires had more freedom in those lawless days, but that didn't guarantee survival. Every place she went, she sought out powerful people. She raised herself up in good society to be the object of every man's desire. She used her talents, her grace, and her sexuality to control people and secure her future.

Lenore is not only charismatic, she's skilled in the Vampire art of charming. There are scenes where she is charming someone and it's not even obvious to the reader.

That's how good she is.

When she returns to Cognito and discovers Christian is no longer buried, she seeks him out immediately. Lenore keeps her friends close and her enemies closer, but she's not clear where Christian falls. Will he come after her, or can she manipulate him once again? Christian was the most loyal person who ever served her. He never exposed her for the simple fact he took responsibility for all his crimes. Once Lenore was secure in knowing he wouldn't come after or kill her, that made her want to bring him into the fold again. Only this time she wouldn't have to worry about his misplaced feelings. If she had Christian again, nothing would stop her.

Well, except for Raven.

Lenore was a different type of villain, and similar to Houdini, there's an uncertainty about her true motives. We know what she did to Christian, but everyone has done unforgivable things. Keystone is a shining example of how people change. At times, she offers Raven honest advice and doesn't appear to pose a threat. She even helped Raven out of a sticky situation. Because of her position and influence, having Lenore as an acquaintance could be useful.

By the end of the series, readers delighted in fantasies of Lenore dying a painful death. After all, she got away with everything. She had others do her dirty work so nothing ever traced back to her. Unfortunately, we've seen how those types of public figures are often the hardest to bring down.

Despite everything, I pitied her. *I know, I know.* But hear me out. I didn't pity the woman she became; I pitied the woman she once was. I imagined her early life similar to Raven's—thrust into a world she wasn't prepared for. Doing whatever necessary to survive. In later years, she became so paranoid about losing her power that she eliminated anyone that she couldn't control. Lenore saw what she was doing as necessary, not evil. In her mind, she was constantly in survival mode.

Raven's life had similar forks in the road. She's in a continual battle to figure out if she stands in the light or the dark. It doesn't take but a few left turns to go in the wrong direction.

Can love change a person? I sometimes wonder if Lenore would have become a different person had she ever been given that chance. Love almost destroyed her, and guess who was there to pick up the pieces and mentor her?

Yep, you got it. The one and only Houdini.

If Houdini taught Lenore anything, it's that there *is* no good or evil. Lenore used that logic to give herself permission to do bad things if it meant her survival. And for her, power and survival were synonymous.

She preyed upon others. She manipulated their emotions to get what she wanted. That's what she did with Viktor. Love and adoration create weakness, and if she can get them to feel something for her, she can control them. That also explains why she was so frustrated with Borislav, one of the three oligarchs. He didn't trust her, so she had to get rid of him. If Lenore could have charmed him and won his affection, she would have dropped Ronald like a hot potato. Lenore believes in power matches—a symbiotic relationship where two individuals can secure their position in the community.

Back in the day, Lenore fed Christian her blood to create a bond—to influence him and secure his loyalty. She never expected him to feel something genuine for her, and when he expressed those feelings, he became a liability. That's why she buried him.

You see, Lenore was smart enough to realize that if you want to be a successful criminal, you never get your hands dirty. You manipulate others and even make them think the crimes were always their idea. But you can't just let anyone do your dirty work either. Christian was the only one she could trust with the truly awful stuff. When he developed feelings toward her, she realized how that might backfire. For one, he refused to follow her request to marry another powerful figure in their world. Had he no feelings for Lenore, he would have done as she asked. After many centuries, Lenore observed how emotions could be a person's downfall. He might even turn on her because of the rejection, so she had to nip it in the bud.

Lenore and Houdini were my favorite villains to write for similar reasons. They were both complex characters who had reasoning behind their motives, each so emotionally distant that they hurt everyone around them.

Sweet dreams, Lenore.

OTHER

This is not a full list of every character who appeared or was mentioned in the series, but it includes secondary characters who had a reoccurring or vital role.

Betty McGuire: Works at Ruby's Diner
Cosmo: Owner of Pawn of the Dead
Hooper: Gem's ex
Marilyn Rothchild (Mary): Relic who is helping Gem with her Mage powers
Matteo Leone: Chitah who attempted to court Blue
Red: Worker in Crush's garage
Ren: Crush's best friend
Sambah Freeman: Leader of his Pride
Tank: Crush's friend
Wizard: Crush's friend, who also does repairs

THE VILLAINS

Audrey: Sensor who ran the fighting ring
Borislav: Vampire oligarch
Cristo: Killed Shepherd's woman
Cyrus, Kallisto, Plato, Lykos, Arcadius: Niko's Mage brothers
Darius Bane: Human killer hunted by Keystone
General (and brothers): Shifter loan shark after Crush
Godfrey Edmond Sparrow III: Mage who put people in the Shadow Realm
Graham Wiggins: Relic who targeted Shifters
Ivar: Chitah oligarch
Li Han: Mage oligarch
Pablo Leonardo Russo: Mage who helped Audrey run fighting rings
Patrick Bane: Mage who raised Hunter
Temple: Vampire buyer involved in Vampire trafficking
Willard Glass: (Detective) - Chitah serial killer

There were also a number of people who played secondary bad guys in the series, but I've only listed the primaries.

PART III

KEYSTONE

Viktor started Keystone because of Gem. He had the idea before, but it all came to fruition after he met her. For years he wanted to do something worthwhile, so creating an organization that hunted criminals felt right—especially with his background experience. Eventually he started picking up other people who fit his specifications and formed a real team.

The Keystone name derives from the keystone on the archways of their house as well as the meaning behind the word. The keystone is the most important stone on which everything else depends.

While certain higher authority members know their identities, they choose to stay underground and not advertise themselves among the criminal element. Their objective is to bring down the most notorious criminals in the Breed world... however they see fit. Only some of their targets are classified as outlaws, which can make hunting them a grey area. Occasionally they might even be in high positions. Keystone does what most bounty hunters can't and what other organizations won't. Because of that, the higher authority grants them a limited amount of protection.

Not all the jobs they accept are received from the higher authority. Keystone works for no one, so there's a vetting process. Viktor may hear about or come across a case to investigate through either his contacts or another source. They're sometimes approached by the Mageri, Councils, and various Breed elders. Viktor also accepts jobs from individuals or businesses. He oversees payment negotiations with those contracting them, assigns cases to certain team members, and determines the payment amount for his people. He's in charge of organizing the investigations, rescue missions, and deliveries.

During downtime, they go relic hunting at pawnshops, searching for any illegal weapons or other items of interest—such as books and historical items—to confiscate. They also research cold cases, transport victims to safe houses, and investigate crimes of fraud or theft. Viktor is very selective of his cases.

Viktor chose his team based on unique skills he felt would benefit them. Because their job is dangerous, he only selects those who have no family or other options. Those who are willing to sacrifice everything for a greater good.

THE TEAM

Leader:

Viktor Kazan

Assigned partners:

Claude Valentine & Gem Laroux

Niko & Blue

Shepherd Moon & Wyatt Blessing

Raven Black & Christian Poe

Order of joining Keystone:

Viktor

Gem

Claude

Niko

Blue

Wyatt

Shepherd

Christian

Raven

NEW MEMBERS: Viktor created a ceremony for welcoming each new member. Using a gold chalice that's been in his family for centuries, he has everyone put a little blood in it. It's not meant for anyone to drink but is a symbol of them becoming one. The chalice is placed at the center of the table while everyone makes a toast with their wineglasses.

KEYSTONE TATTOO: Each Keystone member has a heraldic eagle with a backward *K* for the crown tattooed somewhere on their body. With the exception of Viktor, who put a large one on his chest, everyone else got a small one that's easily hidden.

Viktor created some basic rules. These won't get anyone kicked out. They're designed to create an environment with less conflict. They are followed most of the time.

RULES:
1. Protect each other's lives despite how you may feel about the other person.
2. No one's gifts, abilities, or weaknesses are discussed with anyone outside their group.
3. Eat meals together. This helps to forge bonds and resolve conflict.
4. No sensory exchanges or juicing from one another.
5. New evidence should not be disregarded or ignored even if it slows them down. Evidence is vital for each job.
6. No sex between partners but ideally with no one in the house. A relationship gone wrong can have a negative effect on one's ability to do their job.

. . .

Obviously the last rule became flexible, but as you can see, most of these were made with good intentions. Having lived in a pack, Viktor knows what can lead to conflict. He also understands the value of eating together, because if they go to their separate spots and never assemble except during jobs, they won't form a natural bond or work out their issues.

That's also another reason he created partners. Knowing he would be hiring troubled people, learning to work with partners would also help them learn to work with a team. He paired together people based on how they entered the house, but it's not clear *when* he began pairing off the team. Viktor also believes that no one person should be treated as special in a group. They are all equals, so he can't show favoritism.

Regarding the business card Viktor gave Raven, he doesn't believe in putting the Keystone name or his name on anything. Their organization is known within certain groups but not the wider world. Their card has Zero on it with a number where they can be reached.

THE HOUSE

Keystone property is hundreds of acres and has been in Viktor's family for over three hundred years. The mansion is mostly made of stone and looks more like a castle. It's three stories high and also has several basement-level rooms. There's an underground garage a short distance away from the house, an escape tunnel, and privacy. Stone walls border the property, and there's a black iron gate that's twenty feet high at the entrance. Over that is a stone archway with a keystone of a Roman soldier's head. They can swipe a card to open the gate or push a call button to have Wyatt let them in. At the end of the series, they added wolf and lion statues along the front wall in remembrance of lives sacrificed.

I've listed some rooms below, but the mansion contains many more. Some were mentioned without a description or location specified. Many are used for storage or are closed off. Community rooms are open and available to all. The only rooms with electricity are Wyatt's office, the gym, the rock-climbing room, the medical room, kitchen, laundry, garage, the courtyard (pool and hot tub), and the meeting room next door to Wyatt's office.

. . .

FIRST-LEVEL ROOMS INCLUDE:

- Shepherd's bedroom
- Hunter's bedroom
- Kira's bedroom
- Switch's bedroom
- Viktor's bedroom
- Kitchen and laundry
- Dining room
- Gathering room
- Gem's secret study
- Small library
- Viktor's study
- A second study in the back
- Medical room
- Supply room
- Room that leads to an underground escape tunnel
- Access to courtyard
- Access to gym and other sublevel rooms

SECOND-LEVEL ROOMS INCLUDE:

- Niko's bedroom
- Gem's bedroom
- Claude's bedroom
- Blue's bedroom
- Wyatt's World (Wyatt's office)
- Study
- Soundproof sitting room
- Viktor's office
- Meeting room
- Billiard room with pool, darts, shuffleboard, game tables, chess, and others

THIRD-LEVEL ROOMS INCLUDE:

- Christian's bedroom
- Raven's bedroom
- Wyatt's bedroom
- Interior balcony overlooking the front
- Game room with billiard tables and a bar

SUBLEVEL ROOMS INCLUDE:

- Gym/workout room
- Wine cellar
- Storage basement
- Rock climbing
- Viktor's secret chamber where he keeps artifacts

Note:
Keystone has more than one recreation room, library, and sitting room. There are also several rooms in the mansion with a full bar. One room had a full grey sectional.

Descriptions of the primary rooms used by the team are detailed below. Any locations only briefly mentioned or with sparse descriptions are not included. To help visualize location of furniture and windows, I've given the perspective of most rooms from standing in the doorway.

FRONT ENTRANCE: After passing through the main gates, the long driveway leads up to the house and circles in front. There's a separate road branching to the right that leads to their underground garage.

The front of Keystone faces south. Looking directly at the house, the left side is the west wing and the right is the east wing.

UNDERGROUND GARAGE: *Electricity.* Monitored by Wyatt's security cameras. The outside appears to be a small building with a large garage door. The door is electric, but they have a backup system in case of blackouts. Access is given using an outdoor keypad or electronic opener. Once open, the driveway leads underground. At the bottom, there's a wall up ahead with a workbench and tools. Most of the parking is to the left, but there's also some available to the right. The garage is not massive like a commercial parking lot, but it's large enough to store a number of vehicles. The polished floors and tiled walls are white. It's brightly lit with overhead lights, and there are several columns to help support the structure. To the left in the back corner is a secret entrance to the house, accessed by pressing a specific wall tile.

OUTSIDE PROPERTY: They don't have trees too close to the house where someone could climb them and gain access. The front property is grassy with scattered trees that are denser near the access road. Out back, there's a grove of trees off to the side. One has a rope swing, and there's an iron bench facing the swing. The land is flat and grassy just outside the back door, but it slopes down to a meadow. In the distance, there's a pond, and the trees are spread far apart from each other. Someone cleared a good chunk of the property years ago.

The outside edges of the property are dense with trees, and beyond them is an old stone wall. It wasn't designed to keep people out but to keep rogue animals out and mark the property line. A sidewalk winds around the wooded parts of the property, making it ideal for jogging outside. From the top of the Keystone hill, the scenic view is breathtaking, especially in spring and summer when wildflowers are blooming.

. . .

FRONT INTERIOR: There are three main stairwells in the house, one of which is located in the spacious foyer, just ahead of the front door. When you enter Keystone, on the immediate right of the door is a large winged warrior wielding a sword aimed at those who enter. The hallway to the right side of the stairs leads back to the medical room, Kira's room, and the courtyard.

The east wing is located directly to the right as you enter. Once you reach the far end, you turn left down a long hallway that runs to the back of the house. On the right are beautiful blue-tinted windows. The ceilings are high and arched, the lanterns hung on the walls. An alcove on the left provides access to Gem's secret study. There's also a hallway farther down that cuts through the center of the house where Hunter and Shepherd reside. At the end of the east hallway on the right is a steel door with a bolt that opens to the side of the house.

Back at the main entrance of Keystone, if you go directly left, you enter a short hallway that leads to the dining, kitchen, and gathering rooms.

The floors and walls of the mansion are stone, the ceilings lofty, the doorways arched, and there are countless lanterns and sconces. The architecture is detailed, including the staircases. There are a number of statues throughout of winged warriors, and most of the hallways have arched ceilings. Some of the windows are latticed and others stained glass. Most of the doors are wood, but the soundproof rooms have steel doors.

DINING ROOM: *No electricity.* From the doorway, there's a wall just a few feet to the right. Straight ahead is a stone archway that spans all the way to the left. The open archways that start at waist level allow you to see into the gathering room, and there's a walkway near the dining table. The team sometimes talks over drinks in one of the three booths along the archway. Facing left is the main dining room. The far wall has a window above the liquor table where the westerly sun streams in. A round iron chandelier with candles hangs over a long wooden table. Viktor sits at the far end by the window so he can see everything. Since the table is large, they are able to spread apart or scoot closer. With Hunter joining them, they're more likely to stretch out to include him. At night, they light up the chandelier, lanterns on the walls, and may put candles on the table.

Usual seating arrangement: Facing Viktor, the seating on the left side of the table includes: Wyatt (closest to him), Shepherd, Gem, and Claude. On the other side are Raven, Christian, Blue, and Niko. So Wyatt sits across from Raven, Shepherd across from Christian, et cetera. Hunter is usually at the chair on the opposite side of Viktor, but since they don't have assigned seating, Shepherd will sometimes sit by his son.

Switch and Kira do not eat with the team. Since they are staff, they have separate mealtimes so that the team can discuss work.

GATHERING ROOM: *No electricity.* Along the archways in the dining room, where the booths are located, is an entryway into the gathering room. The entryway is across from the dining table. Upon entering the gathering room is a massive stained glass window on the left with wolves, people, and flowers. The ceiling is lofty, and they sometimes use a bearskin rug in front of the fireplace. Straight ahead to the right is a mammoth fireplace with a long row of stained glass windows on the right that overlook the courtyard. The leather chairs and sofa are across from the fireplace but not close to it. Instead, they're arranged by the stone archways that look into the dining room. The right side of the room is open with a lot of unused space. A floor-to-ceiling bookshelf fills the far right wall. Since the courtyard windows face north, the room isn't especially bright. Aside from the liquor cabinet near the bookshelf, it's fairly empty.

. . .

KITCHEN: *Electricity.* The kitchen entryway is located to the left of the dining table, somewhere behind where Shepherd and Gem sit. You walk through a short passageway into the kitchen, which runs mostly to the left. The pantry is located at the far end. Granite countertops, small windows, a kitchen island with a wood countertop, deep freezer. Small windows.

MEDICAL ROOM: *Electricity.* Located in the hallway to the right of the front stairs. From the doorway, the small room has a metal table straight ahead, the foot of the table closest to the door. There are over-head cabinets and a sink to the left where Shepherd stores most of his supplies. The lower cabinets provide additional storage. He uses a roller stool, and there're a couple of small corner chairs in the back like you might find in a doctor's office. He also has IV poles, and there's a lamp arm affixed to the wall that pulls out over the table when needed.

SHEPHERD'S ROOM: *No electricity or windows.* Located in a private hall off the east wing. His room is on the right, third door down. From the doorway, his low bed is on the right wall, and a rustic desk is next to the door on the immediate right. He stacks his clothes on a bench to the left of the bed, but he doesn't have a large wardrobe. No fireplace. Bathroom entryway is opposite the door. He stores his weapons in a locked armoire on the left wall. The lower drawers hold bullets, throwing stars, and other miscellaneous items. Shepherd medi-tates and exercises on a large green-and-gold carpet in the center of the room. There's a pull-up bar installed above the bathroom entrance. Uses an electric lantern in the bathroom.

. . .

HUNTER'S ROOM: *No electricity.* Located in the same hall as Shepherd's bedroom, only his is the last door at the end. Standing in the doorway, you face a large window that overlooks one corner of the courtyard. The window doesn't open, and battery-operated twinkle lights are strung all around it. There's a short chest of drawers within reach to the right of the door. A play table is located on the left wall along with a plastic scoop chair with metal legs. The bed is to the right with a nightstand and upholstered chair next to it. Since Shepherd doesn't want candles in there, Hunter reads at night with a rechargeable lantern. On the far side of the bed to the right of the window is a bookshelf and round plush rug.

While the walls and floors are stone, the room is filled with color because of his toys, stuffed animals, blocks, books, crayons, and paints. His window faces west, so the warm afternoon sun floods into his room during winter. Hunter has plenty of heavy blankets to keep him warm on chilly nights, but Shepherd is just a few steps down the hall if he ever gets scared or cold. He doesn't have his own bathroom, so he uses Shepherd's or one located in another room.

GEM'S SECRET STUDY: *No electricity or windows.* Located in an alcove off the east wing, just past a small library. To access the room, you push in a faux stone in the wall, triggering the wall to move like a revolving door. It doesn't swing all the way around but opens halfway to allow entry. Lanterns or candles are required to see. High ceiling. Room is roughly twenty by twenty feet. The walls are wooden shelves filled with books and other curiosities. Lanterns are affixed to dividers between the shelves. A large desk (hammered wood) is in the center where Gem does most of her work. Beneath it is an emerald-green rug with gold fringe. A chair behind the desk and a leather chair against a wall provide her with places to sit.

. . .

WYATT'S GAME ROOM (aka Wyatt's World): *Electricity, no windows.* While it has a stone floor like the rest of the house, the walls have drywall and are painted grey. From the doorway looking in, there's a long desk on the right wall with multiple computer monitors, laptops, stress toys, snacks, keyboards, pens, and so forth. Wyatt has color-changing accent lamps behind the monitors. Two leather computer chairs. Opposite the door are two vending machines: one with snacks and one with drinks. To the left of them, a large television with beanbag chairs in front. The team relaxes on the black L-shaped sofa on the left side of the room. There's a trendy red floor lamp behind it and an end table on the right. Colorful pillows brighten up the space. The walls have outlets. While there's a bolt inside the door, the room is usually kept open since the team likes to gather there.

NIKO'S ROOM: *No electricity or windows.* Located on the same floor as Gem but on the opposite side of the house. The door locks with a latch. Wood flooring. From the doorway looking in, his bed is on the left wall. He keeps dried flowers, among other things, in the bedside table next to the bed, which is on the left side of the room. His wardrobe is on the right wall, a long wooden bench beside it. Keeping his possessions organized is crucial. He lines his shoes on the bench with a pair of socks in every other shoe. The bathroom entryway is opposite the door. He has a shower but no bathtub. There's a fireplace located on the far left corner near the bed, and he will often light it on chilly nights. Katanas are mounted on the wall. Texture is important to Niko. His wardrobe has glass knobs, the wood floor is smooth, his blankets soft, and the towels plush. While he doesn't require lanterns or candles to see, he keeps them in his room in case there's a visitor.

GEM'S ROOM: *No electricity.* Envision a colorful room filled with beautiful things. From the doorway looking in, there's a row of floor-to-ceiling windows on the left overlooking the courtyard. Near them, a small open shelf displays her gorgeous raw gemstone and rock collection. Her walls are draped in colorful fabric to hide the dreary stone, some of the fabrics joining together on the ceiling center so it feels like you're inside a tent. Red and gold rugs cover the floor, overlapping in some places. Gem enjoys lounging on large floor pillows by the windows. The armoire to the immediate right of the door is covered in rhinestones. At the right time of day, it sparkles. While she has a fireplace on the wall opposite the door, she doesn't light it for fear of a fire. A curved gold couch is placed in front of it. Her bed is the real showpiece. The king-size canopy on the right-hand wall has purple curtains and lots of pillows. At night, it's magical with all the battery-operated fairy lights strung about the room. She places candles inside colorful mason jars. No bathroom.

CLAUDE'S ROOM: *No electricity.* From the doorway looking in, Claude's large bed is on the right. Because he's a Chitah, it's taller and longer than everyone else's. He loves the masculine look of leather, so he has a leather headboard and also a leather bench at the foot of the bed. Next to the bed is a bedside table and a leather chair in the corner. Opposite the door is an alcove with a white rug and two leather couches facing each other. On the wall between them, a magnificent circular window with blue-tinted glass and a clockwork design. The large window has Roman numerals for the numbers. The hands on the clock are not functional. From outside, the window is a beautiful sight when the room is lit up. On the immediate left of the door against the same wall is a black armoire with a leather stool beside it. Claude's fireplace is across from the bed, a large rectangular mirror mounted above it. Claude sleeps hot, so he doesn't usually light the fireplace.

. . .

BLUE'S ROOM: *No electricity.* Instead of a round doorknob, she has a lever handle. Blue's bedroom receives an abundance of afternoon light since it's located in the northwest part of the house and has several windows. From the doorway looking in, there's a desk and chair by the door on the immediate right. The windows on the left wall continue along the wall opposite the door. Sunlight floods across the floor in the afternoon. Blue has a simple room with a standing mirror on the left wall, an armoire opposite the door, and a bed in the far right corner. No bathroom. She hangs a dreamcatcher just above her pillow. She mounts her tomahawk near the fireplace on the righthand wall.

INTERIOR BALCONY: The interior balcony is located at the front of the house on the third floor and faces south. There's a door on either side. A stone balustrade railing runs along the open archways. The balcony provides a vantage point of the property and driveway leading out to the gate. When the house was built, it was likely used to spot unexpected visitors approaching.

RAVEN'S BEDROOM: *No electricity.* Raven's room is located at the back of the house. Because it faces north, it's darker than most rooms, especially in winter. She has a great view of the property where the hill slopes down into a wide meadow and a pond is visible. From the doorway looking in, you face an alcove on the opposite wall with arched, latticed windows. The sashes open inward. To the immediate right, on the same wall as the door, is an armoire that Raven painted black. Her bathroom entrance is on the other side of it, against the right-hand wall. When you enter and turn left, the toilet and sink are along the left wall, a standing shower straight ahead. The clawfoot tub is her favorite and is against the right wall. There's a small recess next to the tub that allows her to place candles or shampoo in that nook.

Lanterns hang on the walls and provide ample light, but she also enjoys candles when taking a bath.

The ceilings are lofty, and everything is made of stone. She has a cozy fireplace at the foot of the bed on the left wall, though there isn't a mantel. Sometimes she puts a white rug in front of it. Her desk is on the wall opposite the door to the right, close to her bed. She keeps souvenirs from her missions on there along with a childhood jewelry box, photos, and other personal items. Raven spruced up the place to her liking by hanging a large grey-toned image of a forest with a red-leafed tree. The scarlet color matches her blanket. She sleeps in the bed originally given to her, so it's small and has a basic wooden headboard. A red flower arrangement on one nightstand adds more color. Lanterns and candles are located around the room, and a standing mirror is in the left-hand corner by the door.

CHRISTIAN'S ROOM (aka spider central): *No electricity or windows.* From the doorway looking in, the fireplace is on the opposite wall, slightly to the left. His bed is on the right-hand wall, the bathroom entryway on the left, close to the door. Christian's room is minimal—just an armoire, a chair, and a bedside table with a candy dish on it. Near the bed is a wastebasket for his candy wrappers. Because he doesn't require sleep, he only goes to his room when he wants to be alone. Otherwise, he'll spend his time walking around the mansion, reading, or sitting in one of the social rooms. When sharing a bed with Raven, he prefers the left side.

WYATT'S ROOM: *No electricity.* He's located far from Raven's and Christian's rooms. From the doorway looking in, there's a massive black sectional in the center of the room. It's square-shaped with a taller back on the right side. The arms extend all the way toward the fireplace, leaving the foot open. This is what Wyatt sleeps and lounges on. Black shelving surrounds the fireplace, covering the entire left wall. He stores his personal things in the cabinets below. To light up the dark space, there are cylindrical blue lanterns mounted on the dividers and regular lanterns affixed to the walls. On every shelf are gargoyles and cat figurines. If you walk farther in and turn around to face the door, the wall all around the door is painted black with a Pac-Man mural painted in bright neon colors. It displays the maze, the dots, the ghosts, the cherries, and Pac-Man on the run. Wyatt thinks the videogame is a perfect representation of being a Gravewalker. Listens to music on a wireless sound system that connects to his phone.

GYM: *Electricity.* The workout room serves as a place to not only stay in shape but also practice knife and axe throwing. It's the size of a gymnasium. The access point is a door located in the dining room to the right of the entryway. After walking down a long, narrow flight of stairs, you reach a second door. Beyond that is a small recessed hall, and a few steps will lead you into the gym. Ceiling lights keep it brightly lit, and there's every type of exercise equipment a person needs. Most of the equipment is located on the right, along with a pommel horse. On the left is a long rope hanging from the ceiling. The center area has a thin mat used for fighting. The outer perimeter is kept clear for walking. Mounted on the walls are pull-up bars and target boards. They also have kettlebells and jump ropes.

COURTYARD: The courtyard has multiple access points. It's not a perfect rectangle or square but L-shaped. The main entrance opens onto a covered veranda with stone archways. There's a hot tub down to the right and also lounge chairs and a glider. Farther down at the end is a toolshed. In the open grounds toward the left side of the courtyard is the pool, which at night illuminates the water with blue and green lights. The grounds are beautifully kept, mowed grass in some areas and ground cover in others. Too many large trees would obscure the sun and sky, so there are only a couple, one of them being a holly tree. Lots of roses by the walkways. A few benches provide ideal spots to sit and enjoy the private oasis. One of Blue's favorite statues of a winged man is located in the courtyard.

PART IV

THE GOODIE BAG

FUN FACTS

These are behind-the-scenes facts you may not have known regarding the creation of the series, insight, and the writing process.

In the original Keystone manuscript, written back in 2010, the characters included Raven, Christian, Viktor, Niko, Claude, and Wyatt. There was a Vampire named Eli, whom I eliminated. Shepherd's name was originally Luke, but it didn't fit him, so I changed it. Then there's Gem. Originally she was a male Mage who was a hidden enemy within the house. I gave him a full gender and personality change. Blue didn't exist, and I wanted more women to balance out the series. These were all changes that I made when I revisited the manuscript years later.

In the original manuscript, Viktor was named Domino and not at all Russian.

The series has a lot of references to the works of Edgar Allan Poe. Not only Christian's last name, but Raven's first, after a poem entitled "The Raven." I also chose the name Lenore for the woman Christian once held on a pedestal but who ruined him. The name actually appears in a couple of Edgar's poems. In "The Raven," the poem ends with someone rapping at his chamber door. At the end of *Blackout,* someone is knocking on Christian's chamber door. When he opens it, he sees Lenore. It only seemed fitting to name the next book *Nevermore.* And the line written on the headstone on the cover of *Afterlife* is from one of his poems. It would be impossible to read these books and not see the intentional references. I read a lot of poetry in my youth and was heavily influenced by the works of Edgar Allan Poe. It was fun weaving those references into the series.

Houdini's key. I never had any intention of showing what that key leads to and what it reveals about him. It's more of a MacGuffin, an object that helps drive a plot but doesn't serve any other purpose. It became a symbol of Raven and Houdini's warped relationship. Even in the end, she never really understood him. It also gave him a reason to stay in her life. Houdini remains a mystery, just like whatever that key opens. Eventually it became an unnecessary connection between the two, so Raven let it go, deciding the answers weren't as important as being free of him.

While writing Crossbreed, I had numerous documents open at all times. They included:

- Two notes documents. One relating to the overall story arc, the other containing plot points for each individual book, including loose ends that needed addressing. Both documents range between fourteen and twenty pages.
- Chapter summary, where I give a brief description of each chapter including the location and POV.
- Character bios. This document also contains information about the locations they frequent, secondary characters, room descriptions, and villains.
- "Secrets" document. A spreadsheet I used for tracking breadcrumbs and Easter eggs that would reveal more in a later book. This spreadsheet also contains a tab for my characters' vocabulary.

Referring to that many documents is tedious and makes the writing process longer, especially with a series. But it was important to make sure everything came together and was addressed. The more books published in a series, the more complicated the writing gets. Especially with all the subplots I had going on that needed to wrap up.

I also had a separate document for plot and character ideas. Sometimes there were a few things I could work into the story, but most of these ideas never came to fruition. One of those was giving Raven a sister or half sister, but that's not a secret Crush would have kept from her. It would have made it feel like a soap opera, and I only wanted to write storylines or plot twists that made sense. I also considered Blue and Shepherd hooking up, but that pairing wouldn't have worked out. Plus Crossbreed is an urban fantasy and not a paranormal romance. I considered killing off Viktor and having Christian take over the organization, but Viktor is the glue that holds them together. Some ideas never see the light of day for a reason. The characters drive their own story, and most of the time I feel like a passenger in the back seat, yelling at them to slow down.

When coming up with a titling scheme, I considered starting each book with the next sequential letter in the alphabet. I quickly realized readers would expect me to write twenty-six books, so I settled instead for compound words. Each title was thoughtfully chosen to fit the story.

It's not entirely clear if Niko is susceptible to a Vampire's charm or a memory wipe. Most would have never tried on a blind man, but he's also special. Niko's Mage energy restored his eyesight in a unique way where he detects energy in the form of light. Because of this, he assumes that a memory wipe could work if he had to leave Keystone. If Niko were to look into a Vampire's eyes and the Vampire initiated their magic, would he see a unique energy in their eyes *because* of that magic?

I created a world with enough mystery and unknowns that it allows me more flexibility. Special sensory magic could do a memory wipe, and there are Relics with secret knowledge that would blow our minds. It's safe to say that while I never explored this further, Viktor would have made sure he had all his ducks in a row before hiring Niko.

While there are Mageri series crossovers, I avoided the Seven series. In the Mageriverse timeline, *Keystone* takes place after *Shine* ends. Though Christian has only been with Keystone for a few months, it's not mentioned how much time elapsed since he left the Mageri crew. And the thing is, there are two Seven series characters who don't hook up until eight years after *Shine* ends. It's far better to avoid the temptation than to screw up the timeline.

While writing *Ravenheart*, I was so obsessed with the unseen couple in the book, Penny and Lachlan, that I almost wrote a novella about them. We only learned about their love story through a diary, but it goes to show that everyone has a tale to tell. In the end, I chose not to. This is what writers refer to as the shiny object or... Squirrel! Meaning temptations that distract us. Since we knew their ending, it would only be expounding on a tragic tale with no happily-ever-after. Nobody wants to read a love story that's a downer.

LOCATIONS

Crossbreed takes place in a fictional city called Cognito. The exact location has never been disclosed, mostly because I love the mystery of it. But it's situated in the northeast section of the United States, a few hours from the coast. Theoretically, that might place it in New York State. Exact location becomes a distraction since it doesn't exist.

Basing a series in a fictional city allowed me to build that city from the ground up. Readers can't fact-check me, and I don't have to worry about making mistakes—especially since I wanted to base it in an area of the country I don't live. Fictional cities also give authors a ton of freedom, which I needed for a place that has a large Breed population. Because it's an old city with history, it has its own unique culture and subcultures. Breed influence would make a city that's unique, eccentric, and dangerous.

Here are just a few locations mentioned in the Crossbreed series. It does not include any that might have been mentioned exclusively in a different series. These include both Breed and human establishments.

COGNITO:

- Angelo's
- the Angry Hornet
- Arrowhead Bridge
- the Bricks
- Brooks Hotel
- Coyote Burger
- Club Hell
- Club High Jinx
- Cognito Zoo
- Dynasty Star Chicken
- the East River
- Flamingo Hotel
- Flavors
- the Golden Compass
- Magic Hour
- Memorial Hospital of Cognito
- Nine Circles of Hell
- Northern Lights
- Pawn of the Dead
- Razor Sharp
- Rebel's
- Red Door
- Roughnecks
- Ruby's Diner
- Skulls BBQ
- Tia's Taqueria
- White Owl

BELLINGHAM, WASHINGTON:

- Black Cat Tats

WEST VIRGINIA:

- Wonderland

About Breed establishments:

Almost all Breed establishments like to identify themselves as Breed owned by putting a symbol on their windows, door, or even menus. I have never described the symbols used. Shifters have their own, which is usually a paw print. Some are open to all, but since most Breeds like separating themselves from humans, many are membership only. Many restaurants are reservation only, exclusively booking customers who identify themselves as Breed. Doormen are common outside clubs, singling out Breed from the line of humans who are eager to get inside. Shops and other retail places will often cater to both since it's impossible to keep humans out without raising suspicion. Additionally, Breed prefer to circulate their money among their own instead of benefiting humans.

The easiest way to do this is to cluster their businesses together in most major cities. They'll buy up buildings and property on the same streets and block areas, creating what's referred to as a Breed district.

There is a general rule that Breed establishments are neutral ground. They are not the place to stage attacks or start violent fights. Anyone who does runs the risk of getting blacklisted for life. Fights are more common in Shifter bars, and many owners may turn a blind eye. It's really up to the owner on how they run their place.

MUSIC PLAYLIST

I've had a number of readers ask if I listen to music while writing. The answer is no. I require complete silence and even wear sound-canceling headphones if needed. Music taps into the creative side of my brain where my writing is taking place, and it becomes distracting. A melody can inadvertently influence how a scene might be written by altering my mood.

I can't write a scene without being able to hear my characters talking. Music may not detract from the visual story, but I might not hear a twig snapping or the sound of someone's bare feet sweeping across the floor. Every author has a different system based on their needs.

While not part of my writing process, music can still inspire scenes and evoke emotion. I enjoy listening to songs and plotting, and I have a massive playlist. Discovering new music and artists is a passion, and so is compiling music into playlists for each book. If you find songs or artists you love, show your support for their music and make a purchase at your preferred retailer. Artists deserve to be paid for their work.

The songs below are not associated with chapters. Instead, they mark certain scenes in the book, some short and others that span a chapter or two.

Note: The selected songs are not always the original version. Some I intentionally selected because I enjoyed the cover.

Listen to all my playlists on Spotify.

KEYSTONE

"Come with Me Now" by Kongos
"I've Got You under My Skin" by Frank Sinatra
"Galvanize" by the Chemical Brothers
"My Body Is a Cage" by Arcade Fire
"It's Been Awhile" by Staind
"You've Haunted Me All My Life" by Death Cab for Cutie
"This Night" by Black Lab
"Have You Ever Seen the Rain?" by Creedence Clearwater Revival
"Mama" by My Chemical Romance
"Sweet Dreams" by Marilyn Manson
"Everybody Wants to Rule the World" by Lorde
"Various Storms & Saints" by Florence + the Machine
"Long & Lost" by Florence + the Machine
"Take Me to Church" by Hozier
"A Sky Full of Stars" by Coldplay
"Let It Die" by Feist
"Nervous in the Light of Dawn" by Leigh Nash
"Mad World" by Gary Jules
"So Irate" by Delilah
"Bullet with Butterfly Wings" by the Smashing Pumpkins
"Through the Valley" by Shawn James

"Raven Song" by Elephant Revival
"Black Hole Sun" by Nouela
"House on a Hill" by the Pretty Reckless

RAVENHEART

"Can't Feel My Face" by the Weeknd
"You Can Leave Your Hat On" by Joe Cocker
"Counting Stars" by OneRepublic
"Eating Like Kings" by Shawn James
"I Put a Spell on You" by Annie Lennox
"I Still Have a Soul" by Gabriel Shadid & Tobias Marberger
"The Mezzanine" by Liz Durrett
"9 Crimes" by Damien Rice
"Murder by Numbers" by the Police
"My Vampire Heart" by Tom McRae
"The Ghost of You Lingers" by Spoon
"Never Tear Us Apart" by INXS
"My Lover's Gone" by Dido
"You" by Keaton Henson
"Stay with Me" by Sam Smith
"Mercy" by Shiny Toy Guns
"Sirens" by Fleurie
"Who Can It Be Now?" by Men at Work
"Blah Blah Blah" by Say Hi
"I'm Just a Shadow" by SHEL
"Spoonman" by Soundgarden
"You Will Be My Ain True Love" by Alison Krauss

DEATHTRAP

"Black Hole Sun" by Nouela
"Nowhere to Run" by Phil Collins
"Low Life" by X Ambassadors
"Kickstart My Heart" by Mötley Crüe
"Trouble" by Pink
"Have You Seen" by Sharon Van Etten
"Walk Like an Egyptian" by the Bangles
"Bodies" by Drowning Pool
"Air on the G String" by Johann Sebastian Bach
"Fields of Gold" by Eva Cassidy
"King of Pain" by a Band Called Pain
"Love Sex Magic" by Ciara ft. Justin Timberlake
"Making Love out of Nothing at All" by Air Supply
"Coming Down" by Dum Dum Girls
"Couldn't Stop Caring" by Spiritual Machines
"Black Magic" by Ruston Kelly
"Vor í Vanglaskógi" by KALEO
"Every Breath You Take" by Chase Holfelder
"Where the River Bends" by Matthew Barber

GASLIGHT

"Way Down We Go" by KALEO
"Better Love" by Hozier
"Until We Go Down" by Ruelle
"Game of Survival" by Ruelle
"All out of Love" by Air Supply
"I Put a Spell on You" by Annie Lennox
"Your Heart Is as Black as Night" by Beth Hart & Joe Bonamassa

"Wish You Were Here" by Pink Floyd
"Til It Happens to You" by Lady Gaga
"Immigrant Song" by Led Zeppelin
"Rescue My Heart" by Liz Longley
"Constant Craving" by J2 ft. Lesley Roy
"Cheek to Cheek" by Fred Astaire
"A Little Wicked" by Valerie Broussard
"Hurts Like Hell" by Fleurie
"Killer" by Phoebe Bridgers
"A Case of You" by Joni Mitchell
"Falling" by Joshua Radin
"Tear You Apart" by She Wants Revenge

BLACKOUT

"Cold Blooded" by the Pretty Reckless
"Brain Damage" by Pink Floyd
"Goodbye to You" by Ben Harper
"Song for My Father" by Sarah McLachlan
"Mary" by Nightmare Boy
"Mr. Blue Sky" by Electric Light Orchestra
"Africa" by Toto
"Dancing in the Dark" by Nicole Atkins
"Closer" by Nine Inch Nails
"A Country Boy Can Survive" by Hank Williams Jr.
"Baby I'm-a Want You" by Bread
"Some Kind of Wonderful" by Grand Funk Railroad
"Wherever I May Roam" by Metallica
"Just Give Me a Reason" by Pink
"Take Me to Church" by Hozier
"Sara" by Fleetwood Mac

. . .

NEVERMORE

"Madness" by Muse
"Born to Be Wild" by Steppenwolf
"100 years" by Five for Fighting
"Mr. Bojangles" by Sammy Davis Jr.
"What Kind of Man" by Florence + the Machine
"Gold Dust Woman" by Fleetwood Mac
"Take It Easy" by Eagles
"You Belong to Me" by Cat Pierce
"Without You" by Badfinger
"Do I Wanna Know?" by Arctic Monkeys
"Save My Soul" by RIVVRS
"Little Sparrow" by Audra Mae
"American Pie" by Don McLean
"Heartless" by the Fray
"Song for My Father" by Sarah McLachlan
"In Love with My Lover" by Bleu
"Sorry" by Nothing but Thieves
"Hard to Say I'm Sorry" by Chicago
"Count on Me" by NEEDTOBREATHE
"Time Is on My Side" by the Rolling Stones
"Hurricane" by Thirty Seconds to Mars
"Love Me" by the Little Willies
"A Whiter Shade of Pale" by Procol Harum
"All I Want Is You" by U2

MOONSTRUCK

"What Makes a Good Man?" by the Heavy
"Faith" by George Michael
"Even the Nights Are Better" by Air Supply
"Beat It" by Michael Jackson
"Wild Woman" by Sleep Machine
"Dancing in the Moonlight" by Tim Barton
"Game of Survival" by Ruelle
"Man or a Monster" by Zayde Wølf
"All along the Watchtower" by Jimi Hendrix
"Donoughmore" by Rose Cousins
"Moondance" by Liz Longley

SPELLBOUND

"Wise Enough" by Lamb
"Next to You" by Of Rust & Bone
"Something in the Air" by Steelfeather
"Movement" by Hozier
"Hips Don't Lie" by Shakira
"You Got Me" by Gavin DeGraw
"Silver Springs" by Fleetwood Mac
"Comatose" by Sød Ven

HEARTLESS

"I'm Still Standing" by Elton John
"One of These Nights" by Meg Birch

"X" by Welshly Arms
"Heartless" by Kris Allen
"Ain't No Grave" by Renée Elise Goldsberry
"Jungle" by X Ambassadors
"Livin' on a Prayer" by Bon Jovi
"Sunspots" by Nine Inch Nails
"Somebody's Watching Me" by Hidden Citizens
"There's Something Dark" by Dustin Kensrue
"Josephine" by Chris Cornell
"NFWMB" by Hozier
"Earned It" by the Weeknd
"Closer" by Nine Inch Nails
"Light of the Seven" by Ramin Djawadi
"Between the Lines" by Felix Räuber
"Devil Devil" by MILCK
"Mausoleum" by Rafferty
"Bury" by Unions
"The Final Countdown" by Europe
"My Heart Wants Blood" by the Spiritual Machines
"bury a friend" by Billie Eilish
"Crazy Love" by Van Morrison
"Locked" by Welshly Arms

AFTERLIFE

"The Safety Dance" by Men without Hats
"Fortunate Son" by Creedence Clearwater Revival
"42" by Coldplay
"Rival" by Ruelle
"Happy Together" by Gerard Way
"Still of the Night" by Whitesnake

"There's a Ghost" by Fleurie
"Lost It All" by Jill Andrews
"Bad Company" by Bad Company
"bad guy" by Billie Eilish
"The Stroke" by Billy Squier
"Hunt You Down" by Saliva
"California Dreaming" arr. by Chris Proctor
"Kashmir" by Led Zeppelin
"I'm Gonna Be (500 Miles)" by the Proclaimers
"Father and Daughter" by Paul Simon
"With or Without You" by U2

QUICKSILVER

"Dead Man's Party" by Oingo Boingo
"Death and All His Friends" by Coldplay
"(Don't Fear) The Reaper" by Blue Öyster Cult
"Who Let the Dogs Out" by Baha Men
"One I Love" by Shawn James
"I Feel You" by Depeche Mode
"Need You Tonight" by Welshly Arms
"Hazy Shade of Winter" by Gerard Way feat. Ray Toro
"NFWMB" by Hozier
"We Will Rock You" by Queen
"The Lady in Red" by Chris de Burgh
"Let Me Out" by Hidden Citizens
"Für Elise" by Ludwig van Beethoven
"Exit Music (for a Film)" by Radiohead
"Heroes" by Zayde Wølf
"you should see me in a crown" by Billie Eilish
"(Don't Fear) The Reaper" by Denmark + Winter

"Warfare" by Katie Garfield

EVILDOER

"Auld Lang Syne" by Wendy Salisbury
"Something Evil" by the Hot Damns ft. Marc Scibilia
"El Jarabe Tapatío" by Mariachi Vargas de Tecalitlán
"Open Arms" by Journey
"Nobody Loves You" by Rafferty
"Tear You Apart" by She Wants Revenge
"Slowdance I" by the Murder Capital
"Losing My Religion" by R.E.M.
"Wicked Game" by Ursine Vulpine ft. Annaca
"Crazy" by Gnarls Barkley
"Baby Did a Bad Bad Thing" by Chris Isaak
"My Heart Will Go On" by Celine Dion
"Wrecking Ball" by Miley Cyrus
"I'd Do Anything for Love (But I Won't Do That)" by Meat Loaf
"The Wolf in Your Darkest Room" by Matthew Mayfield
"How Villains Are Made" by Madalen Duke
"Part-Time Lover" by Stevie Wonder
"Flesh and Bone" by Black Math
"Send Her My Love" by Journey
"Bloody City" by Sam Tinnesz
"Darkness Inside" by Astyria
"Cheek to Cheek" by Fred Astaire
"Sweet Dreams (Are Made of This)" by Eurythmics
"Dust in the Wind" by Kansas
"Mausoleum" by Rafferty
"Crazy" by Daniela Andrade
"I'll Stand by You" by the Pretenders

. . .

FOREVERMORE

"Time for Me to Fly" by REO Speedwagon
"Don't Stop Believin'" by Journey
"Nothing Else Matters" by Metallica
"All That Is Thirst" by Pati Yang
"You Put a Spell on Me" by Austin Giorgio
"Dancing with Myself" by Billy Idol
"Perfect Day" by Lou Reed
"Imagine" by John Lennon

MY PERSONAL FAVORITE QUOTES

At the end of the writing process, I do a final read as a last proof check once the book has been through the editor and proofreader. I enjoy highlighting my favorite lines or passages, most of which I never share on social media as a quote. These have always been tucked away in their respective book folders for my own personal enjoyment. Readers have their favorite lines and scenes.

Here are a few of mine:

Magic will always find a way to bend the rules.

— KEYSTONE

"The line between good and evil is invisible, and if you cannot sense where it is, it won't take long to cross it. Aspire to be something greater than just a shadow of yourself."

— KEYSTONE

"Sometimes we can't choose our fate, and it is fate that chooses us."

— KEYSTONE

"Vampires are about as cuddly as barbed wire."

— KEYSTONE

"Most human cemeteries don't even like raised headstones anymore. They look more like a golf course. It offends the dead."

— KEYSTONE

Christian had never believed in karma, but lying in the casket with old Martha Cleavy was giving him second thoughts about divine justice.

— KEYSTONE

"He's an evil man who kills humans. You can't justify that."

Niko sat up straight, his eyes seeming to look at mine. "That is true. But we're not born evil. His desire to reclaim what he lost blinded him from making the right choices. Sometimes what we desire the most can change who we are, and it's up to us to decide if that's for better or worse. You must learn to control those desires so that you're always on the right path, even if that means never attaining or holding on to the thing you want most."

— KEYSTONE

Christian folded his arms. "So how do you take a man down?"

I shrugged. "Usually I do a scissor move with my legs and asphyxiate them."

He lowered his arms and strolled around me. "So... you can put a man's head between your legs until he passes out?" Christian leaned in close to my ear and lowered his voice. "That's not something I'd brag about, lass."

— KEYSTONE

"Ambition can destroy you if you don't learn to balance it with sacrifice."

— KEYSTONE

Christian's mouth latched onto my neck, and he thrust his hips forward. There was no concealing his arousal as it pressed against me like granite, awakening my desire to be touched by a man.

"Your skin tastes like the Dead Sea," he whispered against my neck.

I tried not to think about Christian's words of seduction, but they kept repeating in my head until I erupted with laughter.

— KEYSTONE

"If that man were a sock, he'd be the one that goes missing."

— KEYSTONE

"This looks like something we'll need to deny later."

— RAVENHEART

"True enemies will never come for you; they will spend a lifetime planning your ruin and savor the moment when they have broken you."

— RAVENHEART

"The only way to move forward is to face your past."

— RAVENHEART

What compels a man to risk his life to save another? That's a quality many people claim to possess but don't actually have. That stranger, who had run through fire to save a little girl, was the best example of a man.

— RAVENHEART

"Do you know how a sword is made? The steel is heated, placed on an anvil, and forged with a hammer. It's bent out of shape, repeatedly struck, and reheated. This process can go on for weeks to craft it to perfection. The point I'm trying to make is that the sword will never come into existence unless it's been challenged by the elements and by force. It becomes a weapon, but it's also a protector."

— RAVENHEART

Niko closed his eyes. "The fates will always reunite two souls that are destined for each other. You shouldn't weep for her death, but rejoice."

— RAVENHEART

"You're an addiction I've never known before."

— DEATHTRAP

I was terrified of how my father would react when he saw me alive. Terrified that the truth might send him into cardiac arrest. Terrified that seeing him might be a mistake. Would he resent me for abandoning him? Maybe I wasn't ready for the truth that my father might be happier without me in his life. But I needed that final good-bye. That was all I really wanted—a hug from my daddy and maybe his forgiveness.

— DEATHTRAP

I peered up. "Don't chop it all off. I know how you guys *love* to turn two inches into seven."

Claude stirred with laughter. "Actually, it's eight. But don't tell anyone."

— DEATHTRAP

"There's a dark side to our world, Raven. Even darker than you can imagine. Immortality breeds the most evil men imaginable."

— DEATHTRAP

"Just relax and close your eyes," he said, massaging my neck.

"That's what I say to all my victims."

— DEATHTRAP

There were a lot of things I'd do in life, but eating tiny turtles wasn't one of them.

"Is something the matter?" Patrick inquired.

My stomach churned as I stared down at my bowl, knowing what lurked beneath.

Shepherd chuckled. "She's suffering from reptile dysfunction."

— DEATHTRAP

"A sharp intellect is deadlier than a sharp knife."

— DEATHTRAP

A tire rolled off the truck and zipped past Shepherd. He stopped short and surveyed the carnage. Wyatt had jammed a MoonPie into his mouth while stacking the undamaged boxes.

Christian offered me his hand and helped me up. We stood amid twisted metal, chocolate, and an open gas line spilling fuel onto the road.

Shepherd kicked one of the packages with the tip of his boot and stuffed his hands into his pockets. "This looks like something we'll have to deny later."

— DEATHTRAP

Christian folded his arms and sighed. "Do you think men sit around and share their innermost secrets over a glass of ale?"

"Don't you?"

"We talk about which nipples are the most beautiful and which knives are the most effective when severing a head."

"So which are best?"

He circled his fingers around his chest. "I'm partial to the larger ones that aren't too dark or too pink. It depends on the size of the breast. If they're too small, a large nipple will only—"

"I meant the knives."

— DEATHTRAP

"We might be done with the past, but the past isn't done with us."

— DEATHTRAP

"The most difficult decision you'll ever make is to let go of the thing you want most."

— DEATHTRAP

"Don't get your heart attached to me, Precious. I'm not a thing to love."

— DEATHTRAP

"I should know better than to feel anything for a man who treats love like a venereal disease."

— DEATHTRAP

"One thing I know about that girl is Raven'll never give her whole heart to a man who doesn't ink himself for her. She grew up around that kind of devotion, so it's all she knows. You got any ink?"

— DEATHTRAP

A cryptic look flickered in his expression, and he gazed at me so intently that I found myself drawn to him. Christian had captivating eyes—like two obsidian stones encased in porcelain. Without warning, he cradled my neck and kissed me, his tongue delving deep and flooding my senses. It was the only warmth my body felt, and I surrendered myself completely. Christian's kiss was like a passionate tide rocking and swelling against my shore, but it was the undercurrent of emotion that threatened to pull me under.

— DEATHTRAP

A dark hunger flickered in his eyes, and his voice became rough and sexy. "The things I'll do to you will make your ancestors blush."

— DEATHTRAP

He didn't speak, and neither did I. There was an understanding in our touch that transcended words, reminding me that despite all my doubts and apprehensions, I needed him. For reasons I might never understand, Christian filled a void I'd carried since my mother's death. I closed my eyes and surrendered to his touch.

— GASLIGHT

"You want so desperately to believe in good and evil, to fit yourself somewhere in that spectrum. There *is* no good and evil. There's only cause and effect."

— GASLIGHT

"And in the end, you'll be reminded of something you've forgotten."

"Which is what?"

His footsteps drew closer. "That killing is what you do best. Flap your wings and cause some chaos, Butterfly. That's *your* purpose, just as giving you immortality was mine."

— GASLIGHT

"Because he's her maker, she sees herself in him. And to see him as evil is to see herself as evil."

— GASLIGHT

"You can't keep secrets from the dead."

— GASLIGHT

"My memories have too many holes, so I need to make new ones."

"Worry not, lass. I'll fill your holes."

Too tired to laugh, I yawned, drifting to a quiet space in my head. "Do you think I would have drowned in the ocean or frozen to death first?"

"Killer whales. That's where I'd put my money."

"Not sea lions?"

"Jaysus no. All they'd do is take a nip and swim off. But you don't want to feck around with a pod of hungry orcas."

"They don't eat people."

"Don't they now? Orcas are the wolves of the sea. I once saw a whale eat a moose."

"There would have been nothing left of me."

He kissed my head. "They can't digest bones."

"I'm not sure what bothers me more—this conversation or how much you know about whales."

— GASLIGHT

"I might ruin your life."

Christian cupped my face in his hands and pressed his forehead to mine. "If that be the truth, then ruin me, Precious. *Ruin me.*"

— GASLIGHT

"Home is not a place—it's the people you love and the time that you inhabit."

— BLACKOUT

"As long as men shape their beliefs by the actions of the past, the chasm between our Breeds will always exist."

— BLACKOUT

"People cheat in life because they're afraid of failure."

— BLACKOUT

"I thought you had reservations," I said, shivering from the gust of wind.

Christian leaned forward and twiddled his thumbs. When he looked over his shoulder at me, his fangs were out in a vicious display. "That fecking arseface knows I called a week ago. It's in his bloody book. If they can't find a table, they need to throw out one of these shitebags and make room. And if that eejit walks over one more time and offers a glass of water while we wait, I'm going to rip his heart out through his belly button and serve it on a platter to the next customer who steals a table that should've been ours a half hour ago."

I crossed my legs. "Stop. You're making my nipples hard."

— BLACKOUT

"What did the blonde with the red lipstick say?" I asked, jerking my thumb toward the back where the woman had been sitting.

He twisted his torso, his heated gaze melting me in my seat. "What's revealed to me in that confessional is confidential. I'm merely the Lord's instrument to listen."

"You're not an instrument. You're a tool."

— BLACKOUT

"The journey to understanding begins with a leap of faith."

— BLACKOUT

"I used to dream about my family finding me and coming to my rescue. I didn't care if they were perfect or rich. I just wanted someone who was willing to love me unconditionally. I never got that, Shep. Never in my whole life. Even my Creator didn't love me. She cared for my well-being and had compassion for my plight, but I don't know what it feels like to be loved. I thought I had that with Hooper, but now I'm not so sure even *that* was real."

— BLACKOUT

"I want you, Raven. I just don't know how to have you."

— BLACKOUT

She reached out and tugged on his beard. "Did you forget how to shave, or are you trying to repel women on purpose?"

"Perhaps next time you should bury me with a razor."

Her lips thinned, but her smiling eyes belied her contempt. "I don't want to quarrel on such a festive night, and my skin is a lot thicker than it used to be."

"Perhaps you should have used sunscreen."

"You have strong features, Chrissy. You shouldn't hide them behind all that hair."

He bristled at her use of the pet name she'd given him long ago. There was a time when having a special name meant something, but now it just felt like talons pricking at his heart.

— NEVERMORE

I cruised inside and flung my coat over the back of the kitchen chair. Crush was sprawled out in his brown recliner, the footrest up and a tray of food on his lap. He cackled at some old comedian on the public access station.

I lifted the tray and stared at the empty TV dinner plate. "I bought you all that healthy food and went back yesterday for more. Why are you eating this crap?"

"Did all that food come with a cooking lesson?"

I sighed and walked around to the kitchen. "You need to eat the fresh stuff first before it goes bad. The TV dinners are for the zombie apocalypse."

"I think I saw one outside earlier."

"That was just your reflection in the window."

— NEVERMORE

Crush held his side. "No hospital."

"You could be hemorrhaging."

"If you take me to a hospital, the only thing hemorrhaging will be my bank account."

— NEVERMORE

"Nobody gives you a manual on love. The rules are different for everyone."

— NEVERMORE

"Wicked deeds are thorny vines that weave into your soul."

— NEVERMORE

"The heart wants what it wants."

— NEVERMORE

"You bewitch me, Raven Black. Through and through. My soul is dark, but I feel the light when you're near."

— MOONSTRUCK

"People who do nothing change nothing."

— MOONSTRUCK

"His bags were packed, but his heart wasn't ready to go."

— MOONSTRUCK

"Careful, lass. You might fall and break your neck." Christian draped my leather jacket across my shoulders.

"What would you do if I died? Carry me all the way back home?"

"I'd bury you in the potatoes and sing you a song."

"The potatoes?"

"Think of all the lives you'd save with your rotting corpse nourishing the crops."

"You always say the things that make my heart go pit-a-pat." While I put my arms in the sleeves of my coat, Christian gripped the back of my sweatpants with one hand as if I might fly over the edge.

"Then perhaps I can make you swoon by pointing out that you still reek of urine."

"I'd bathe in the pond, but I might get a parasite."

"*Oh, Danny boy, the pipes, the pipes are calling,*" he sang.

"You're a terrible singer."

"I have to practice. Ashes to ashes, dust to dust."

"Potatoes to potatoes."

"Nothing beats a warm bowl of Irish coddle."

— MOONSTRUCK

"We all are both heroes and villains in our own story."

— SPELLBOUND

"Raven's so lucky. Crush is such a fun guy, and I just love all his wrinkles and grey hair."

Wyatt knocked on the floor. "That's a strange compliment."

Gem felt no need to explain. She adored the elderly. They were both fragile and strong, and they were also something she'd never be. The life they'd lived was mapped on their skin, and Gem could see that Crush had experienced tremendous hardship but also joy. From the deep frown lines on his forehead to the laugh lines around his eyes, he was a man who had truly lived life.

— SPELLBOUND

"When you're given a weapon, you have an obligation to learn how to use it."

— SPELLBOUND

"When you are two halves of a whole, there are people on both sides who will never accept you."

— SPELLBOUND

"Love transcends the physical."

— SPELLBOUND

"Old flames are hard to put out because they've burned the longest."

— HEARTLESS

Before either Claude or Gem heard anything, Christian picked up the sound of an electric vehicle. But the noise was quickly drowned out by keyboard synthesizers that erased the silence.

Claude stood and squinted at the fast-approaching vehicle. "Is he playing 'The Final Countdown' in a cemetery?"

A golf cart weaved around headstones and trampled the plaques on the ground. Wyatt not only had headlights mounted to the vehicle but flashlights taped to the bars that held up the roof.

As soon as the lyrics to the eighties song kicked in, he moved in a snakelike motion toward them. After another reckless minute, he clipped a bench and lost control. Wyatt flew out of the vehicle and rolled across the grass.

"Now that's a bloody shame," Christian said with derision.

— HEARTLESS

"The stillness of life makes us dizzy with regrets."

— HEARTLESS

Christian gestured to Wyatt. "What's on that computer of yours?"

Wyatt opened up a plastic wrapper and admired a chocolate cake with white filling. "The blinking light."

Christian gave him an icy stare.

After chomping into his pastry, Wyatt set it down on the dash and put on his loose beanie. "Look, I'm three sheets to the wind. I smoked a doobie before you called, and maybe I had another drink for the road. If you get me worked up, I'm gonna get paranoid and have a panic attack. Nobody wants to see that."

Gem played with the quartz pendant around her neck. "I haven't heard the word doobie in an awfully long time. Did you know that they're starting to make it legal?"

Wyatt reached for his chocolate pastry. "If only I cared about human laws."

Christian tipped his head to the side. "You're not concerned about brain function?"

Wyatt furrowed his brow. "It's only temporary. It's not like it affects my hippopotamus."

Gem giggled. "You mean *hippocampus*."

"You see? Who needs the internet when you have a word nerd?"

— HEARTLESS

Christian averted his gaze. "I see you're still bathing in milk."

"You're welcome to join me."

"I'm afraid I'm lactose intolerant."

Lenore set the glass aside. "It's not the same as fresh milk from the cow. No one knows where food comes from anymore. It's just cartons on a shelf."

"That's udderly fascinating."

"Perhaps I should purchase a few goats."

"You'll need a lot of teats to fill that tub."

— HEARTLESS

I approached and rested my hand on the stone newel. "Anything good on TV tonight?"

Still chewing, he said, "I watched a fight that turned into an amateur sex movie."

I gave him a lethal glare.

"Don't worry, buttercup. It was too dark to see anything. I turned it off before I was scarred for life by Christian's woody."

"Woody?" I snorted. "What are you, nine? I thought men looked at each other all the time in bathrooms and locker rooms."

He finished off the last of his candy and left the empty box on the stairs. "There's a difference between hard candy and soft candy."

"It's all candy to me."

"Well, someone needs to keep that candy *wrapped*."

— HEARTLESS

"I'll move time for you, Precious. All you need do is ask."

— AFTERLIFE

"Some people enjoy the life that others pity them for."

— AFTERLIFE

Ren stood up and stretched out his arms. "Can't complain about his mood lately. He's struttin' around like a peacock. I don't think I've seen him this happy since you came back. Besides, it'll give him exercise." After finishing his soda, Ren lit up a smoke and moseyed toward the door. "If I were you, I'd keep an eye on him when he goes for those long walks."

"Why's that?"

Ren put on his aviators and cracked a smile. "I'd bet my left nut he took that dog up the road to shit in Lou Johnson's yard. Those two haven't been on speaking terms since Lou knocked over his mailbox. See ya."

As I held my spot in the doorway, I noticed Crush ambling back. Harley was trotting alongside him, tail wagging and looking about three pounds lighter.

— AFTERLIFE

"You can't let the pain of death steal away the memories of life."

— AFTERLIFE

"You never appreciate the time you're in until it's gone."

— QUICKSILVER

"I did *not* come this far in my life to be ruled by a man."

Christian hooked the strap over his shoulder. "Fecking hell. You and your fancy balls. I should have learned my lesson years ago."

"Stop your whining, Chrissy." She paused in front of a mirror and touched her hair. "This is exactly why you should always look your best. You never know when you might be wearing your clothes forever."

He strode toward the door. "It looks like a cat spit up tinsel all over you."

"You're one to talk. I haven't seen that much silver on a man since they dipped that butler in a vat of it. Remember? He stole from the most powerful Vampire in town." She turned, a wistful look in her dark eyes. "Those were the good old days, as they say. It was easier to kill a person without consequences."

"The night is young."

Lenore approached and straightened his tie. "You have more venom in your tongue than a snake."

He reached up and loosened his tie in a fluster. "Viktor's waiting. And for your information, a snake's venom is stored in their glands, not their fecking tongue."

Lenore sighed and walked off. "You were always so literal."

— QUICKSILVER

"We've been through this, Cookie. When it's my time, it's my time. I've had a good long life, but I'm not scared of dying. Let me tell you a little secret. When you're young, you want to live forever. You have your whole life ahead of you, you're healthy, you're full of energy. But when you're old, you don't want that. You know what people my age want? To do it all over again. To be young, to fix all the mistakes we made, to seize those missed opportunities, to grab life by the balls. I've had my run. I'm gonna stick around for as long as I can and do right by you, but I'm ready for the next chapter. What if your mama's waiting for me out there? Maybe this time I won't fuck it up."

— QUICKSILVER

"I've spent a thousand lifetimes searching for you."

— QUICKSILVER

I snuggled close against his naked body, missing how he used to make me warm. "So after buying a computer and contacting Wyatt's friend, you had time to stop by the store and buy mint-green sheets and a new blanket?"

"You know how I feel about hotel linens."

"I'm just trying to imagine you picking out blankets and pillows at Macy's." I refrained from laughing as I stared at the hotel comforter and sheets piled on the other bed. "What stopped you from buying a whole new mattress?"

"Don't think it didn't cross my mind. Do you know how many mites are living in this thing?"

"No, but I'm sure you do."

"Enough to repopulate the entire planet. They have cities in here and favorite vacation spots."

"I love your pillow talk."

— QUICKSILVER

Houdini stepped into my line of view, his hazel eyes sparkling and watchful. "Be the youngling I've never had. Let me be the maker you've always wanted. Together, we're capable of so much. I understand you in a way he never will."

— QUICKSILVER

"If you look up the definition, you'll see a villain is simply the person who opposes the hero in a story. But not all heroes are good. And by that standard, not all villains must be evil. They are two opposites driven by purpose. There's no good and evil, Raven. Only intentions. Only desires. Only purpose. It's a fluid concept. One action creates an equal and opposite reaction."

— QUICKSILVER

Christian took hold of me and gave me a fervent gaze. It was as if in that moment, he could see right into my soul. When our lips met, we lived a lifetime in that kiss. His lips were a memory of every moment we'd shared, his warm embrace proof of his convictions. Could I do this? He had so much faith in me—more than anyone. If these were our last moments together, I wanted him to know that I never wavered. That I did everything I could.

— QUICKSILVER

"I'm not a man who bends the knee, and I'm not a man who gives a ring. But my heart belongs to no other. Dead or alive, you're the only woman I desire. I spent a decade in a pine box staring into darkness, and I've carried that darkness with me ever since. The first time I saw you, it was as if someone struck a match and lit a fire in my soul. I'm a wicked man, Raven. I've done wicked things. You know everything about me, and yet here you are." He tenderly stroked my cheek with his thumb. "If you think I'm not enough, then say no. If you'd rather be alone in life, say no. But if you can love a man like me for more than a short time, say yes. We don't need a ceremony. We can exchange vows right here and now."

— QUICKSILVER

Footfalls quickly approached as a wolf skidded to a stop. It shifted to human form, and a very naked Switch knelt beside us. "Is she okay? I saw the flash of light."

"*Jaysus wept.* Cover that up, will ya? Grab a leaf or something."

"News flash: there isn't a leaf big enough to cover what I've got."

I frowned. "Where did you come from?"

He raked his long hair away from his face. "I've been here since it began."

"You fought?" I rubbed my temple.

"Is something wrong with her?"

Christian scooped me up in his arms. "Aye. Your balls dancing in her face like two baby hamsters wrestling in a water balloon. Now if you all don't mind, Raven's done saving the world for the night. We'll be upstairs, and I'll ask everyone for a wee bit of privacy."

— QUICKSILVER

I went into the empty kitchen and came back out. "Claude's not in there."

When Wyatt sat on the edge of the chair and it wobbled, he began laughing uncontrollably as he caught himself before falling. "I guess it's Claudie. All this time, I thought he was in the kitchen making me pie. Doesn't chocolate pie sound out of sight?"

"I think you need to lay off the mushrooms."

Gem wheeled in and gasped when she saw the goodies. She dragged one skate behind her, using the rubber toe stop to slow down. "Wyatt Blessing! I was only joking when I said to put everything we have on the table."

"Ah, but you didn't *say* you were joking," he pointed out. "Welcome to Wyatt's buffet of dreams."

— QUICKSILVER

"I'm not gonna defend the way I choose to love and be loved."

— EVILDOER

"I would tear down the world for you."

— EVILDOER

"If you kill my maker *and* my Creator, how the hell am I ever going to trust leaving you alone with my dad?"

— EVILDOER

Crush pointed a finger in Christian's face. "You're walking on thin ice. You got that?" He turned away and stormed into the kitchen. "I would have *killed* that sonofabitch."

"And what kind of punishment is that?" Christian fired back. "I made him suffer. I made him scream. And I would have done it for years longer before I gave him the sweet relief of death." Christian wrapped his arms around me from behind. "I won't let him come after her again."

Crush turned and leaned against the sink. "Your promise isn't good enough. Why didn't you tell her?"

"Because I wanted him to myself. And Raven wasn't ready to face him. Deep down, I think she knows it. She's the strongest woman I've ever met. The toughest. The bravest. But the wound was too fresh. I didn't want him dead. Not yet. Not without suffering. I planned to offer him to her if and when she was ready. And if you think I don't know about suffering, I do. The demons we carry are all different, but they haunt us just the same. I wanted nothing more than to murder my demon straight away. Doing so would have wrecked me. I've spent years becoming a stronger man, and when I finally face that person, it'll be with a smile and not with a tear."

— EVILDOER

Viktor knocked on the table. "I need your attention. Normally we would do this in the morning when we are rested and sober, but I want to get to work as soon as possible. I have taken a very sensitive case. That is why we are in this soundproof room. While I trust our help, I cannot take chances." He pushed a button on the laptop, and a blue image appeared on the screen behind him. When he tapped a few more keys, cursing under his breath, a video suddenly played. We watched cupcakes glide down a factory conveyer belt while a machine drizzled chocolate over them.

"Hold your ponies." Wyatt launched out of his chair and rushed to Viktor's aid.

"What the hell is that?" Shepherd leaned forward and squinted at the images.

Blue scoffed. "Food porn."

Wyatt switched off the overhead lights and then tapped a few keys on his computer before a photo came up of three men talking. "There. Now don't click on the wrong file or I can't promise what else you might see."

"Your fetish for gargoyles?" Christian offered under his breath. "There are fantasy clubs for that."

— EVILDOER

"If you can't control your mind, then you can't control your body."

— EVILDOER

Christian pitched the broken metal into the hearth. "Lenore means to win this war. It's personal now. She's throwing chum in the water —Fletcher being the chum—and waiting for the sharks."

"And I guess we're the sharks?"

"We're the orcas."

"Jesus." I sat down in the chair.

Christian sat at my feet, his black eyes glittering with firelight. "I know what you're gonna say; just hear me out. I used to admire sharks. They're rogues, like us. But lately I'm feeling less like a shark and more like—"

"Free Willy?"

He scratched his beard. "Orcas are intelligent apex predators. They're strategic and hunt in deadly pods of twenty or more. They're the ones who prey on the sharks. They use echolocation to hunt."

"I guess that explains your exceptional hearing. You're just communicating with your pod."

— EVILDOER

I couldn't take watching *Ghostbusters* another minute longer, not with Wyatt giving a dissertation on the impossibility of sucking a soul into a positron collider.

— EVILDOER

"We spend a lot of time figuring out *where* we're supposed to be instead of *who* we're supposed to be."

— EVILDOER

"Powerful men have others fight their battles."

— EVILDOER

"Nothing warms the cockles of my heart like watching my lover's father's dog taking a shite. Say, do you think we can get someone to print that on one of those T-shirts?" He gestured to a row of white tees.

"How much do you love me?"

Christian cupped my cheek with his hand and turned my head to face him, ensnaring me with his fierce gaze. "I would climb into the pits of hell to retrieve your soul. I would become a scourge in the belly of civilization until I punished every last enemy of yours. I would build you an army if you wanted to rule. I would abandon my soul if it meant saving yours. I would give up immortality."

"Will you look after my father if anything happens to me?"

"But I won't do that."

— EVILDOER

"A phoenix rises from the ashes because it cannot burn in them."

— EVILDOER

"Dreams are a life unrealized."

— EVILDOER

He rubbed my back several times. "Did you finally learn how to swim?"

"No."

"Hmm. Then I'm curious—did you get used to it underwater?"

I looked up and speared him with a glance. "What do you think? It was a nightmare. I felt like I was dying or dead. I couldn't think, I could barely swim, and my entire chest felt like it was going to explode."

"It's a wonder you ever survived the womb."

"The East River is not a womb. It's the opposite. Cold, dirty, and confusing."

Christian kissed my head. "Like my first sexual experience."

— EVILDOER

"We can be Vampires without being monsters, can't we?"

— EVILDOER

"Never bring something into your life because of how it looks but rather by how it makes you feel."

— FOREVERMORE

Gem flattened her back against the door, eyes wide.

Wyatt slowly set down his gun. "I was going to fill it in," he explained, backing up with his hands held out. "Now I have to do it all over again. Bad dog!"

"Oh shit," Shepherd muttered from his seat. He put his smoke out on the bottom of his shoe and slowly stood. "You better run, Spooky."

Gem opened the door and flew out.

Wyatt slowly backed up and looked over his shoulder at the door. "I didn't mean it. Good dog. Good boy."

Blue shook her head because she knew Viktor might still be listening.

Wyatt looked at her pleadingly. "Help a guy out, Shifter girl!"

"Serves you right," she muttered just as Viktor launched off the table.

Wyatt slipped as he pivoted and fled the room. "Son of a ghost! I didn't mean it!"

Viktor's vicious barks trailed behind him, and Wyatt shrieked.

"Should we go after him?" Shepherd asked, rounding the table.

Niko clasped his hands in front of him. "Perhaps we should give them a moment alone so Wyatt can rethink his choice of words to his leader."

— FOREVERMORE

"It feels like we were always meant to be together. I don't know how long forever is with two immortals—I guess I just wanna see how it all ends. Christian's my other half. He's not perfect, I'm not perfect, but he gets me. And I get him. I know what made him the way he is, and I can't fault him for it. He makes mistakes, but he also tries to be a better man. I've had bad experiences with men, and I've had unremarkable experiences. It's different with him. I know he'll always have my back. Besides that, he's sexy as hell and he makes me laugh."

— FOREVERMORE

Christian lowered himself on top of me, still fully dressed. "You have bewitched me, Raven Black. And tomorrow you'll be my bride forevermore." The deep timbre of his voice made me shiver beneath him.

"No talking," I whispered against his lips. "Save the romance for tomorrow when our hearts and souls marry. Tonight our bodies marry. So marry me, Christian." I kissed his face and worked my way to his earlobe. "Marry me hard."

— FOREVERMORE

Passion tangled with love and devotion. In that moment, we connected. It wouldn't matter if we never married. Our souls had bonded, and our hearts had already fused.

— FOREVERMORE

He tilted his head to the side. "Is that jealousy twinkling in those mischievous eyes?"

"I trust you."

"As you should. I'll never betray you. I'll never deceive you. Every ocean I crossed, every suffering I endured, every mistake I made, I'd do it all again if it led me back to you. I'll always protect you and fight by your side. I can't promise to be a perfect husband..."

"I don't want a perfect husband. I want someone who's more

like me. Maybe I'm not the most beautiful woman in the room, but I'll make you feel like the only man on earth. I need someone who's patient, because I'm still figuring stuff out. I just want us to always be honest with each other even if it's hard." I touched his soft lips. "I promise that if I die first, I'll wait for you. I'll always wait for you." I gazed into his onyx-colored eyes. "Will you wait for me?"

Christian caressed my cheek. "Aye, Precious. Should I perish in flames, I'll wait for you." He ran his hands up and down the length of my back, and I felt those quenched desires burning once again. "Just don't be taking too long. I know how much you love making me wait."

I kissed his mouth. "Save me a seat on the ferry, and I promise I'll make it up to you."

He chuckled.

"What's so funny?"

"I doubt you'll need to worry about saving a seat. Something tells me the Grim Reaper can't wait for you to take over his job."

"Mmm." I nuzzled against him. "I love job security."

"Don't be daft. You just want the sickle."

"Shut up and kiss me, Poe."

— FOREVERMORE

Wyatt held the smile of a man who had no complaints about being covered in twenty pounds of cake. "Want a bite?"

Shepherd stared down at the tiny bride and groom stuck to the bottom of Wyatt's boot. The groom's head was missing. "This looks like something we'll have to deny later."

— FOREVERMORE

"Do you promise to protect my daughter, put her needs above all else, take care of her when she's having a bad day, and always make her feel empowered by your love and not ruined by it? Do you promise to battle any demons that would harm her even if they're your own?"

Christian lifted his gaze to my father. "I do."

— FOREVERMORE

Christian smiled handsomely as he cradled my head in his hands. "You'll always be my Precious."

I rested my hands on his chest. "And you'll always be my heart."

— FOREVERMORE

SPOILERS

WARNING: This section contains major spoilers to the Mageri series as well as *this* series. Be sure you've read them all before going any further so you can enjoy those little surprises as they happen. This also includes the two short stories included in this Insider's Guide. I'd recommend reading those first and then looping back around to this section.

The reason I'm sometimes elusive with names or providing too many details in certain crossovers is that I don't want to be so obvious as to ruin it for those who haven't yet read the other series. And what I mean by that is sometimes there were very revealing facts about a Mageri character as part of the crossover. I do my best to give just enough information that loyal fans of the Mageri or Seven series will easily spot those magical moments. But some of my Easter eggs are very well hidden.

I carved out all the crossovers and placed them here in the *Spoilers* section. I've had so many readers reach out to see if they missed anything or if someone I mentioned is the person they were thinking about. This will provide you with all the answers. And those who haven't read the Mageri books can bookmark this page and return after they do their read. Please note that spoilers may also exist regarding the short stories included in this Insider's Guide, so you may want to read the short stories first before diving in.

Are you ready to see how many you got right? I've broken these down by book.

RAVENHEART/MAGERI SERIES CONNECTION

Let's talk about John the ghost. In *Ravenheart*, Keystone is investigating a murder case when a ghost follows them home. In order to get rid of the specter, Wyatt makes a deal with him. To those who haven't read the Mageri series, John is just a ghost, and the storyline stands on its own. But to those who have, you might have already pieced together that John is Knox.

I had to be careful about using his real name so I wouldn't spoil anything for those who planned on reading the Mageri series next. The thing is, when ghosts linger behind, they start to lose pieces of themselves. John remembered his first name, which was revealed in the book *Risk*. There were enough clues in addition to his attitude and looks that it would be easy enough to identify him. But for those who hadn't read the Mageri series in a while, they might not have figured it out. Often it's during a reread when a light bulb comes on and a reader contacts me.

When I added John into the story, it created an opportunity to learn more about Gravewalkers. It allowed readers to see life (and death) through Wyatt's eyes—what it's like to deal with the dead. We not only learn more about ghost behavior, we get to see it firsthand. Why do some move on and others don't? What happens to the ones who don't? Often small roles can serve a greater purpose, so even if there hadn't been a Mageri link, John was still vital in giving us more insight.

A lot of readers grieved over his death, but his passing was an important part of that series. It reminded the characters (and us) how fragile life his—how precious our loved ones are. How a person can affect people and how they continue to have an impact long after they're gone. Knox taught us to seize all the moments and never leave things unsaid. *Risk* fast-forwarded a couple of years to show the positive impact he had on those around him.

I didn't want to erase his existence, and so inserting him in *Ravenheart* was my gift to Mageri readers. It was closure for not only him but also us. Knox had stubbornly stayed behind after his death and became lost. I thought his final scene was beautiful—both bittersweet and yet hopeful. He left with peace in his heart and with nothing left unsaid.

Sunny and Knox's love will stand the test of time, and I'm certain they will one day find each other in another life.

OTHER MAGERI SERIES APPEARANCES OR MENTIONS

JUSTUS DE GRADI

Justus appears in the following scenes:

1. His first cameo is in *Deathtrap*, chapter sixteen. He's described as a man with a tribal tattoo sitting at the bar, and a waitress flirts with him. (Justus is a Charmer)

2. Gem reveals in *Spellbound* that HALO rescued her from her captors, and Justus was one of them.

3. He also makes an appearance in *Heartless* during a raid and briefly exchanges words with Christian.

4. Mentioned by name in *Afterlife* by Remi.

5. Meets Christian for the first time in the short story *A Bleak December*.

LEO CROSS

1. In the *Heartless* raid scene, the Chitah accompanying Justus has reddish-blond hair. That's Leo. Another hint is members of HALO wear what looks like a wedding band on their finger.
2. He's mentioned by name in *Nevermore* as someone Viktor was talking to at a party.

LOGAN/SILVER

1. In *Keystone*, a familiar Chitah walks into the bar and Christian bails. No Chitah would make him uncomfortable enough to leave other than Logan Cross.
2. In *Heartless*, Logan and Silver appear in the Chinese restaurant, sitting at a nearby table. The obvious clue is the sugar donuts. Logan approaches Raven's table to make sure everything is okay.

REMI

Remi makes an obvious cameo in *Afterlife*. He is mentioned by name, so it's no secret who Raven is having a meeting with.

You'll find there are also name drops of other characters. Finn is mentioned in *Afterlife*. In *Keystone*, Christian talks about guarding a woman who no longer needed his services, and that was referring to Silver.

SEVEN SERIES CONNECTIONS

RAVEN'S ANCESTRY

Crush revealed in *Nevermore* that they had a Relic ancestor in the family line with the last name of Graves. Since Relics are the closest to humans genetically, they are the only ones able to have children with them. Most won't since the Relic gifts would likely cancel out. The ancestor came from the UK. If you read the Seven series, there's a Relic named Edward Graves who has an English accent. It stands to reason they are related.

BLUE KNOWS IZZY

In *Moonstruck*, Blue reveals her Shifter craving is green olives. In the Seven series, Izzy mentioned that she once knew a girl whose craving was green olives.

EASTER EGGS

What are Easter eggs in books? This is a term used to describe when authors leave little surprises in their books just for readers. They are sometimes hidden and can be a person, place, object or a reference given in dialogue. It can make rereading a book enjoyable when you stumble across them. I separated the spoilery crossovers into a different section since some readers may not want to see them until they are done reading all the books in the Mageriverse.

Some of these I also refer to as breadcrumbs since they might be hints dropped about a revelation that happens later on. They're not always easily spotted, even during a reread.

Raven and Christian: The first time they meet. The first time Raven and Christian met was when Raven was a little girl. He saved her in a fire. While this isn't discovered until later, I dropped a few hints early on.

She was more complicated than any woman he'd ever met, and there was an unshakable feeling that he somehow knew her.

— RAVENHEART

There was a sense of familiarity like nothing I'd ever known when he held me in his arms—a feeling of protection and safety.

— RAVENHEART

HOUDINI

Mr. Elusive. Sometimes I had him in a scene or involved in something and he was never mentioned or identified. Some of these were revealed later in the series, but here's a full rundown of the scenes where Houdini appeared either in human or animal form:

KEYSTONE

- He's the man in the bakery.
- He's the one who stakes Christian and puts him in the crypt.
- He's also the white cat wandering on Keystone's property.
- Houdini carried Raven from the bathtub to her bed by sneaking through the window.

RAVENHEART

- He's the white panther in the bar that rubs up against Raven.
- He broke into Pawn of the Dead in search of the key.

- He was dressed as the Phantom of the Opera at the masquerade ball.

DEATHTRAP

- He's the man in the salon getting his hair bleached.
- He stole Shepherd's keys, filled the tank with gas, and left the keys for Raven to find.
- He was also the man (Chaos) she meets at Club Nine and spends time talking to. Of course, we find this out later.

GASLIGHT

- He dug up the bodies of the three men Raven killed in the woods.

NEVERMORE

- He returned the red truck and was the white wolf standing next to it.

MORE HOUDINI SECRETS

In *Evildoer*, Raven and Christian are sitting in a truck outside the Mexican restaurant. She tells him that she wishes someone would drop Lenore off on her doorstep with a note that says: "She's all yours." Earlier, Houdini was in the parking lot in owl form. While there's no sign of him in that scene with Christian and Raven, he was nearby and overheard her request. That's why in the end, he granted her wish and put a note on Lenore with the same message. Raven may not have realized it since she likely forgot she said those words to Christian.

In *Heartless,* someone on the black market site gave Wyatt the full blueprints to the auction house at the eleventh hour. That someone was Houdini, which I revealed in the next book. I didn't expect anyone would figure this one out, but the clue was in the user name 24267. If you look this up on a keypad (such as a telephone), you'll see it spells out CHAOS.

In *Quicksilver*, Houdini used the same code (24267) to grant access to his underground home next door.

ABOUT THE COVERS

One thing readers may not realize is that I design my own covers, both front and back. I also insert the back cover at the end of my e-books after the final chapter, so if you missed them, check your table of contents!

There is a lot of work that goes into cover design, aside from the tedious task of sorting through hundreds of images. Sometimes one cover can have as many as fifteen or more individual images put together. Most of the models for Raven are the same. There are some instances when I used a different model, mainly due to the lack of options. Hopefully I've made them similar enough that it's not noticeable. The covers using a different model from the one I identify as Raven are: *Keystone, Gaslight,* and *Blackout. Spellbound* obviously has a different model since that cover is supposed to represent Gem.

Most authors don't do custom photo shoots. Some traditionally published books also use images that are easily identifiable as stock art by those of us who peruse stock websites on the daily. Even with expensive custom shoots, the photographer owns the rights and can license that image or every shot from the photo session out to other buyers. In many cases, it's not always possible (or financially feasible) to get exclusive rights to every photograph in a custom photo shoot. The author selects the images they want for their cover or series and can opt to pay extra for exclusive rights to only those images. All this depends on what they work out contractually with the photographer.

The other alternative is to purchase stock images, which most cover designers do, and that grants them a royalty-free license. It's up to them whether they use the photo as is or alter the image to make it unique. If no changes are rendered, there's an increased risk that someone else's book cover could look nearly identical. I've done my best to use numerous images and modify them through cropping, erasing elements, adding elements, colorizing, et cetera.

You've likely seen book covers using the same models. While there are thousands of models to use on stock sites, not all of them are suitable for a book cover. Some also have a larger portfolio, so their faces become more ubiquitous. Then you get into whether the image is right for the genre or character description. I've done my best with the Crossbreed series to create unique covers that are, for the most part, edited to high heaven. You would be surprised at how many layers of images are often used for one cover. All the special effects are added, the filters, the backgrounds, the objects. Even the model's body can be modified in what some designers lovingly refer to as frankenshopping, which combines the words Frankenstein with photoshopping.

You get the picture.

When designing a cover, sometimes I hit the nail on the head the first time. Other times, I might have over sixty mock-up designs, each different. I'm probably too hard on myself, but I really want to produce a worthy cover. They are a labor of love.

Here's a behind-the-scenes look of each cover in the Crossbreed series.

Note: This section talks about the original covers as of 2023.

KEYSTONE

The most important part of designing the first book in the series is ensuring the series will have strong branding. What that means is creating a look that visually connects with the other books in the series. This is done not only through the artwork but also typography and additional elements. For that reason, the first book is almost always the hardest to design. With the Crossbreed series, the series-branding elements are the same typography, a title bar across the center with the series name, usually fog placed somewhere and a sparkle effect, a Keystone logo in the upper right corner, and an overall look of realism instead of a digital painting.

Keystone had less than twenty mock-ups. I was heavily leaning toward a woman in a trench coat walking away, but that imagery felt removed, like it was excluding the reader. I also had a few designs that didn't have a model because, let's face it, designing a cover with models is a giant stress ball. Let me tell you why...

When writing a series, it's important to find a model that fits your image. Once you do that, you also need to make sure there are enough shots of that model that you can work with for all the books. Poses are less important since you can frankenshop body parts. When I first began the Crossbreed series, I thought it might be just a few books long. I had no idea it would go past ten books, so I wasn't fully prepared for the work that lay ahead.

Once I found the model I wanted to use for *Keystone*, I worked on the background and color. Raven is emotionally lost in this book, so I wanted her to appear more vulnerable than on the other book covers. I added a push dagger to her belt. The ravens flying overhead represent her and are found on every cover except *Spellbound*. Even *Forevermore* has raven feathers in the background. In *Keystone*, the ravens are soaring across the sky with a graveyard beneath them. The image feels solitary and desolate, and that's how we first meet Raven in the series. She's a loner, leaving a wake of bodies in her path. She has no direction in life and no sense of hope.

That's the feeling I wanted to convey.

Back cover: On the back cover, Christian is sitting on a crypt. If you look closely, you'll see the name on the crypt is Martha Cleavy. Martha played an important part in Christian's past as one of his first enemies, though it was back when he was human. He also spent a little time in her tomb. Some of the back covers on the paperbacks are slightly different from the e-book versions in order to fit the book description. In the e-book, Christian is sitting on top of the crypt. But on the paperback, I moved him down to the ground so I could fit the synopsis in the open space above.

RAVENHEART

This is my Raven. I used this model's face on most of the covers. Raven isn't meant to be a knockout. She's tough and beautiful in her own way. Once I found the image I wanted, I needed to seat her on something. So I used a scene from the book. The chair is meant to represent Detective Glass's house. It's described as having damask wallpaper in vintage green and baroque furniture. Backgrounds don't necessarily have to be literal all the time. Sometimes a road can symbolize a journey, or a forest might indicate the book takes place outside the city. It's nice to have that creative freedom.

After I put the knife in her hand and added blood, I decided to get creative with placing the raven. At this point, readers weren't aware that I was including a raven on each cover and might wonder why there's a bird hanging out in the room. So I used the shadow of the raven and placed it on the floor beneath the chair. I wanted to make it look like a natural shadow from either Raven or the chair, so the beak is touching the heel of Raven's kick-ass boot.

This model didn't have very many images to use, so on many of my covers, I found a body pose I liked from a different model and then overlaid the Raven model's head. On this cover, this is her actual body. But every other cover where I used this particular model's face, I put it on a different body that fit the look I was going for.

This is the first cover featuring the ruby heart pendant. It's also the first time we get to see her mismatched eyes.

Fun fact: I painted her fingernails black. Sometimes when I'm doing the finishing touches, I laugh. I've got the image zoomed in to a ridiculous size, and there I am, painting her fingernails. Most people won't even notice, but that's how detailed I am.

I go the extra mile.

Back Cover: The back cover is Christian opening up his long coat. I added the little tattoo (which was temporary) on his neck that says DRINK ME based on a funny scene in the book.

DEATHTRAP

This cover was the death of me. It was an absolute fucking nightmare to come up with a design. I had different poses, different faces on different bodies, and an insane number of background options. Just looking at my archive folder with all the mock-ups gives me hives. Most of the images had Raven standing by a staircase to represent the apartment fire she survived as a child. I liked the concept, but the stairwell wasn't working on a front cover.

Instead, I placed her in a room that's on fire. It challenged me as a designer to add flames and embers since it was my first time. I wanted to create an impending sense of danger while at the same time capturing an introspective emotion. After all, this was a turning point in her and Christian's relationship. The stuffed bear was added in the background to help readers connect this image to the tragic events of her past.

The location of the raven is outside the window.

Back Cover: Christian is standing at the foot of a staircase. Flames are glowing at the top as embers are showering him. His coat is on fire, a nod to him running through fire to save a little girl. If there's one thing that can kill a Vampire, it's fire. Christian has a dark soul, and we later find out just how dark it is. And yet this one defining moment showed his humanity. It also changed the course of events, directly impacting his fate.

GASLIGHT

This book exposed Houdini and put him in the spotlight. Raven was caught in a storm, and I wanted to reflect that chaos on the cover. Niko says a line in this book about how she needs to walk into the storm to find her answers. I tried several models, but my backgrounds were always of a storm. I knew that was the direction I wanted to go with the design, so it was a matter of finding a model with the right expression. Not a helpless one. Even though Raven faces the nightmares of her past with Fletcher, she comes out of that storm.

Readers immediately noticed the necklace wasn't on her neck but flying in the air. Panic ensued. It had nothing to do with Christian but what Raven was willing to trade—what she almost lost.

The location of the raven is on Raven's shirt.

. . .

Back cover: Christian doesn't appear on this back cover. I didn't plan nor commit from the beginning to always have Christian on the back cover. I was always open to ideas according to what felt right. The tornado represents both Houdini and Raven—the butterfly caught in a chaotic storm.

***

BLACKOUT

I think this cover fully displays Raven's badassery. This is an edgy side we haven't seen on previous covers—weapons in hand, ready for battle. Because of the dark forces at play and the urban fight scenes, I used a city for the background. This particular book spawned some of the worst mock-up covers I've designed. I'm not gonna lie—some just make me laugh out loud. Part of the issue is the title *Blackout*. The cover needed to take place at night, and that can be hard to pull off where the model is visible. One concept I liked was her casually sitting on a rooftop that overlooks a dark city, but one advantage of trying different designs is that during the pursuit, you often find or come up with exactly what you're looking for.

Once I found the model, I sifted through dozens of images until I found the right one. I almost made the cover gold but settled on a turquoise shade.

The raven is flying over the moon.

Back Cover: I wasn't going to design this cover without Christian in a cassock. That was a given. I almost chose a full-body shot but really loved that close-up, smoldering look where all that's visible is the clerical collar.

NEVERMORE

This is the cover I'm the most proud of. I wanted a bike on the cover since Raven is returning home and her father repairs and modifies bikes for a living. Not to mention Christian rides a Ducati. A few of the early mock-ups depicted Raven inside a garage, sitting on a bike or a car. The garage had too many distractions that took the focus away from Raven, so after I moved the scene outside, I searched for the right bike. Once I found that, I would know which pose Raven needed to be in—either sitting on the bike or standing beside it.

There are a lot of layers in this picture. Each layer can be anything from an object to an effect. For instance, the raven is a layer, the headlamp is a layer, the smoke is a layer. The model had a pose and look I really liked, but the lower half of her body wasn't visible. That meant I had to find her a pair of legs. The bike had a ton of grass in the background and odd reflections in the chrome, which I removed. It also didn't have a working headlamp, so I had to figure out how to brighten it up in a realistic way. There aren't always tutorials for this, so it's just a matter of playing around with ideas until you figure it out. Once I got it working so it's illuminating a little of the fog, I applied shading and brightening techniques I learned from basic art class in seventh grade. I noticed the direction the light was shining and highlighted the underside of Raven's hand and fingers, her jacket, and her pant leg to give it a more natural look.

It's necessary in shadowy images to look at all the objects and highlight or shade accordingly based on ambient or direct light. For instance, I darkened the top of her right boot and also darkened the motorcycle completely as the original image was shiny and bright.

The raven is located on top of the bike in this shot. I felt midseries that Raven was coming into her own, and with that, the bird is perched and calm instead of flying in chaos or hiding. I also colored the right eye blue like hers.

Many wondered about the clock in the background and whether the time meant anything. The clock was a symbol that Raven was racing against the clock in this book.

Back Cover: Christian is standing in fog, and we can see a peek of his raven tattoo. I've had readers ask why I haven't shown a cover with the full tattoo design. The truth is, I would have to create a custom image and wrap it around his body the way I imagine it, and that's something only a skilled tattoo artist can do. I don't think my manipulating an image would do it justice.

MOONSTRUCK

Raven was going on a trip, so the best place to pose her was in a train station or near a train. The backpack on the ground connects to the story of them traveling. While Raven can wield energy, it's something I've mostly avoided on the covers. I wanted her displaying a little of that Mage power because that's where her mindset is at the beginning. But then she kills a lion using her Vampire instincts, and little by little, Raven is learning to accept her true self.

I searched high and low for the right image of a train. My initial plan was to have her leaning against it, standing on the front, or sitting at the top. None of the images worked. Since part of the story takes place in the woods, I tested out a few backgrounds with trees, but that idea didn't work either. Sometimes the background is a literal scene, other times it's symbolic. Regardless, the images and model need to be visually compelling, and a background of a forest was too weak. Plus we wouldn't want Raven to inadvertently start a fire.

The escalator worked surprisingly well, and all I had to do was add a sign on the wall to indicate where she was. In addition to giving the model a new body and rips in her jeans, I added a dagger to her leg.

The raven is located on the backpack as a print design.

Back Cover: This was the only cover where I put Raven and Christian together. They connected in this book on a deeper level as Raven is finally accepting her Vampire nature. She's always been afraid of it—afraid of people seeing her as a monster. But Christian isn't going anywhere.

SPELLBOUND

I had this model saved in my favorites long before I had the notion to write a book featuring Gem. It reminded me so much of her spirit. Instead of adding new hair, I used the existing model's dark hair and figured out how to lighten it. Once I did, I switched the shade to Gem's hair color, paying attention to the fading and highlighting techniques that Claude applies. I tinted her eye color and added a mole to her cheek. The butterfly was in the original image, and I found I didn't have to remove it since it tied in with a scene in the book where she gives Niko a thoughtful gift using stones. Perhaps it was meant to be.

I wanted her sitting in her secret library, so having her leaning on a stack of books made so much sense. The red book at the bottom with the bright light between the pages represents the spellbook that Niko had spent centuries protecting.

Back cover: Searching for my Niko was a fruitless task, but it wasn't necessary that he be on the cover. Instead, I used an ouroboros symbol since it was on the cover of Niko's spellbook. An ouroboros is an ancient symbol of a serpent or dragon eating its tail. I chose it as the symbol because it represents eternity.

HEARTLESS

The cover that almost put Raven in a coffin. Not only would it be a spoiler, it was too cliché. Since Raven is working undercover in a club, I put her in a club scene. I placed a neon heart on the wall with a chunk taken out of it. It seemed fitting with the title. Instead of alcohol, there's a bottle of love potion on the table. This isn't a literal representation of the bottle Houdini gave her, but it's the first time we hear about love potion as a Sensor creation. The potion also comes up in later books, so if Houdini had never given her that gift, she wouldn't have made the connection down the road when she found out what Lenore was up to.

In *Heartless*, Raven is turning to the bottle as a coping mechanism. She knows how drinking almost destroyed her father's life, but she rationalizes the habit since she's immortal. Drinking won't kill her, so what's the harm? More than she realizes when Houdini decides to teach her a lesson.

The one item you can't see on this cover is her black necklace. She has an onyx pendant with a hidden camera inside. I went through the trouble of adding it only to find that the title was going to cover it up. Honestly, I didn't feel like shortening the chain, so I left it as is.

The ravens are located on the shot glasses.

Back Cover: Christian looking hotter than hell. I am partial to all my front covers, but regarding back covers, I have a favorite, and this is it. On the front cover is a neon heart, but on the back cover, the neon heart has horns. Christian is a tormented soul who has done bad things. He spent years trying to rectify that as a guard, but now he's feeling that darkness all over again when it comes to protecting the woman he loves.

AFTERLIFE

This is an example of a design that came together quickly. I knew exactly which pose I wanted and that Raven would be sitting on either a headstone or a crypt. They're dealing with a lot of victims in this book and trying to piece together a crime. Wyatt almost dies, and Blue is reliving the trauma from her past. A graveyard seemed fitting and also captured the genre. I really love how this one turned out.

Since this book focuses on Shifters, I put a wolf on the cover. The wolf isn't meant to represent any particular Shifter. Because of the story focusing on all these deaths, the imagery of the tombstone and skull worked. The writing on the tombstone is a nod to Edgar Allan Poe. At the time, I chose that quote because it encapsulates the fragility of life and wondering if what we do even matters. In the poem, the narrator can't even hold on to grains of sand. All the victims were once loved and slipped through the hands of those who loved them. And now the survivors are left to pick up the pieces and figure out the meaning of life because that's what we do when tragedy strikes. We grieve, we rage, and we question everything. Blue realizes it wasn't all for naught. She will never be the same after the death of her sons, but it led her to something that helps others. Now she holds the power to prevent others from experiencing the loss she carries with her every day. Amid the crashing waves of life, she has found meaning.

The raven is located on Raven's shoulder. It's smaller than it should be, but anything larger would have obscured her face.

. . .

Back Cover: Christian is sitting on a motorcycle in a graveyard. I added the onyx ring Raven gave him to his finger even though most readers would have to break out a magnifying glass to notice. I could have left him in the scene alone, but I wanted to create depth to the image by placing something in the foreground. Harley needed a little love, and honestly some of my favorite scenes in the series involve Harley chasing Christian on his bike. The skull is a great look, but do you know why I really put it there? Too many doggy bits showing. I needed something large to cover it all up, and a femur wasn't big enough. I like the look since Harley is just living his best life, protecting his daddy from immortals.

QUICKSILVER

Ah, yes. Another book where I spent time painting Raven's fingernails. Because the book takes place in winter, I put her in a winter scene. I love the contrast that certain colors can create against snow. The circle of light behind her represents the power of Godfrey Sparrow—the same power she later acquires temporarily.

Once again, readers panicked when they noticed she wasn't wearing her ruby necklace. Instead, it's dangling from the raven's mouth. Any time something happened where Raven had to give up her necklace, I didn't want her wearing it on the cover. But it's always hers, which is why the raven has it.

She spent most of this book in a dress, but that didn't work for the cover. Aside from that, it wouldn't have been easy to find the exact dress she wore to the ball. I incorporated the red leather jacket she wore to the party though. The skull in the scene represents the looming threat of the Keystone team living among the dead.

When I look at this cover, I remember how challenging it was to create the look of a light fog over snow. I had to think about the falling snow and direction, because that signaled wind. I remember adding flyaway hair to create movement, burying her fingertips in the snow, and creating a shadow behind her hand and shoe. It's all the little things that go into a cover that I notice when I look back. The time, the attention, the detail.

The raven is standing on a skull with the necklace in its beak. I colored the eye brown to match Raven's left eye color.

Back Cover: This is my second-favorite Christian back cover. It's just a simple design that conveys the imminent threat with the Grim Reaper off in the background and Christian's look of determination. The fun part was adding snow to the shoulder of his jacket. It wasn't as easy as it looks. I don't spend much time doing graphic design since that's only one aspect of my job as a writer. I don't get to spend hours on end researching techniques and practicing the way I'd like. Each cover design is a concept in my brain and a crash course in how to accomplish that goal. I'm constantly challenged in new ways, and even if I wasn't a writer, I would still enjoy graphic design and digital art.

EVILDOER

With this being the final full-length novel in the series, I worked hard designing the right cover. I had a few concepts, including one where Raven looked more like a fantasy character in a cape made of black feathers.

That was a bit much.

Evildoer takes place in winter, but I wasn't certain about designing another winter background since *Quicksilver* had one as well. The story takes us through several locations, so I had plenty of options. Probably the most important element was creating the right atmosphere, so I didn't eliminate the idea of a snowy backdrop.

Evildoer has a lot of revelations, so I wanted an air of mystery. The scene with Raven falling into the river was a moment, not only because Raven overcomes her fear but also because we learn who was flying that helicopter. I decided to put water in the background to draw us back to that place. Instead of daylight, which would wash everything out, I chose an evening setting with a mysterious moon. As for the shooting star, I like to think it's Raven's wish coming true. But to be honest, it was included with the background. While I could have easily removed it, I liked the meaning behind it.

On this cover, the raven is front and center. Not a shadow, not in the background, not off to the side. I placed the head in front of the title bar to bring it closer to the reader. The bird is a representation of Raven, and she has finally come into her own. Notice the direction the two are facing. The bird is looking left, which is considered looking back or in the past, whereas Raven is facing right and looking ahead. The duality makes sense. In order to move forward and look to the future, Raven had to finally confront her past in a big way.

The key in her hand was a big part of the story. Raven kept a key for most of the series that belonged to Houdini. It's an important symbol of Raven moving on. If you look over her shoulder, you'll notice a white owl flying beneath the moon. That's Houdini. He played a vital role in not just her origin story but her understanding of the person she wanted to become.

Once again, I painted her nails since Raven mostly only wears black nail polish. There's a push dagger added to her belt. I like her stance on this cover. It's confident. While her body language is a little closed off, it's also relaxed. Raven learned a lot about what she can survive. When she tumbled into the frigid waters, she powered through the pain, knowing that it wouldn't last unless she allowed it to. That's how I see her living the rest of her life.

. . .

Back cover: Instead of designing a new shot with Raven, I used her image from *Afterlife*. The writing on the headstone was changed to another Edgar Allan Poe quote. We can't get enough of sexy Christian, and I'm glad I discovered this model because he's pretty close to how I see him. I could probably add more beard, but it doesn't really matter since his beard length and shape will vary depending on how long he lets it go. I put a little teaser of his tattoo, but as mentioned in the *Nevermore* section, I'm not a tattoo artist. Designing the full wraparound image of how I see it in my mind wouldn't do it justice. I added the onyx ring Raven gave him on his finger.

FOREVERMORE

While all the covers in the series have a model on them, I wanted *Forevermore* to be an object cover just like my other series novellas. When I came up with the idea of using black feathers in the background, the concept pulled together. Raven wore a cape with black feathers on the shoulders. It's a simple design, but it's elegant and it works. One thing I changed was the font location and style. I could think of nothing better to add to the cover than a ruby heart.

Though Christian purchased the ruby necklace for another woman, Raven was the only one who had accepted his heart. The necklace is a treasure to Raven, but not as much as Christian's love. It's a symbol of their trials and tribulations as a couple. In the end, their bond was unbreakable.

Back cover: I was initially going to carry over the feathers, but then I started toying around with the idea of roses, hearts, skulls, and ravens. I thought of Raven's remark about their trip to Africa and getting eaten by lions. They're always joking about death, and that's when the idea of skeletons in love hit me. I'm pretty sure they would get a kick out of seeing their bones in a romantic embrace. If anyone means forever-more, it's these two. During the ceremony, butterflies appear, and Crush suggests that it means her mama was watching. Butterflies also represent transformation, and these two have been on a spiritual jour-ney. Even death will never keep Raven and Christian apart.

GLOSSARY

alpha: *Shifter term.* Dominant Shifter who is born to lead. This can refer to any animal type, not just wolves.

ancients: A general term used when referring to a Breed who is over one thousand years old

Architect: *Mage term.* Type of Unique. See *Gifts* under *Part 7: Mage.*

beta: *Shifter term.* Second dominant Shifter (aka: second-in-command). The beta's role is to keep everyone in line.

binding: *Mage term.* Mage transference of sexual energy with another Mage.

Blockers: *Mage term.* Anyone can be a Blocker, though it's rare. They have a natural ability to block various types of powers from different Breeds. A Blocker is also a rare Mage gift where they are able to block other Mage gifts.

blood sharing: *Vampire term.* Exchange of Vampire blood, typically between two Vampires.

bloodlust: *Vampire term.* When a Vampire youngling or a human is consumed by the desire to drink blood.

bloodslave: *Vampire term.* A person (particularly a Vampire) who is used for blood consumption by another Vampire. It is also a term for Vampires who were once kept against their will by other Breeds so their blood could be used for healing.

bonding: *Mage term.* Mage ceremony between a committed couple where they are bonded. Just another word for marriage.

bounty hunters: They work independently, tracking declared outlaws for the reward. This is a popular job among alpha and beta Shifters prior to forming a pack.

Breed: A collective term for all species of supernaturals. Also a general term when referring to an individual species.
Example 1: "The Breed live in secret among humans," meaning all supernaturals.
Example 2: "He doesn't date outside his Breed," referring to his specific Breed type.

Breed district: Every city has an area of town that is predominantly run by either Breed or trusted humans. This area often includes places of business as well as homes and apartments. Clustering homes and businesses allows immortals to live separately from humans and reduce their interactions with them.

Breed jail: Most cities have a Breed jail. Those waiting for sentencing or those who have been sentenced to serve time are housed here. The size of each facility, what it looks like, and how much security is required varies from one location to the next.

the Bricks: An area in Cognito that the higher authority carved aside for the criminal element so they don't mingle with upstanding citizens. Crime lords live here, and there are also underground dwellings and tunnels.

charged: *Mage term.* When a Mage is overfueled with energy.

Charmer: *Mage term.* Rare Mage gift. See *Gifts* under *Part 7: Mage.*

charm/charming: *Vampire term.* A Vampire using their gift to put someone in a trance so they'll provide information they wouldn't otherwise give up. It is also the process of planting suggestions and influencing behavior.

cleaners: They're called to a scene to clean up evidence of Breed activity and/or dispose of bodies. This is done so humans won't discover any Breed bodies or open an investigation. Cleaners report their findings to the appropriate local Breed law enforcement, but there are also cleaners who work under the table and, for the right price, will clean up a crime scene without notifying the authorities.

concealing light: *Mage term.* Refers to hiding energy so they are not detectible by any Mage in the immediate area. Mage energy can be strong and fluctuate due to emotions.

core light: *Mage term.* Used to describe the central energy within each Mage that is the source of their power and immortality.

Council: A body of officials within territories who oversee and investigate matters within their own Breed. They might also conduct mating ceremonies or work with private investigators. This term can apply to all Breeds. Among Shifters, they're generally made up of Packmasters and leaders of other animal groups.

coven: *Vampire term.* Long ago, some Vampires stayed in groups for protection. They called these covens.

Creator: *Mage term.* A Mage who has the ability to make another Mage. It is also the name used when a Mage is referring to the person who created them by giving them their first spark. Not all Mage have this ability.

Creator's mark: *Mage term.* When a Mage is given their first spark, they inherit the same mark as their Creator, which is a symbol that appears somewhere on their body. Each Creator has their own unique mark. This makes it easy to identify their progeny. The exception is if a Mage is given their first spark and one of their Mage gifts is that they are also a Creator. They will have a unique mark from anyone else that they'll pass down to their progeny, should they have any.

dead receptors: *Sensor term.* A Sensor who is unable to pick up, transfer, or store emotions.

crossbreed: Someone who is more than one Breed type. Sometimes they are referred to as hybrids.

districts: There are often references made to Breed districts and human districts. Because immortals are not known to humans, this is just a general term to describe an area where the majority of Breed conducts business. They like to purchase shops and businesses in the same area where they can also live in apartments and houses that are Breed only. Most Breeds feel more comfortable around their own kind and prefer to separate themselves as much as possible from humans.

Over time, they take over many different areas of major cities and even smaller towns.

dreamwalk: *Chitah term.* Some Chitahs have the gift to appear in people's dreams.

Easter eggs: A term used to describe when authors leave little surprises in their books for readers. They are sometimes hidden and can be a person, place, object, or a reference given in dialogue. It can make rereading a book more enjoyable when you stumble across them. You'll often find Easter eggs in movies, video games, and other creative works as well.

elders: Body of elders who ensure that the law is upheld. Among Chitahs, they are respected, but elders serve the Lords. It will vary by each Breed.

Enforcers: Mage police. Enforcers work for the Mageri. Only a Mage can work in this position.

fang: *Vampire term.* A derogatory word for a Vampire. *"Who let the fang in?"*

fanghole: *Vampire term.* Pejorative describing a Vampire. Same as calling someone an asshole.

fangdaddy: *Vampire term.* Slang for a Vampire maker.

fates: Many Breeds refer to the fates. It could be seen as their explanation of how the universe works, the gods, karma, et cetera.

favors/favor trading: Among immortals, favors are more valuable than currency and are respected in the Breed world. Even villains will honor a favor if they are indebted to someone. To hold a favor in your pocket is just a way of saying that you can call on a favor from that person at any time, so long as what is asked is equal to what you did to help them. Favors have to be agreed to by both parties, and sometimes terms are set. If you don't honor the trade, you could damage your reputation and others will not do any favor trading with you. If they do and discover you do not honor your end of the bargain, they could rescind any favor owed. Favors can be highly valuable in the future in unforeseen circumstances, especially if the person who owes you has become wealthy or powerful.

feeders: *Vampire term.* Rogue Vampires who feed on people's blood by force.

firebrand: Sensor term. When a Sensor puts magic into someone that feels like fire.

first change: *Shifter term.* The first time a Shifter shifts into their animal.

first spark: *Mage term.* The creation of a new Mage by a Creator.

flare/flaring: *Mage term.* Flaring is customary for a Mage when entering an establishment, especially if they're an outsider or it's a private club. It basically announces to others that they are a Mage in order to avoid conflict with another Mage who might think they are concealing their light to hide something or stage an attack. It's not required and isn't the law, but immortals are paranoid, so this is just a show of trust.

flash/flashing: *Mage term but also can be a Chitah term.* Flashing is when a Mage channels their light to run at fast speeds. The term is also used to describe a Chitah running at Chitah speed.

fleshwalker: *Gravewalker term.* Slang referring to the living when differentiating them from ghosts.

freshy/freshies: *Gravewalker term.* The recently deceased.

Gathering: *Chitah term.* Formal assembly of Chitahs to search for their kindred spirit.

Ghuardian/Ghuardianship: *Mage term.* Ancient word for a Mage who is assigned by the Mageri to teach a Learner to use their abilities. Not their Creator.

guard: Job title. Guards can be any Breed, but Vampires are often selected because their presence can go undetected among most Breeds and they can work longer hours. Guards typically protect officials, important people, or are hired independently. They work for themselves and decide which jobs they'll take.

HALO: An independent organization located in Cognito that conducts internal investigations and enforces the law. Like Keystone, they accept various jobs from officials and individuals. HALO appears in the Mageri series.

HEA: A Happily-Ever-After, a happy ending

higher authority: They are a higher order of law composed of numerous representatives from different Breeds. Technically not an established form of government that rules all Breed since there are different groups within major cities. They let Councils and elders handle the day-to-day affairs and oversee larger issues such as trying and convicting criminals. They also carry out executions. They establish common laws that must be upheld by all Breed. Regulators of the Security Force (aka Regulators or RSF) carry out orders on their behalf and issue warrants.

hybrid: A word some might use to describe a crossbreed

impalement wood: *Vampire term.* Weapons used against Vampires to paralyze them. Only certain woods, such as cedar and beech, can effectively paralyze when left inside a Vampire's body.

imprint: *Chitah term.* Also can be a Mage term. Used to describe a Chitah's unique scent or a Mage's unique energy. It's not something you do to another person.

Infuser: *Mage term.* Rare Mage gift. See *Gifts* under *Part 7: Mage.*

interbreeding: General term describing when people fool around with others outside their Breed. Among most Breeds, many frown upon it. Especially any Breed that produces offspring.

joyrunning: A loose term some Shifters use referring to those who let their animal run on private property where they're not allowed

juicer: *Mage term.* Mage rogues who have a light addiction. They steal energy from another Mage for a high, which is called juicing. They usually target Learners or those who might be inebriated since a victim with a powerful gift could end them. It's illegal. Most wait around Breed clubs or bars, looking for easy targets.

Jumper: *Mage term.* Rare Mage gift. See *Gifts* under *Part 7: Mage.*

kindred spirit: *Chitah term.* Two souls made for each other.

Lady: *Chitah term.* A Lord's mate.

Learner: *Mage term.* A newly made Mage not yet living independently.

leveling down: *Mage term.* When a Mage's energy level spikes and isn't controlled, it can cause them to black out and suffer exhaustion that lasts for days. It can spike due to high emotion or lack of control. One way to reduce excess energy is to use it, such as flashing. Otherwise, they have to control the energy before it peaks by reducing it. This is done internally. Think of it as a power surge. This is typically only an issue among Learners who have not mastered their energy.

life mate: *Shifter term but also occasionally used by Chitahs.* What Shifters often refer to as a soul mate—the one they were born to love. Occasionally that strong bond will give some a sixth sense when the other is in danger. Not always the case, but it'll be a panicky feeling about their mate and they'll feel ill, like something is very wrong. Some Chitahs also use this term to describe the person they've chosen to mate with, especially those who are not their kindred spirit.

lifeblood: *Vampire term.* Slang for Vampire blood.

liquid fire: (not illegal) An extract of an unknown origin. When applied to a wound, burn, or tattoo, it will seal it permanently. For tattoos, the ink will retain its original vibrancy and never fade. It's called liquid fire because it burns like hell when applied. Most Breeds have self-healing magic that heals wounds and absorbs tattoo ink. Liquid fire stops the healing process. Many Shifters consider certain scars a badge of honor and want to keep them. It's recommended they wait a little or shift once to seal the wound prior to applying so it'll make for a less grotesque scar. Liquid fire has the consistency of petroleum jelly. It's thick and difficult, if not impossible, to put in aerosol form (there has been one known exception). Liquid fire is dangerous when ingested if the victim sustains life-threatening injuries or ingests poison. It has to naturally work its way out of the system before the victim is in the clear.

Lord: *Chitah term.* Leader of a Chitah Pride.

Mageri: Higher order of law among every Mage. They oversee the Mage Councils within individual territories. *Pronounced MA-juree (MA sound like in Mad)*

maker: *Vampire term (occasionally Mage).* Used by Vampires when referring to the one who gave them immortal life. It is also sometimes a general term that a Mage might use when referring to their Creator since it implies the person who made them.

Mageriverse: *Author's term.* This is what I have named my entire universe as all series to date are written in the same world.

measure: *Mage term.* Formal ceremony when the Council members document the gifts of a new Mage by measuring their light. They review their strengths and weaknesses. The Council swore an oath of privacy so that each Mage recorded in their books doesn't have their information shared or leaked.

memory wipe: *Vampire term.* Process of a Vampire erasing all of someone's life memories.

Mentalist: *Mage term.* Rare Mage gift. See *Gifts* under *Part 7: Mage.*

official: Higher authority members are called either officials or reps

omega: *Shifter term.* In order to keep peace in a pack, all wolves follow a rank. Omegas are the lowest ranking, so there may be more conflict between the bottom two than the other wolves in the house.

outlaw: Anyone deemed a criminal by Breed standards. This is an official title given by the higher authority for hard-core criminals or those who have fled when a warrant was served. Outlaws are typically wanted dead or alive and can be a lucrative target for bounty hunters.

Overlord: *Chitah term.* Leader of all Chitahs. Has authority over all the Lords.

own a scent: *Chitah term.* When a Chitah puts someone's personal scent to memory. Usually it's family or an enemy. They refer to it as owning their scent because they will remember it for the rest of their life. That can make it easier to track someone or pick up their scent in a public place.

Packmaster: *Shifter term.* Leader of a wolf pack and typically an alpha. Anyone other than an alpha leading a pack creates friction among the packmates, who might challenge him for the position. This is another reason a Packmaster won't invite another alpha to live in their house—only alphas can challenge for the leadership role. All children, including and especially young alphas, are expected to leave the pack when they are old enough to live independently while they find a new pack and get their life together.

packmate: *Shifter term.* A general term used to describe members of a wolf pack.

peace party: *Shifter term.* An organized party where Packmasters from different packs are invited along with their packmates. Regardless of the occasion, it's an opportunity to form alliances, share information, and build trust. Typically those present are not allowed to shift since their animals could fight and it might create friction between individuals or packs.

pets: *Shifter term.* Humans who voluntarily live with a Shifter as their plaything. It can be sexual, platonic, or otherwise. Some may just want a companion without a physical relationship. It is a mutual agreement with a trusted human, and typically they'll wear a collar that shows who they belong to. That will keep them protected from other Shifters. Pets aren't a common custom among Shifters, and most frown upon it. Because it's consensual, it's perfectly legal.

POV: *Writing term.* Point of View. Perspective in which the scene or story is told.

Pride: *Chitah term.* Cities are broken up into territories, and each one forms a Pride, ruled by a Lord. This term is also used by Shifter lions to describe a family group, and in that instance, it is lowercased.

private investigator: Job title. They usually work locally with minimal travel. They're independent, so they might accept jobs from local law enforcement, the higher authority, bounty hunters, or individuals. They are for hire and work for the public, but they are expected to adhere to the law and turn in or report criminals to the proper authorities.

progeny: *Mage and Vampire term.* Used by Creators and makers to describe the ones they made.

pureblood: *Shifter term.* These Shifters are rare and were once considered royalty. Their family line has never crossed with a different animal from their own. Most come from the Old World. Purebloods live longer than the average Shifter and have stronger powers. All the original Shifters were once considered pureblood, but over the years, most mated with those outside their animal. In some cases they mated with someone who was of mixed ancestry. Those who were confirmed purebloods became fewer, so they were treated as royalty at one period in time. Their line was easily traced, and arranged marriages with other purebloods became the way. There aren't many left.

Regulators: *Aka: Regulators or RSF (Regulators of the Security Force).* Higher authority law enforcement officers. They serve warrants, conduct arrests, work in Breed jails, and carry out executions. Many are Chitahs. They usually wear all-black attire with a katana on one hip and a dagger on the other.

scrubbing: *Vampire term.* When a Vampire erases select memories.

second-in-command: *Shifter term.* The beta wolf in a pack.

Sensor pops: *Sensor term.* A novelty candy Sensors lace with emotions to show off their wares.

Sensorship: *Sensor term.* Some believe Sensors should be able to sell any experience, even illegal ones. When the law steps in to forbid it, those individuals cry Sensorship.

sensory exchange: *Sensor term.* When a Sensor sells an emotion and pushes it into their customer. Sensory magic is interchangeable and can also be acquired by the Sensor.

sentries: Mentioned in the Mageri series specifically. A sentry works on the street, keeping crime in check. They don't work for any organization, but they share information with other sentries. They are paid by the higher authority but typically only in the nicer areas. Some are paid by local shopkeepers or tenants who want to keep crime in check. It's not a high-paying job, so there aren't a lot of them.

shadow walk: *Vampire term.* Vampire gift of moving quickly through dark shadows.

sharpening light: *Mage term.* When a Mage brings their energy to their fingertips in preparation or anticipation of an attack.

Shielder: *Mage term.* Type of Unique. See *Gifts* under *Part 7: Mage.*

Shiner: *Mage term.* Type of Unique. See *Gifts* under *Part 7: Mage.*

Sire: *Chitah term.* How Chitahs address their Overlord.

spellbooks: Very rare. Written in a dead language. The books are usually indestructible except by the only weapon created to specifically destroy it. The paper won't burn, the ink won't smudge, and the pages can't be torn. A Mage infused special powers into the words by writing it using a phoenix feather. Only a Mage can unlock the spells by touching their fingers to the words while reading them aloud. The book pulls energy from the Mage and activates the spell. The weapon to destroy it is typically a stone infused with a special power driven through it.

stunners: *Mage term.* These are weapons specifically designed to incapacitate a Mage. The metal is infused with old magic, and when impaling a Mage, it will temporarily paralyze them. They are illegal to sell but not to own.

Summoner: *Mage term.* Type of Unique. See *Gifts* under *Part 7: Mage.*

Thermal: *Mage term.* Rare Mage gift. See *Gifts* under *Part 7: Mage.*

trusted humans: Humans who are aware of the Breed world and are either invited or accepted by officials. They will typically make themselves known to local leadership to prevent someone from mistakenly scrubbing their memories. Some work closely with Breed, sharing

information or creating job openings for them in human government
or organizations the higher authority might want to monitor. They
must keep the Breed world a secret or else the penalty could be severe.
Humans are typically protected by Breed law, but betraying them
would be a violation of trust that could result in a memory wipe or
worse. Many trusted humans don't have family since it would be difficult to keep secrets from them. Additionally, being involved with the
Breed world can be dangerous.

Unique: *Mage term.* A rare Mage who is not like the others and has
extraordinary abilities beyond common or rare gifts.

Vamp: *Vampire term.* A derogatory word for a Vampire.

watchdog: *Shifter term.* A Shifter who takes on the responsibility of
protecting a woman or child who does not have a protector in their life
such as a father or a mate. It would be less common for an adult
woman to have a watchdog unless there are circumstances that would
put her in danger. Among Shifters, it's a great honor to serve as a
watchdog.

youngling: *Vampire term.* A newly made Vampire, a term their maker
would use when referring to them.

Also: When addressing someone by their Breed instead of their name,
it's usually considered derogatory. This is done between different
Breeds.
Example: "Tell me what you want, *Vampire.*"

A FINAL WORD

Toward the end of the Seven series when I was looking for a new series to write, I found *Keystone* tucked away in a folder. I had seven books planned for the Seven series, and it was coming to a close. My original plan was to work on something else, but Christian called to me.

I never imagined the series would go on this long. I thought I'd give it a few books, see how it did. At the time, my readers were hard-core Mageri and Seven series fans. I knew I might lose some Seven series fans who were looking for more romance, so it was a gamble to move back to urban fantasy. I write in two genres, both inhabiting the same universe. I love urban fantasy because it allows me to write from one protagonist's point of view and follow her journey. But I also love paranormal romance. Not only can it be just as riveting and action-packed, it's also that beautiful journey of a couple finding their way to love. My hope is that while some books may have more romance and others may have more action, what readers love about these stories will shine through regardless of the series they choose. There have been some special crossovers that readers will miss if they choose not to try out a different series.

So how did it go? Twelve full-length books and one novella. That's a lot of dedication to one story arc. At some point, every series writer will face the tough decision of when to end it, and there are so many reasons why that might happen. Book sales can often be a driving force, so if you love a book, post reviews and recommend it to everyone. Another is lack of passion. That's not to say the author doesn't love their story and characters to pieces, but there comes a time when an author is ready to move on. Forcing out more books might satisfy the core fan base, but the story could suffer. And a thirty-book series can often drive away new readers.

I always let the story tell itself, whether that turns out to be three books or thirteen. With a series that follows one protagonist, there's an overall story arc that reveals the hero's journey. Once I've reached the other side, it's time to wrap up loose ends and say goodbye. If I go beyond that, what readers love about the books and characters could lose its magic. Or it could turn into a soap opera where readers never want to reread the books again. I'd rather end things on a high note.

I couldn't be more grateful for the love and support I've received from readers over the years for the Crossbreed books. Each character was special to me, and it's tough to juggle a large supporting cast and give each one the proper page time. Every book was a labor of love. Never once did I rush a story or just give up at the end. I worked for hours, weeks, and months on every book, making sure never to release it until it was exactly the story I envisioned.

I'm especially grateful for those who came on board from either the Mageri or Seven series, trusting that I would deliver a different kind of story they could love but with the same magic. Thank you to those who will continue the journey with me down a new path in the Mageriverse. I can't promise they'll be like what I've published before. I want each series to feel special and unique from the others—to have its own voice and story to tell. Black Arrowhead is one I'm proud of and hope to expand upon. Future books and series may be grittier while others softer. They'll have different kinds of heroes and heroines. They'll open up the Mageriverse just a little bit wider each time.

The way I look at it, had I never walked away from the Mageri books, I wouldn't have written the Seven series. No Wheeler, no Denny, no Izzy. Had I never ended the Seven series, there would be no Raven, no Crush, and no Spooky.

It's important to note that while this document contains many known facts, laws, and rules, my world is always expanding. I didn't want to create too many limitations from the beginning, so the more books that come out, the richer this world becomes.

To all my loyal readers who have stuck with me through every series and have reread them more times than I ever will, thank you from the bottom of my heart for your trust. I will always do my best to write meaningful stories that compel you to turn the page.

"Every new beginning comes from some other beginning's end."

— SENECA

PART V

CHITAHS

ABOUT

CHITAH: Pronounced like *cheetah*
An original Breed created by Dannika Dark.

What is a Chitah?

In the Mageriverse, Chitahs are a Breed with animalistic traits and supernatural gifts. However, they are not a Shifter and do not morph into an animal.

When I came up with these supernaturals, I liked the idea of shaping their behavior and abilities around cheetah cats. It's pronounced the same, but to differentiate them, I changed the spelling. I wanted Chitahs to have primal instincts like an animal without the spirit of an animal living inside them. Though some may refer to their inner animal or similar, this is just another side of them—like Jekyll and Hyde. Chitahs are unique and one of my most beloved Breeds.

The first time I introduced them was in the Mageri series. A character I meant to write as a Vampire didn't quite feel right. I imagined him as very tall, and when he lifted his eyes, I saw gold instead of black. Yet I still pictured him with fangs. From there, I crafted a unique Breed with many admirable traits. They are fierce, protective, respectful to women, and dangerous. So if you want to read more about this Breed, be sure to check out the Mageri series! I also hope to write more about them in other books.

A note on the plural form: Some characters may use Chitah as plural and others Chitahs. Either is correct. Language among Breed can sometimes be fluid since they don't have Breed dictionaries.

Their word is their bond. This is a common saying among them. When a Chitah gives his or her word, it's solid. They stake their life on keeping their word so people will trust them. Occasionally one might also say, "On my word as a Chitah."

PHYSICAL CHARACTERISTICS

Eyes: All Chitahs have a distinct eye color that is described as yellow, golden, or amber. But all Chitahs range from pale yellow to golden brown. They are not known to have blue, green, hazel, or brown eyes. *Note:* When their switch is flipped, their eyes turn black. Read more under *Gifts*.

Skin: Their skin is normal in appearance. Chitahs are most commonly Caucasian, but they can be *any* race. Regardless, they will still adhere to the common physical traits of a Chitah, such as golden eyes and light hair with their normal skin tone and features.
Note: When their switch is flipped or if they are excited or aroused, a spotted cheetah-like pattern will ripple across their skin like a mirage. The pattern, location of spotting, and overall look is unique with each person. Read more in the *Gifts* section.

Hair: Most Chitahs have light-blond hair, but any shade ranging from white to reddish blond is acceptable.

Teeth: Chitahs have four canines like most wildcats—two on top and two on bottom. They are concealed with their regular teeth unless the Chitah is provoked or aroused, in which case the fangs elongate involuntarily. They can also force them to appear at will. Their canines are longer than a Vampire's but not excessively. Read more under *Gifts* regarding venom.

Height: Anything over six feet tall is considered a normal height. Anything shorter is not. The most desirable height is usually 6'5" or taller.

Body: Generally speaking, many Chitahs have conditioned bodies with lean muscle due to how fast they can run. Appearances vary.

Important note: Those who do not have eye color, hair color, or height within the normal range are seen as less desirable to the opposite sex and are considered defects. They would be less likely to find a mate since those defects could be passed down to offspring, and there is an assumption they might have weaker gifts. Skin color or race is irrelevant.

JOB PREFERENCES

Chitahs are especially good trackers and might seek work as bounty hunters or personal guards. Their occupations vary. More Chitahs work as Regulators for the higher authority than any other Breed.

CHITAH HISTORY

Chitahs have a varied history depending on where they lived or settled. Like other Breeds, no one knows their origin. Some believe they might be distantly related to Shifters because they often refer to their inner animal even though they don't shift.

Because of their natural ability to run faster than a Mage and kill them with their venom, they were likely used to hunt and track Mage throughout history. Given they are family oriented to this day, Chitahs likely used to live in large family units as a form of protection, same as most Shifters.

Chitahs are highly organized with their Prides and leaders. They value order and structure.

CHITAH FACTS

LIFESPAN

Once a Chitah reaches maturity, the aging process slows down dramatically. After that, it can take hundreds of years for a Chitah to physically age five years. Lifespans vary. They have the ability to live well over a thousand years. Since Chitahs can die, there aren't a lot of old ones. In the course of a long life, it's easy to get struck down by enemies, wars, accidents, or even suicide. They are not as difficult to kill as Vampires, for instance.

HEALING

Lost most Breeds, Chitahs have accelerated healing in comparison to humans. It takes more to kill them as they are resilient. Stab wounds won't necessarily kill a Chitah unless there is significant blood loss that can't be stopped. There are some in the Breed world who have acquired knives with metals that prevent wounds from sealing, causing the victim to bleed out. In general, there are a number of rare and mysterious weapons that float around on the black market. It's important to remember that Chitahs are not immortal, and while they have an extended life and accelerated healing, they can still die.

INJURIES/SICKNESS:

Chitahs don't carry diseases, catch viruses, develop infections, or get sick.

DEATH

- Chitahs can drown
- Chitahs can burn to death
- Chitahs can die from significantly high falls, especially if they result in a traumatic head injury
- Chitahs can die from substantial blood loss if there's no way to stop it. They are typically resilient, but certain weapons can be used that prevent healing. Situations vary.

NATURAL ENEMY

A Mage is a Chitah's natural enemy. Chitahs are the only Breed who possess a gift specifically designed to kill a Mage, and it's their venom.

DEFECTS

Like any Breed, some Chitahs have defects. That could include limitations to or an absence of natural gifts such as running fast, healing with saliva, venom, fangs, or flipping their switch. They're also considered a defect if they don't have the physical characteristics that are ubiquitous among Chitahs such as golden eyes and light-colored hair. A Chitah of another race is *not* considered a defect so long as they have the characteristic traits known to their Breed. Those who don't possess those physical traits are less desirable to the opposite sex, who might question if they're a pure Chitah or a crossbreed.

Author's note: When it comes to defects, I don't embrace the reason behind *why* Breeds single out those who are different. The explanation given is that each Breed guards the traits that make them unique from other Breeds, and passing down defects could eventually render them defenseless against other Breeds because of weaker abilities. This is one quality that makes immortals an imperfect species—their inability to accept what is different. That's illustrated many times in the books. As the creator of this world, I love writing about the outcasts and the challenges they face.

PETS
Like Shifters, most Chitahs don't believe in owning pets. This is referencing animals, not human pets. They don't believe in human pets either, which is something only Shifters practice.

THE GATHERING
All Chitahs have a kindred spirit—someone they were born to love. But there is no guarantee they'll ever find them. That soul mate might live far away or have been born in another time. Maybe not even born yet. Chitahs will often wait years or even centuries to find their kindred spirit. To facilitate the search, they created the Gathering to help find their kindred spirits.

The Gathering occurs every three years locally, every five years nationally, and every six years globally. This event is a large party held on private property and is usually three days but will vary based on demand. This allows Chitahs the opportunity to attend different events where others assemble in hopes of increasing the odds of finding their kindred spirit. If the male finds his match, he will know her by scent. It is not uncommon for the male to mark her with his personal scent as a way of claiming her in front of the elders to make it official and to signal to other males to stay away. To learn more about kindred spirits and marking, read the *Family/Sex* section.

NAMING CONVENTION
Chitahs have an unusual naming convention within their families. All male children's first names begin with the same letter as their father. So

if the father's name is Paul, all of his son's names will begin with a *P*. The girls will use the same first letter as their mother.

If there are a lot of family members (uncles, cousins, brothers) where they feel the letter is overused in a family and they are running out of names, they can choose a new letter. But the new naming convention must start with the firstborn in a family so that all their siblings will have the same name letter.

COMMONLY USED TERMS

Chitahs have a unique vocabulary when it comes to certain common words. It's important to know that when the word *female* is used, it is usually with reverence.

- *Female* - Woman
- *Male* - Man
- *My female* - A term of endearment
- *My male* - A term of endearment
- *Owning a scent* - Putting someone's personal scent to memory. (e.g., "I own his scent.")
- *Young* - Children

CHITAH LAWS

While the higher authority has laws that all Breeds must follow, every Breed has their own subset of laws created by their lawmakers. There are also a number of ancient laws that are still in place according to books and may have to be followed for specific situations that might arise. Some of these were revealed in the Mageri series, and others are worldbuilding rules I have listed in my master document.

OVERLORD

The Overlord is the ruler of all Chitahs. All Lords serve beneath him. Under the advisement of trusted elders, the Overlord can create new laws or overturn decisions. It is imperative for peace that the Overlord enforces the law, even ancient ones, and that he follows the process set forth to make any changes under the guidance of the elders. He is not a king and must therefore follow the process in order to prevent chaos among the territories or an uprising.

LORDS

Each Pride is run by a Lord (his mate is called a Lady). Lords are in charge of keeping order within their territory and also carrying out the Overlord's commands.

PRIDES

Cities are broken up into territories, and each one is called a Pride. Every Pride is run by a Lord. Trusted elders may serve the Lord in providing advice and helping with all business matters. Chitahs should go directly to their Lord or the elders to resolve any conflict within their territory.

CHALLENGING FOR THE TITLE OF LORD

Every fifty years, a Lord can be challenged for his title. Each Pride runs on a different schedule to prevent a massive shift in leadership all at once. A challenge in some cases can mean a physical fight, but mostly it's just vying for the position with the vote of elders. There can be a physical show of their natural abilities, but it is a grueling process of proving one's worth, which also involves elaborate questioning. Typically with Chitahs, the eldest born is the strongest male and most favored to lead. For that reason, only firstborns will challenge for the position of Lord. There may be exceptions as far as which male in the family is inherently the most powerful, but it works similar to Shifters with the strongest (alpha) usually being the firstborn.

CHALLENGING FOR THE TITLE OF OVERLORD

The Overlord has a designated time period when there is the potential for a shift in power, but only Lords can challenge for the position. Challenge traditions are typically the same as with Lords and not open to the public. The Overlord is addressed as *Sire* or *my Lord*.

LAWS

- Killing humans is against the law.
- Exposing the Breed world to humans intentionally is against the law. This refers to deliberate acts on a higher scale.
- Treason is a high crime. This includes plotting to overthrow any leadership body or assassinate leaders.
- Old Chitah law allows fair competition when it comes to kindred spirits. If a female is mated or promised to another and her kindred spirit finds her, the law will support the kindred's request to pursue courtship. Her consent is not required. Courtship does not involve physical intimacy; it only allows the male to courteously get to know his soul mate and prove his worth. He must respect her, or the courtship period will end prematurely. Once the allotted time has elapsed, the female will make her choice. If she rejects her kindred, he must accept her wishes. The law was created because of issues that occurred with females already mated when their kindred spirit found them. What the male feels for his kindred is powerful and undeniable, and problems arose out of this, such as him challenging her mate to the death or families being broken apart. The courtship gives the male a chance so they can also have closure if it doesn't work out. An enforced courtship will also give the female a blanket of protection from the law if the male causes any problems for her or her family in the future.
- Chitah law does not recognize the union between different Breeds. While no Breed can forbid a coupling, they are not entitled to the same rights as a Chitah couple would be. Elders consider the union an insult because interbreeding

rarely produces a child, and when it does, the gifts are most often canceled out.

FAMILY/SEX

Like other Breeds (with the exception of Relics), Chitahs cannot have babies with humans.

However, Chitahs have something that separates them from other Breeds. When two Chitahs produce a child, that child can be born either a Chitah or a human. There isn't a lot known about the early origins of Breed, what might have crossed into their bloodline. Perhaps at some point humans or another extinct Breed close to humans were able to mate with Chitahs. In any case, something in the Chitah DNA allows them to have both human *and* Chitah babies. Having a human child is uncommon, but this might also be nature's way of controlling the Chitah population.

KINDRED SPIRITS: Chitahs believe they are born with a perfect match and that a kindred spirit is the only one meant for them. It doesn't mean they can't fall in love or build a life with anyone else, only that kindreds are two souls compatible from birth. The intensity of emotion between them is something everyone covets. It's important to know that life choices can make two kindred spirits incompatible as adults. Perhaps that is why Mother Nature only gives males the ability to know with absolute certainty, because it will be up to them to prove they can love and provide for her the way she needs. While soul mates exist, so does free will and the ability to choose.

If their kindred spirit dies, they will never have another. Not all Chitahs find their kindred spirit. Many choose to wait and search for years, while others may decide to get on with their lives. But settling comes with risks.

- **Only the male feels the pull and knows with certainty when he has found his kindred spirit.** He will know the first time he sees or takes in her scent.
- **The female does not know who her kindred spirit is.** If a male claims her as his, she can only take his word for it. That's why the decision always lies in her hands, so she won't choose a bad mate just because they're soul mates. She will always follow her heart, so the male has to prove that he is the best suitor who can provide her with the respect, love, and happiness she deserves.
- **If a male has found his kindred spirit and she rejects him,** it will be difficult for him to get over. Many fall into depression or reject the idea of forming other relationships. That's why most good men will do whatever it takes to change and be the male she deserves. They will conquer their demons, give up habits, and strive toward becoming a better person.
- **If a Chitah finds his kindred spirit and she is promised to another man or even mated to him,** the law allows for fair competition. The elders respect the bond and will determine how long he is allowed to court her before she makes the final decision. This is done to reduce conflict, allowing both parties to know with certainty if

they're compatible so that there aren't any regrets or feelings of animosity.

- **Same-sex kindred spirits have not yet been explored.** Some Chitahs believe they don't exist since nature would only pair up couples for the purpose of procreating. But this is a door left open. Regardless, couples can choose whom they love.
- **Some Chitahs have a sixth sense when their kindred spirit is in danger.** Sometimes they know which direction to go even if they don't know the destination.

COURTSHIP: There is no determined period of courtship when a male announces his intention to court a female. It will go on until the female either accepts or rejects him. Chitahs have interesting courtship traditions!

- **Hair cutting:** While courting, the males will not cut their hair. There's a superstition many believe in that to cut your hair is to cut your chances. Not all practice this, but many do just to convey to the female how serious they are.
- **Sex:** During courtship, males will often refrain from initiating sexual relations to show restraint.
- **Marking:** Also during courtship, the male will sometimes mark her or her things with his personal scent to keep other males away by announcing that she's claimed. Typically this is not something a male will do on a first date unless it's his kindred spirit. Marking is a serious matter, and in most cases, it's only done with kindred spirits. For that reason, males who scent a marked female will stay away. Keep reading for more on marking. It's not what you think!

For information about enforced courtships, refer to the *Chitah Laws* section.

CHOOSING A MATE: Most Chitahs will hold out for as long as it takes in order to find their kindred spirit. Until then, they will have casual partners. Mating with someone who is not your kindred is referred to as "settling." It poses a risk even if the couple is deeply in love. Since the male always knows his intended, if he settles and later finds his kindred spirit, it could mean great heartache for everyone involved. He might feel an obsessive pull toward a woman other than his mate.

If a female settles with someone other than her kindred spirit, her soul mate might find her one day and disrupt the life she's built, especially if he requests an enforced courtship.

When someone's kindred spirit dies, the surviving partner might choose not to mate with anyone else. They often believe they can never possess a love as powerful as the one they felt with their kindred spirit.

When two Chitahs decide to make their relationship permanent, it's called mating. Most Chitahs won't mate with someone outside their Breed for a number of reasons. Many in society won't accept them, they may not be able to have children, and any children conceived are likely to have defects.

SETTLING: In some cases if a Chitah doesn't find his or her kindred spirit, they might choose to settle for someone they love so that they can experience the love of partnership and family. Many do not settle, fearing that after they build a home with someone, their kindred spirit might come along.

. . .

MALE PERSONAL SCENT (MARKING): Chitah males each have a unique scent that is powerful when they use it to claim what's theirs. To other males, it's a warning. To females, it can be an aphrodisiac. The scent comes off their skin, and sometimes a male has no control over it when he feels a strong connection with a female, especially if it's their kindred spirit. It's common for males to "mark" their kindred or claimed female to ward off other males. He just has to stand close enough as the scent will lift off his skin with an incredible punch to the senses. If the female is uninterested, the scent will be unpleasant to her. It's as if her body chemistry knows which males she's compatible with. See the section on *Gifts* for more about marking.

MATE/MATING: Mate has two meanings among Chitahs. Mating is what Chitahs do when they choose a life partner, but it's also another word for sex. Male Chitahs will often fight to the death for their mate.

FEMALES IN HEAT: Similar to Shifters, Chitah females experience a period of going into heat. Only with less urgency and less pain. It's Mother Nature's way of signaling that they're ready to have young. They experience mild discomfort, such as muscle cramps. Her skin will display spotted patterns that fluctuate and are brief. The duration varies from person to person. Sometimes it might last a few days, other times a few hours. Females go into heat once a year or less. Pregnancy outside of a heat cycle is unlikely but not impossible.

SEX: Males will sometimes flip their switch during sex as their primal instinct takes over. There's nothing dangerous about it. Sex is an act that displays vulnerability, and often a fierce protective instinct takes over. Females sometimes bite the male on the neck to incite climax. They might also lick his Adam's apple to arouse him.

. . .

PREGNANCY/CHILDBIRTH: When a Chitah becomes pregnant, her body stops the rejuvenation process that helps her heal. In order to carry the child, the magic within her is suppressed. This is the most vulnerable time in her life and when complications can arise. Males are highly protective of pregnant females for that reason. Some will also become unexplainably protective over a pregnant female even if they aren't aware she's pregnant. This is due to her changing body chemistry. Males can often scent when a female is pregnant, and some females just know it. During childbirth, the females rarely take drugs, especially since human medicine doesn't work the same and dosing would be difficult. Because their healing magic is suppressed, childbirth is always high risk to the mother.

BABIES: As mentioned above, babies are born with golden eyes, light hair, and usually display the spotted pattern across their skin. The pattern fades but is visible with newborns since they're not able to control it. That makes it easy to distinguish if a baby is human or Chitah. The parents always know, but a Relic can also confirm if there's uncertainty.

CHILDREN: Girls are less common in a Chitah family. That's not to say a couple can't conceive a girl, only that it might require more attempts. Because of that, the males are highly protective of them. Unlike Shifters, who prefer males in hopes of producing an alpha leader, Chitahs hope for girls. Having a female child is a great honor. Some families might end up with a number of male children as a result of trying for a girl. There could be some families who have nothing *but* female children, so they might be inclined to produce more offspring to help with the male-to-female ratio.

It's not uncommon for children to sleep in the parents' bedroom for the first years in order to bond with them.

Similar to Shifters, the firstborn in the family is usually the most powerful—like an alpha. Chitahs don't place any importance on whether the firstborn is a male, let alone has more inherent power. They don't live in packs where a hierarchy is essential. The firstborn has more potential to rise to power than his younger siblings. There are always exceptions where genetics might give more power to a younger child instead of the older one. The only instance where the firstborn power might be of any importance is if they want to seek the position of Lord. See section on *Chitah Laws*.

HUMAN CHILDREN: If the baby is born human, most parents will give up their babies to be adopted by humans in order to shield them from the dangers of the Breed world. They might have enemies or those who seek out their vulnerabilities. Chitahs know little about human illnesses and diseases and wouldn't be able to properly care for a human child, let alone protect them from harm. They would be an outcast in the Breed world. It is considered the ultimate sacrifice. It's also proven traumatic for them to watch their human children grow up fast and die. That child might also marry a human and separate from the Breed world to protect their own children, causing the family to split apart. Chitahs believe that giving those babies to a human family is the best option for the child's happiness.

FAMILY AND SOCIAL GROUPS: While it isn't always the case, siblings will often stay together even after they find a mate. They develop a close bond and find protection in numbers. They might dwell in a large home or in the same apartment building to stay close. Females are the exception. After finding a mate, she might choose to live with her mate and possibly his family.

· · ·

CHITAH BEHAVIOR: Chitahs have their own unique customs and traits. Here are just a few:

1. Purring: All Chitahs can purr. Males often use it to produce a calming effect in a distressed female. But like a cat, it also shows when they are content and happy.

2. Nuzzling: Nuzzling is a form of affection among Chitahs and comes instinctually. They might nuzzle against someone's neck or into their hair, but it's a gesture typically seen between those who are in an intimate relationship. It's less common outside of that unless one of them might be seeking comfort.

3. Hand-feeding: Among Chitahs, hand-feeding is seen as a symbol of trust between lovers. It carries a lot of connotations and isn't something you would do with an acquaintance lest you risk giving them the wrong idea. It's considered an intimate act. This might be something the male attempts during courtship to see if he has won her trust and affection. It would be forward and presumptuous for a male to do this on a first date. Hand-feeding goes both ways between a couple.

4. Sleeping habits: It's common for young siblings to have bonded by sharing a bed for warmth during winter. As with cheetah cats, they might sleep close to keep each other warm. As adults, they have separate rooms and don't engage in this juvenile sleeping pattern. But they will still offer themselves when someone they love is injured or in need of emotional support. This applies to anyone they care about, regardless of relationship or Breed. In such instances, the Chitah will usually drape him or herself over the person's feet or legs to offer warmth and emotional support. Sometimes they will simply sleep at the foot of the bed. In their culture, this instinct strengthens relationships by reinforcing their loyalty and support.

5. Females are rarely abused in a family: It's impossible to say never as it depends on the family and other factors. But generally speaking,

Chitah males are born and raised with a protective instinct toward females. It's one of their Breed traits and reinforced within the community, but negative influences can always factor in. From an early age, they see how vulnerable women are during pregnancy and how uncommon female children are within a family. Brothers will live and die to protect their sisters, so it would be hard for someone in the family to abuse her without the others stopping if not preventing it. Because they can scent emotions, it would be difficult to conceal one's malicious intent or past actions and for her to hide her emotions as a victim.

6. Chitahs use nonverbal sounds to express themselves: These can include purrs, roars, chirping, and others.

7. Cooking and cleaning: Domestic duties are reversed in Chitah homes. Most males do the cooking in a household. They believe the males should be the ones serving the females. Separate from that, cooking and providing food for the opposite sex can also hold special meaning between unmated couples. These rituals stir up primal instincts, so if a female isn't interested, she might reject his offerings. Most males clean up after themselves as it would be disrespectful to expect the female to do it. That's not to say females never cook or clean (job duties may vary by household), but most males treat them as queens and prefer them to focus on their passions or jobs.

GIFTS

All Chitahs share the same common abilities—some stronger than others. When a Chitah lacks any of these traits, they are considered a defect. It might hinder their ability to find a mate as it would have to be someone willing to accept a partner who's incapable of producing venom, has no exceptional sense of smell, or can't run at Chitah speed. The concern would be passing along those defects to offspring. Lacking any of these gifts could also make them or their family vulnerable against enemies.

CHITAH GIFTS

- **Venom:** Their bite contains venom that's harmless to every Breed except one. If a Mage receives venom from four fangs, it's a quick death. Anything less will cause suffering. Chitah venom is secreted similar to a snake's and works with venom ducts carrying venom to the fang. Three puncture marks is extremely rare, but the injection of more venom means temporary paralysis, agony, and possibly death. Two fangs or fewer is not considered fatal. Venom causes the body to immediately warm, the heart rate to speed up, and the veins to burn hot. The Mage becomes hypersensitive—their skin a raw nerve. Pain rips through every muscle, and they might experience chills, chest constriction, convulsions, and temporary blindness. Disoriented, they become paralyzed with pain and may slip in and out of consciousness. The symptoms and severity are greater with each puncture, and permanent damage could result if one survives three or four fangs. Venom is secreted at will, meaning a Chitah could sink all four canines into a Mage and not kill him if he only wanted to issue a warning or intimidate them.

- **Eyesight:** A Chitah's eyesight in the dark is better than average, like any nocturnal animal. But it's nowhere near as good as a Vampire's.
- **Speed:** Most Chitahs can outrun a Mage. They will refer to this as running at Chitah speed or even flashing.
- **Sense of smell:** Chitahs possess an acute sense of smell that allows them to scent emotions. Often when pulling in a scent, they take several puffs of air, or their nostrils will flare. Those who have refined their gift can decipher mixed emotions. This allows them to tell whether someone is lying, angry, afraid, or anything else that belies their demeanor. They trust a person's emotional scent more than their words. Skill sets vary. *Read further for limitations.*
- **Flipping their switch:** When a Chitah loses control of their emotions, they flip their switch. This can also occur when they're angered, aroused, or even protective. Flipping one's switch means allowing their primal instincts to take

over. Some may refer to it as their animal coming out, which is just another way of referring to their primal side. They are completely aware of what is happening, but they no longer have control. Some describe it as being a passenger in their own body, able to see and hear everything in a dreamlike state. They can't understand language or be reasoned with. They're operating on emotions and animal instinct only, responding to vocal tones, emotional scent, and body movements. When a Chitah flips their switch, their eyes turn black and a unique spotted pattern flashes across their skin. Their fangs also punch out. They'll only switch back when the threat is gone or a loved one talks them down. They respond to that person's tone and scent, trusting them. If a Chitah flips their switch to protect someone they love or their kindred, they will fight to the death. This is primarily a male trait— not all females have the ability, but when they do flip their switch, it happens for entirely different reasons. Instead of it happening whenever they're angry, they might flip their switch to protect their young. If they flip their switch during sex, it won't last, and their partner is never in any danger.

- **Healing saliva:** Chitahs have a healing agent in their saliva and can heal superficial wounds by licking them. Puncture wounds and serious injuries won't heal using this method.
- **Marking:** Male Chitahs can mark people or objects with their personal scent. For their mate or kindred, the scent is intoxicating and may have an arousing effect on them. This is not a casual gesture but only done when the male has found the woman he loves or wishes to claim. The scent will lift from the scent glands all over their skin. This isn't an act done by spraying or urinating, but that should go without saying. It might be an involuntary reaction when

meeting their kindred spirit. Not all females are attracted to the scent. Some may be repulsed by it, which could indicate there is a chemical reaction happening based on whether there's attraction or not. To males, it's a distinct scent, and they'll typically avoid a female if she, her home, or her possessions carry the scent of another male. Read more in the *Family/Sex* section about kindred spirits.

- **Dreamwalking:** Not all Chitahs possess this ability. Dreamwalking allows some Chitahs to enter into other people's dreams. There are limitations. They have no control over the dream and can only witness what is happening. They might be able to interact with the dreamer and other times not. The dreamer is not aware of what's real, so it's often pointless to communicate.

- **Owning a scent:** Chitahs are able to put someone's personal scent to memory. They call it "owning their scent." With those they love, they only do it so they're able to track them if something were to ever happen. A new baby in the family might have their scent memorized by siblings and parents. However, it's also done when a Chitah wants to put his sworn enemy to memory. This is not something they would do if they're just tracking a criminal. It's a very personal and intentional act.

- **Sixth sense with kindred spirit:** Some Chitahs have the ability to sense when their kindred spirit is in mortal danger.

LIMITATIONS

- **Chitahs cannot scent Vampires**. Everyone has a unique personal scent. Vampires do not. The Chitah might be able to detect their cologne or shampoo. While Chitahs have sensitive noses, their abilities aren't extreme. They can't smell what someone is eating from across the room. Each Chitah's skill set varies.

- **Some females cannot flip their switch.** Those who do will do it for different reasons than aggression, such as defending their young. Females are not as reactive as males.

PART VI

GRAVEWALKERS

ABOUT

GRAVEWALKER
An original Breed created by Dannika Dark.

What is a Gravewalker?

In the Mageriverse, Gravewalkers are a Breed who possess the ability to see and communicate with ghosts. That is not the extent of their abilities. They can also sense who doesn't belong in a graveyard.

Not all Gravewalkers like their gifts. Seeing ghosts on a daily basis can be emotionally exhausting, and some ghosts may harass and threaten them, causing mental distress. While it's natural to gravitate toward professions you are naturally skilled at, some Gravewalkers choose an occupation where they don't have to deal with ghosts. It's not common, and there are people who believe they are traitors to their Breed by shunning their own gifts.

The dead cannot look at a person and tell if they're a Gravewalker. A Gravewalker would have to make direct eye contact with them or acknowledge their presence in some way. Sometimes it can be tricky to tell who the ghosts are. Acknowledging random ghosts comes with risk as they may follow the Gravewalker home and refuse to leave until they get what they want.

PHYSICAL CHARACTERISTICS

Gravewalkers look like everyone else and do not have any physical traits that are unique to their Breed. Like all other Breeds, tattoo ink will only stay on their body if they seal it with liquid fire.

JOB PREFERENCES

Long ago, Gravewalkers earned money by walking through graveyards to locate buried Vampires. Staking Vampires and burying them was common practice, especially when humans believed that was how you killed them. Other Breeds could have also been buried alive, but Vampires were more commonly put in the ground either intentionally by their enemies or by those who assumed they were dead.

Gravewalkers perform an array of services to earn money. They receive offers from both the living and the dead. If a ghost wants help, they must find a way to secure payment with the Gravewalker through a living person or hidden valuables. The dead may ask a Gravewalker to help settle their affairs, give someone a message or other item, identify their killer, or even help them plot revenge against someone. Gravewalkers are the middleman, so if the ghost wants someone dead, the Gravewalker would have to find a hitman.

Gravewalkers might also act as a spiritual medium in the human world, going to people's homes to determine if ghosts are present. They would help the living and the dead communicate. Breed might hire a Grave-walker to make sure their home doesn't have any lingering ghosts that might spy on them.

While ghosts in theory could help solve crimes, they're not reliable, especially the older they are since their memory will fade. For that reason, Gravewalkers are less likely to work for law enforcement unless they have other skills unrelated to their gifts.

See section on *Ghosts*.

GRAVEWALKER HISTORY

Gravewalkers are not a powerful Breed and were often used by others to locate buried individuals or communicate with the dead. Throughout history, there has been a wealth of opportunity in both the human and Breed world for Gravewalkers. Jobs included but were not limited to cleaning houses of ghosts, communicating with the dead as a medium, working in a circus as a psychic, and using information ghosts provided to blackmail people. There are a number of creative ways that a Gravewalker can make money, some ethically questionable. Leaders or other powerful men might have hired them to find a ghost willing to spy on their enemy. In current times, someone might want a ghost to spy on their competitor or uncover sensitive information.

For those reasons, Gravewalkers are seen by some as a potential threat. Their jobs can be dangerous, and they might lose their life should they cross the wrong person. Since the living can't get rid of ghosts, who may be the source of the problem, they will eliminate the next best thing: the Gravewalker who's working with them. Especially if they feel that Gravewalker is conspiring with their enemy or someone they killed.

GRAVEWALKER FACTS

LIFESPAN

Once a Gravewalker reaches maturity, the aging process slows down. Gravewalkers can live to a thousand.

HEALING

Like most Breeds, they are far more resilient than humans and heal at an accelerated rate, just not as immediate as some Breeds who can shift or draw sunlight to heal. Because of that, they're more vulnerable than some Breeds, which is why you may not see a lot of really old Gravewalkers. They don't have any additional gifts that produce healing effects. Gravewalkers can scar. Tattoos are only permanent after sealing them with liquid fire.

INJURIES/SICKNESS

Gravewalkers do not get sick or develop diseases. Like other Breeds, they experience temporary ailments such as stomachaches or headaches. A Mage Healer or Vampire blood can heal any potentially fatal injuries incurred. Some Gravewalkers may have secured favors with those who can heal them should the need ever arise.

DEATH

Most Gravewalkers will not linger behind when they die. They will go wherever spirits go because they know firsthand the plight of lost souls who chose to stay behind and found themselves trapped in the dead realm, unable to move on.

WARDING OFF GHOSTS

Some Gravewalkers keep figurines of gargoyles or cats in their house or bedroom to ward off ghosts. Ghosts are said to have an aversion to them. It may not always work, but the more there are, the better. Real cats can also see the dead and typically don't like them, so for that reason, Gravewalkers might choose to have a pet cat or two.

AVOIDED LOCATIONS

Gravewalkers who want to avoid being around too many ghosts will stay away from places like newer cemeteries, funeral homes, and hospitals, especially since most of those locations would have ghosts who were formerly human. Gravewalkers can't always negotiate profitable deals with a human.

FAMILY/SEX

Gravewalkers are born into their Breed. You cannot "make" a Gravewalker the same way you can make a Vampire or a Mage. They can't have babies with humans.

RELATIONSHIPS: Like most Breeds, Gravewalkers prefer to marry their own kind. Having children with another Breed is uncommon, and any children born between an interbred couple will likely have gifts canceled out. Anyone living in the Breed world who has no gifts or weaker gifts is more vulnerable and less likely to find good work. Other Breeds find it too creepy to date a Gravewalker, knowing that they have conversations with people they can't see. There are no special courtship rituals.

CHILDREN: Because of their lifespan, Gravewalkers can reproduce for centuries. For obvious reasons, most would prefer to have their children early in life so they're not continually raising them. The kids will also be closer in age and, because of that, form better relationships.

They cannot have children with humans. If they *are* able to produce a child with another Breed, the child likely won't have any Gravewalker gifts since gifts are usually canceled out. While many Gravewalkers struggle with their unusual life, they accept that they're a valuable asset to the Breed world and can help people. For that reason, they want to ensure that they don't go extinct.

GIFTS

All Gravewalkers are born with the ability to see and communicate with ghosts who exist in the dead realm. Those souls rejected moving on and lingered behind, often because they left something unfinished. Gravewalkers use their gifts in any way they can to make money. Some have powerful skills, whereas others may have defective traits.

GRAVEWALKER GIFTS

- **Seeing the dead:** Gravewalkers can see spirits who haven't moved to the next realm. They can also see a person who just died, moments before they transition to the next realm. When a spirit moves on, Gravewalkers cannot see or hear what or who is calling that spirit. They might hear the ghost mention something before they disappear. Gravewalkers also don't know where they go after that. Sometimes it can be difficult to visually distinguish the living from the dead. See the section on *Ghosts* for more.

- **Communicating with the dead:** Gravewalkers can hear and speak to the dead, but they can't make physical contact. It's advisable to ignore them in public because once a specter discovers a living person can see them, they might follow them home and pester them for years.
- **Locating Vampires:** Gravewalkers have an uncanny gift of knowing who doesn't belong in a cemetery—Vampire or not. People used to bury Vampires as punishment or revenge, so Gravewalkers were hired by individuals or even local leaders to locate them since a Mage can't feel a Vampire's energy and a Chitah can't scent them. If the Vampire is impaled when buried, they wouldn't be able to scream or make noise. The Gravewalker will often walk around the area until they pick up a vibe. Sometimes souls will guide them. Rarely it will be the spirit of a living Vampire whose soul jumped out of their body when the heart was stopped (read more under *Vampires*). Locating a person buried alive is easier when there are a number of other dead people buried in the same area. It's more challenging to locate a buried Vampire off in the woods because of the acreage. It really depends on the ability of the Gravewalker. *Note:* buried individual must still be alive for a Gravewalker to find them.

LIMITATIONS

Gravewalkers can't just dial the dead and summon any spirit they want. They might hold a séance to give off the impression that they can, but the specter has to be in proximity for them to communicate.

MORE ON GHOSTS

Everything you always wanted to know about ghosts but were afraid to ask.

Gravewalkers are unable to see where specters go when they die and move on. Whether they go with an unseen entity, walk into a light, skip down a tunnel, or get teleported up into a mother ship, only the dead know. But it has been revealed in the Crossbreed series that an unseen entity arrives to collect any left behind who are given a second chance. There is light, and there are voices.

When a person dies and they choose to stay behind, they are stuck in this world but live in a dead realm where the living can't see them. It's rare that they are given a second chance to move on. People stay behind for different reasons. Some refuse to accept their death. Others might feel they have unresolved issues. Then there are those who want to seek revenge against the person who killed them in the first place.

Two ways they can move on is by making peace with whatever they were holding on to or by doing something extraordinary like saving a life or helping the living with something of great importance. Not every spirit moves on if they missed the first boat, and it typically requires a selfless and noble act.

ABOUT GHOSTS

- **Appearance:** How a spirit looks when they die varies. Some will appear as they remember themself, others might have been so traumatized by their death that they still look freshly killed. They might be wet, burned, or covered in blood. Death is personal for everyone.
- **Dead clothes:** The dead usually wear the clothes they died in and are unable to change at will. It's possible they might see themselves differently from how they died and for that clothing to appear on them. For example, a person who was a former soldier might only see themselves in a uniform.
- **Ghosts are sometimes difficult to identify.** While some are easy to spot because of their physical appearance, others may blend in with the living more easily. Most will exhibit certain behaviors that are characteristic of the dead. Another telltale sign is if no one else can see them.
- **Ghosts don't cast shadows.** This is another way to visually identify them.
- **Electricity confuses the dead.** They are more drawn to spaces without electricity. It doesn't mean they'll avoid clubs or places that are wired, only that they don't make those their regular hangouts. Sometimes they stare at light sources. They also have the ability to create power surges and make the lights flicker or shut off.
- **Freshies (**newly dead) are often found in cemeteries, hospitals, and funeral homes. Occasionally they might

linger in the location they died, but a soul would be inclined to follow wherever their body is taken.

- **The dead lose their memory with time.** Spirits don't have any real sense of time. The longer a ghost lingers in the dead realm, the more scattered their memories. Their thoughts become fragmented like pieces of different jigsaw puzzles put together. They're also easily distracted. The living world confuses them because no one is able to see them. They are lost souls. Some will hang around familiar places, but if they wander, it's likely they will forget their life or even who they are. Some of those memories might mix with memories of past lives. Gravewalkers liken them to having the memory of a goldfish since the older ones can't be relied on for information. There are always exceptions, but in general, being a ghost is like having dementia.

- **Ghosts notice anyone who makes eye contact.** The living world around them ignores their existence. Inhabiting the dead realm will cause many ghosts to become irate, desperate, and confused by not being seen. Conversing with other ghosts isn't a pleasant experience when many of them are mentally unstable, easily distracted, and unable to have cohesive conversations. Plus it's a reminder of what they are. When a Gravewalker notices them, they might follow that person, desperate for help. Sometimes they just like to be seen. It can be infuriating if the Gravewalker chooses to ignore them. Some just like harassing Gravewalkers for fun. The older ones may prefer to be left alone.

- **The dead can influence the living.** When a living person is asleep, half-asleep, or even weak-minded, a ghost can put thoughts in their head or influence their emotions. While the person is asleep, the ghost might make them dream or see things. It's not a possession, so they can't control a person's body or even their thoughts. Not all ghosts are aware they can do this.

- **It's unhealthy for a ghost to get attached to the living.** They don't belong here, and in time, they'll go mad if they form an emotional attachment to a person they can't remember. They might even forget they're dead, confused as to why no one can see them or why they can't touch people.
- **The dead cannot eat or drink.** Not unless they died with food in their hand, in which case they might be walking around the afterlife with a hot dog. Awkward.
- **Ghosts can't move things.** Because they have no physical form, they're unable to carry, possess, or move objects from the living world.
- **The dead can travel.** Ghosts can travel as passengers in cars, bikes, airplanes, and any other mode of transportation.
- **Transportation by thought.** It's entirely possible for ghosts to transport themselves to a different location by focusing on a person. Most may not be aware and others may not know how. It could also happen by accident. Some ghosts may be incapable or can only do it immediately after their soul leaves their body. There's no handbook for the dead.
- **Aversion to figurines of gargoyles and cats.** Some Gravewalkers possess these figurines in their home to make their living space less attractive to a ghost. It's likely the reason gargoyles were put onto old buildings. Since cats can see the dead and don't especially like them, Gravewalkers might have a pet or two around the house.

WHAT HAPPENS AFTER THEY MOVE ON

- It is believed by many that souls are reincarnated into a new life.
- If a human did a good deed helping out Breed in either their life or in ghost form, it's likely they will be reborn as Breed.
- Ancients believe that all human children who die are reincarnated as Breed in order to gift them an extended life for the sacrifice of their short one.

Some Gravewalker terms for the dead:

- Ghost/Ghosties
- Spooks
- Freshy/Freshies (new ghosts)
- Specters
- Spirits

Other terms:

- Eternity box (a coffin)
- Fleshwalkers (the living but not a Gravewalker)

PART VII

MAGE

ABOUT

MAGE
A previously written supernatural reimagined by Dannika Dark.

What is a Mage?

A mage is often portrayed as a sorcerer or magician. When I decided to use them in my world, I wanted a unique spin that redefined what a mage is. I looked at their gifts from the perspective of a human. The whole concept of the Mageriverse is that there are supernaturals secretly living among us. I thought it would be exciting to explore how they're portrayed in books, TV, and film to show how humans in the past misunderstood their gifts.

I had already created a Breed that could harness energy, but I didn't want to add a magical element to it. They have excess energy within them that they can control, but they're also affected by outside energy. Once I developed the core idea of a Mage, I could build upon it, layer by layer. These supernaturals can store, manipulate, and weaponize energy. Long ago, humans who witnessed their gifts thought it looked like they were performing magic. They had no explanation for what they were seeing, and that's how the myth was written into stories. That inspired me to create a unique Breed, building a collection of gifts, abilities, history, and laws within the Mageriverse.

A note on the plural form: In the Mageriverse, most will use *Mage* as the plural form rather than Mages. That's not to say that *Mages* is incorrect since there is no Breed dictionary, but that is usually how the plural form is treated. While the word is a familiar one to us humans, to the Mage, they are something entirely different from the sorcerers in fables.

PHYSICAL CHARACTERISTICS

They do not have Breed-specific physical characteristics since almost every Mage was formerly a human. Some of the ancients have light flickering in their irises.

Every Mage has a Creator's mark located somewhere on their body. The symbol matches the one their Creator has. The only exception is when the new Mage is also a Creator, in which case they'll have their own unique mark to pass down to their progeny (should they make any).

JOB PREFERENCES

There are no specific professions that a Mage is better suited for than any other Breed. Long ago, they might have gravitated toward jobs as warriors, guards, or even messengers since they can flash for short periods. Certain rare gifts possessed by a Mage might give them advantages in a profession, but the Breed overall doesn't dominate any particular field.

MAGE HISTORY

Mage history is a dark one. They hunted their own kind—those whose powers were too strong or not understood. To protect themselves from enemies, Creators gave immortality to those who would guard them. Some were made against their will.

Throughout history, Mage were notorious for keeping Shifters as slaves who served them in either animal or human form. Immortals once feared the power and numbers that Shifters had, so stronger Breeds tried to control them.

Mage are now one of the most organized Breeds. They formed the first recognized body of law—the Mageri. Their violent past might be one reason they got organized and created laws to abide by. If they had kept fighting themselves and other Breeds, they might have gone extinct. Creators no longer have a need to build armies, and many don't want the responsibility of mentoring a new Mage.

Long ago, some called them Lightwalkers. Little was understood about the rare and common gifts that every Mage possesses. Energy is addictive, so there were numerous attacks. Some kept light slaves so they wouldn't get arrested for murder or witchery. The Mageri keeps tabs on murders, making it harder for those with a light addiction.

Instead of attacking people on the street, Creators with a light addiction might make a new Learner for the sole purpose of juicing their energy. Juicing is a crime, but penalties against Creators aren't especially severe since they're the only ones who can replenish the population. Because the Mageri has more control over who is chosen to become a Mage, there are fewer issues than there once were. Light addiction will always exist, as will crime, but now they keep tabs on everyone and are better able to govern how many new Learners are created.

Women also have a dark history in the Mage world. Long ago, men sought power. Creators primarily chose male Learners to guard and serve them, so there were always fewer women than men. It's likely that most women brought into their world were done so as a light slave or someone to bind with. Binding is a pleasurable experience where sexual energy is shared, and it can only be done with another Mage. Female Creators could have been seen as a threat. These were ancient times, so all one needs to do is think about the obstacles women faced in history when men were consumed with fighting battles, conquering new lands, and increasing their power.

Even today there are far more men than women. Some of those ancient women who experienced hardships now hold positions of power, especially with the Mageri and higher authority. Not only have they struggled long enough, their positions (or statuses of wealth) secure their safety so that women never have to go back to the Dark Ages again.

MAGE FACTS

LIFESPAN

Immortal. In theory, they can live forever. However, all things created can be destroyed. See farther down under *Death* for more on how a Mage can die.

ENERGY

A Mage's energy is a weapon when used on other Breeds (except Vampires). But they can't blast another Mage with energy. All it will do is juice them up. Energy may be visible in the hands, especially when transferring energy to or from another Mage. But it doesn't shoot out like lightning or radiate around them. Healing light often resembles electric spiderwebs floating in the wind from their fingertips. If a Mage is charged up with energy, light might drip from their fingertips. Large amounts of energy, such as what Wielders can manipulate, are visible as energy balls. An ancient may have the ability to create small globes of energy they can hold in their hand, but they can't use them as weapons. That's only something a Wielder can make. If a Mage Healer uses their gift on someone, it will create a flash of light. Because they have more energy, they might also be more prone to static electricity.

. . .

HEALING

Like most Breeds, Mage have accelerated healing abilities. What's more, they can instantly heal by pulling healing light from either another Mage or direct sunlight.

Healing from a Mage: Healing light is mixed in with regular light— it's a very specific energy source. It takes practice to learn how to extract healing light and how to freely give it. One must learn how to separate that light from the rest because simply pulling energy from a Mage is not enough. The light is diluted, and all it will do is juice them up. Healing light doesn't have to be given freely—it can be taken. Because light is addictive, most prefer sunlight even if it means waiting through the night.

Healing from other Breeds: It's possible to extract healing energy from other Breeds, but it's not enough to heal severe injuries and could kill that person. Vampire blood can heal a Mage, but most Vampires don't give that up freely.

Healing with sunlight: Simply exposing their body to the sun will not have a healing effect. The process requires careful infusing of just a small amount of sunlight into their body by will, so they have to be conscious. Direct sunlight is required; a cloudy day that is bright is not sufficient. Because sunlight is powerful and too much could knock them out for days or even kill a young Learner, they need to be taught by an experienced Mage how to do this. Healing by sunlight is natural and a better source than taking from another Mage or Breed. For that reason, fighting in the daytime is advantageous for a Mage. If the injury is severe and sunshine isn't in the forecast, they're better off taking light from another Mage lest they suffer.

If none of these methods are performed, a Mage will still heal from their injuries. But depending on the severity, it could be a painful wait.

Usually a bone needs to be realigned so it'll fuse together properly. Otherwise, it may need to be rebroken. The extent of injuries and how much of their core energy was drained all play a factor in how long the natural healing process will take.

STUNNERS AND CHITAH BITES

Mage have two vulnerabilities: stunners and Chitah venom. Stunners are made of a type of metal fashioned into knives and other weapons that, when impaling a Mage, cause temporary paralysis. They will be vulnerable for as long as the weapon remains inside them. Most stunners are collected, traded, found, or stolen since they're illegal to sell. No one knows their origin. Stunners don't leave scars.

Chitah bites cause severe pain and even death. Chitah bites scar.

Venom: Their bite contains venom that's harmless to every Breed except one. If a Mage receives venom from four fangs, it's a quick death. Anything less will cause suffering. Chitah venom is secreted similar to a snake's and works with venom ducts carrying venom to the fang. Three puncture marks is extremely rare, but the injection of more venom means temporary paralysis, agony, and possibly death. Two fangs or less is not considered fatal. Venom causes the body to immediately warm, the heart rate to speed up, and the veins to burn hot. The Mage becomes hypersensitive— their skin a raw nerve. Pain rips through every muscle, and they might experience chills, chest constriction, convulsions, and temporary blindness. Disoriented, they become paralyzed with pain and may slip in and out of consciousness. The symptoms and severity are greater with each puncture, and permanent damage could result if one survives three or four fangs. Venom is secreted at will, meaning a Chitah could sink all four canines into a Mage and not kill him if he only wanted to issue a warning or intimidate them.

INJURIES/SICKNESS

- A Mage cannot catch viruses, develop diseases, or get infections.
- **Drowning:** A Mage cannot die by drowning. Their core light won't allow it. They might be so overwhelmed by the pain and shock that they choose to lie at the bottom and fall unconscious. With determination, a Mage can walk to the shore despite the agony of water in their lungs. Their heart will still beat, and no cells will die.
- **Buried alive:** A Mage won't die in a coffin from lack of oxygen, but it's possible they might waste away if they're not able to eat or drink. They still experience hunger and require food. It would likely take years since their core light won't let them die that easily. Even if they waste away to bones, there have been rumors that if brought into the sun or given healing light from a Mage, they could mend.
- **Broken bones:** These will heal, but it's generally a good idea to realign the bone if it snapped in half and moved out of place. If they heal misaligned, they might have to be rebroken. It doesn't have to be an exact alignment, but if the bones are lined up side by side, that would become an issue. Bones that are shattered may not heal right. In extreme cases, it's always best to seek out someone with knowledge to advise on proper healing, such as a Relic.
- **Poison:** Because poisons remain in the body for varying lengths of time, a Mage can't use healing energy to recover from the physical effects any more than they can use energy

to undo sensory magic. Poison alone can't kill a Mage—not unless they somehow ingested liquid fire. Time is required for it to leave the system. The same applies to venom from snakebites, for example.

- **Severed body parts:** If they lose a limb, it won't grow back. However, it's entirely possible they could hold their limb together, align the bone, and use healing light or Vampire blood to reattach it. A Healer's gifts might also work. If the limb is severely mangled, the odds are slim to none. Usually in these scenarios, a Mage will seek out a Relic.

- **Scars:** All wounds heal, so a Mage doesn't scar. They can keep scars or tattoos by using liquid fire. They also retain any scars they acquired as a human before their first spark. *Exception:* Chitah bites always leave a permanent scar because of the venom not allowing the wound to heal properly.

- **Tartar and cavities:** They don't develop any issues with gum disease, decay, cavities, or even tartar. Their body is self-healing, and that includes teeth. Broken teeth work like broken bones and will likely fuse back together. Otherwise, there would be a lot of Mage out there with dentures.

- **Stomachaches and headaches:** Although a Mage cannot get sick, they experience stomachaches and headaches from alcohol, food, stress, et cetera. They simply have to wait it out or take human medicine.

- **Human medicine:** In general, human medicine is weak for most Breed. If they take any, they often will increase the recommended dosage.

- **Weight:** A Mage will typically maintain the same weight as when they were made. Their body resists excessive fat retention unless they were overweight as a human. That said, a person's consistent diet and lifestyle allows them to add muscle or even lose weight. It's also worth noting that flashing burns a lot of calories.

DEATH

Examples of how a Mage can die:

- Beheading
- Fire
- Chitah bites. See farther up under *Venom*.
- Core light can be removed by a Stealer, rendering them mortal. After that, they are as vulnerable as a human.
- It's possible if both their blood and energy are drained simultaneously (particularly if they are a new Mage whose light isn't developed and strong) that they will die.
- Shifter wolves and other predators (wolves especially) are able to kill a Mage by working together. First they will rip off their hands to remove their ability to use energy. Then they tear them apart. Their head still needs to be removed for certain death, but Shifters going for the kill will finish the job.
- They can also succumb to rare gifts used on them by another Mage, such as a Wielder's ability to incinerate people with energy balls.

NATURAL ENEMY

A Mage's mortal enemy is the Chitah. Most Chitahs can outrun a Mage, and their venom can kill or paralyze. Because Chitahs are also excellent trackers, that can make it difficult for a Mage to fight or even flee from a Chitah. Fighting would put them in close proximity to a

Chitah's fangs, and unless they're also a Jumper, running would use up their core energy, which they need in order to fight. Nature has given the Chitah a number of advantages over a Mage.

CREATOR'S MARK

Every Mage has a Creator's mark somewhere on their body. The symbol matches that of their Creator and appears after their first spark. These marks make it easy to identify a Creator's progeny. Because they're a symbol, people might initially mistake it for a tattoo. But upon closer examination, there's no ink. All Creators have a mark unique from other Creators. If one or more of their progeny also receives the rare gift of Creator, they will have their own unique mark. That's what makes the gift easy to identify with a new Learner, whereas other gifts might take years to discover.

DEFECTS

Like every other Breed, defects exist. They might have weaker light, not flash as fast, or lack common Mage gifts.

TATTOOS

Like scars, a Mage's body will self-heal. Tattoos will only last a few days before the body absorbs the ink and it's gone. Like other Breeds, if they want a permanent tattoo, they'll need to seal it with liquid fire.

COMMONLY USED TERMS

There are many Mage-specific terms you'll see in the books. Refer to the glossary for definitions, or this section, which will elaborate on some of these.

- *binding*
- *bonding*
- *charged*
- *concealing light*

- *core light*
- *Creator's mark*
- *first spark*
- *flare/flaring*
- *flash/flashing*
- *Ghuardian/Ghuardianship*
- *juicing/juicer*
- *Learner*
- *leveling down*
- *measured*
- *sharpening light*
- *Unique*

MAGE LAWS

While the higher authority has laws that all Breeds must follow, such as it being illegal to kill humans, each Breed has their own separate laws created by their lawmakers. Some of these are unique, and some merely enforce the higher law. This document may not encompass all laws but lists the ones mentioned to date.

THE MAGERI

The Mageri is the governing body that rules every Mage. They are one of the most organized groups and formed the first body of law. The Mageri is located in every major city. They also form a Council for each territory, comprising at least four members. Councilmen work on behalf of the Mageri, resolving issues, monitoring Learners, overseeing investigations, and measuring every new Mage.

While Creators can make a new Mage of their choosing, the Mageri likes to select from a list of trusted humans who will contribute something to their way of life. That way they have more control over who is brought into their world and it's not complete chaos. Most Creators prefer it this way. Problems can arise when a human is brought into their world by force or without the Mageri's approval. They might not have fully comprehended what they were accepting or may wish to return to their old life. If the Learner becomes violent or commits treason, the law decrees that the Mageri can "put them down." Trusted humans are a safer bet since they know about the Breed world, the laws, and understand what they are getting into.

Creators who make their own progeny without approval aren't breaking the law. They can rectify the situation by facing the Council, who will make note in their record books and assess the Learner's gifts. Even if a Creator abandons their progeny, the Mageri will show leniency since Creators are the only ones who hold the power to give the first spark. If a Creator doesn't wish to mentor his or her Learner, the Mageri will usually assign a Ghuardian to do the job. They won't leave a Learner to their own devices. Their goal is to make sure that all who enter their world are of sound mind and will obey the laws.

The Council and all others who work for the Mageri have sworn an oath to protect the privacy of each Mage they record in their books. Anyone with access to Mage records or those who conduct interviews and investigations are beholden to those vows. Betraying their oath is treason. They would face the harshest penalty, which could be death. This consequence fosters a trusting environment between the Mageri and every Mage.

ENFORCERS

Enforcers are officers who work for the Mageri. Some of their duties include serving warrants, making arrests, escorting prisoners, conducting searches, and occasionally providing backup on big cases worked by third-party organizations. All Enforcers are Mage.

LAWS

Aside from the laws set forth by the higher authority, there are a number of Mage laws created by the Mageri. The Council will review

each case to determine the appropriate punishment. Some of these laws
include:

- Killing one's own Creator is a high crime and punishable
  by death. The lucky ones spend the rest of their life in
  Breed jail. There is no statute of limitations.
- Juicing energy from another person against their will is
  illegal. It's especially dangerous since it can kill the victim,
  especially humans.
- Killing humans is against the law.
- Revealing oneself to the human world is forbidden (this
  applies to all Breeds). There are exceptions when it's to an
  individual. This law is targeted toward those who are
  deliberate with their attempt to expose their identity and
  secrets to a large body of people or even the government.
- Plotting to overthrow the government is a high crime.
  Traitors can be executed, and this includes those who work
  for the Mageri. They are not offered immunity for treason.
- The Councils have sworn an oath to privacy when it comes
  to measuring each Mage's talent. They document the
  Learner's abilities in their record books, but they cannot
  share or leak that information. To do so would mean death,
  which ensures that no one violates their oath. Each Mage is
  free to talk about their gifts to anyone they choose, as that
  is their right. This law also creates a more trusting
  relationship between the Mageri and their community.

While using Mage gifts like flashing around humans is discouraged,
punishment may not be severe unless the intention was to expose
Breed to humans. The Mageri has no way to police every single infrac-
tion, let alone dole out punishments since they don't have a small-
crimes court. Immortals work in various jobs in the human world to

help erase evidence, such as video and police records, that could expose them.

In a world where anyone can take videos with a cell phone, it's increasingly important to make sure immortals comply with what's expected of them. That's another reason Breed will buy up businesses and homes in certain areas of the city and create a Breed district. It gives immortals a place to use their gifts more freely with less concern about human witnesses.

FAMILY/SEX

A person is not born a Mage. While there is one exception of that happening in my books, usually a Mage Creator must give either a human or Relic their first spark. It's good practice to select a candidate who doesn't have a family. Otherwise, the temptation is strong for them to either return to their family or reveal the Breed world to them.

FIRST SPARK: The act of making a Mage involves a Creator putting his or her light into the individual and creating a channel. Then they pull that light out and mix it with their own. It's a complex and exact process. When successfully done, this is called the first spark.

LEARNERS: A new Mage who is not yet independent of their Creator is called a Learner. It means they are still in the learning phase of not only figuring out how to use their powers but also learning about the Breed world and Mage history. Some refer to any young Mage as a Learner even if they're independent of their Creator. In those instances, it's often an insult, implying they still have much to learn.

CREATORS: Being a Creator is a rare Mage gift. They are the only ones with the power to create another Mage. Creators are responsible for caring for their progeny and teaching them the laws, helping them to refine their gifts, and showing them how to survive. Their Learner will live with them until they are deemed fit for independence. Length of time will vary per person and also depend on how invested their Creator is. For that reason, many Creators in the modern world have no interest in giving another immortality, especially if they have a busy life.

GHUARDIAN: This is an ancient word used to describe someone who voluntarily accepts responsibility over another Mage to teach them the way a Creator would. In modern times, if a Creator is unwilling to care for the progeny the Mageri has selected for them, the Mageri would assign them a Ghuardian. Sometimes the Mageri finds a Learner whose Creator died or abandoned them, and they need guidance. It's an honorable position that few volunteer for.

HOW THEY ARE NAMED: It's up to the Creator if they want to rename their progeny. It's a time-honored tradition for many as it symbolizes the transition of leaving their old life behind and starting anew. Learners usually take their Creator's surname, if they have one. It is always up to the Creator if they want to also change their progeny's first name. The new Mage may or may not have any say in the matter. If a Creator has no surname, which was common long ago in many cultures, they will often give the Learner a new first name, and that is all they will go by. This renaming tradition explains why names don't always fit the individual. A Swedish man might have a Spanish name because their Creator was from Spain.

FAMILY/SEX:

- **A Mage cannot have children.** The energy coursing through them is too powerful for them to either conceive or impregnate. Mage sperm will destroy the eggs of a non-Mage. A female Mage does not menstruate and cannot have children by a Mage or otherwise. Lab experiments or items infused with magic are another story...

- **A Mage can only have "safe" sex with another Mage or a Vampire.** During intercourse, sexual energy manifests in their light. Excess energy escapes through their hands, and they have little control over it. With any other Breed, they risk shocking or electrocuting them—possibly enough to kill. They have to be careful not to touch the other person, which makes it complicated to have sex with a non-Mage. With their own kind, not only do they not have to worry about excess energy, they can also choose to bind with their partner (see below). Vampires are unaffected by Mage light, so they don't feel anything if a Mage pushes it into them. But sex with a Vampire is dangerous for the Mage because of a Vampire's strength.

- **Binding is the act of sharing sexual energy with another Mage.** During intercourse or otherwise, sexual energy manifests in a Mage's light and channels into their hands. When joining hands with another Mage, a channel opens, transferring sexual energy. They feel what the other is feeling. When they close their eyes, they see images in the other person's mind. Many consider it the ultimate sexual experience—better than the real thing.

The lines between fantasy and reality are blurred. When the channel is open, the energy continually flows in and out of the couple. It taps into the desire in their core light, which is far more intense. Binding doesn't have the same effect as juicing since the energy is a separate stream from their core light. While binding can be done during intercourse, most prefer to engage in the act without getting physical.

- **Most do not marry (bond)**. Immortality is a long, long time. Most fear a commitment that likely won't last and might end ugly. When they do make a permanent relationship, most prefer their own kind. It makes the act of sex easier without having to worry about killing their partner by accident. They might not care about a love match so much as finding a partner who can help elevate them financially or socially.

BONDING: When a couple chooses to commit to a permanent relationship, it's called bonding. Not to be confused with binding, which is the transference of sexual energy. Sometimes there's a ceremony and the woman has the male's Creator's mark inked on her body. Because tattoo ink looks different from the Creator's mark, they are easily distinguishable. The tattoo might be placed in a concealed area or even displayed openly to show that she's claimed by another. Mostly it's for them.

NOTE ON RELICS:

Relics are the only Breed who can become a Mage since they are closest to humans genetically. That said, most Relics don't. A Relic's gift and sole purpose is to acquire knowledge and pass it on to their offspring. Most Relics have at least one child. If they became a Mage, they would not only have to live under a Creator's constant guidance, they would likely have to give up their job.

That's not all they would give up. As a Mage, they wouldn't be able to produce any more children. If they already had kids, they would experience the tragic loss of watching their children and all their descendants grow old and die. Some might suffer illness or tragic accidents. It would be a selfish choice for the Relic to make because of the emotional trauma. When a Relic is selected by the Mageri, they prefer candidates who don't have families. If the Relic is chosen by a Creator, the Mageri can't forbid it. The only reason the Mageri might select a Relic is if they have specific and beneficial knowledge to Mage and are too old or unable to have children.

GIFTS

Upon their first spark, every Mage receives both common gifts and at least one rare gift. Common gifts are abilities that every Mage possesses. Rare gifts are extra abilities that only some or few may have. Most Mage have one rare gift—that is the norm.

Rare gifts are not inherited from their Creator. It's possible that they could receive the same gift by coincidence, but when a Mage is given their first spark, the light within them is unique. Not every Mage susses out their gift right away. Sometimes they stumble upon it later in life by accident. Part of the process of being measured by the Mageri is that through their experience, they're often able to discover rare gifts the Learner may not have known they had. The Mageri Council will also determine the strength of their core energy and limitations of their gifts. If a Mage doesn't uncover their rare gift right away, it could take many years before they do.

All gifts, whether common or rare, require training. If a Mage is not taught how to flash, heal, or even sense direction, they'll never master those abilities. There are tips and tricks one can only learn from another Mage. How well they learn depends on their Creator or Ghuardian in addition to whether they have defects or limitations.

The exception is with rare gifts. Some of those gifts come naturally, such as being a Charmer. There's nothing they need to do since that gift is always switched on. But other gifts require mastery through experience. If their Creator doesn't possess the same gift, they won't know how to properly guide the Learner in using it. The young Mage will have to teach themself with practice and time unless there is someone willing to mentor them. It might not be easy to locate a Mage with the same gift willing to teach them, so Relics are valuable resources.

COMMON MAGE GIFTS

- **Blasting:** This term is used to describe weaponizing Mage energy. A Mage can channel a surge of energy and blast it into another person, shocking them. Depending on how strong the energy, it can knock the other person out or even kill them if they're weak. Blasting does *not* work on Vampires, who are unaffected by Mage energy. Additionally, it doesn't work on another Mage. They are each power sources, so pushing energy into another Mage will only power them up (juicing). That's why they'll fight each other using weapons combined with flashing and/or their rare gifts.
- **Flashing:** A Mage can harness their energy and run at high rates of speed. Because flashing uses up energy, it's not done for long distances or periods of time as it will drain their core energy and weaken them. *Note:* most Chitahs can run faster than a Mage can flash.
- **Healing:** Every Mage has the ability to heal at an accelerated rate. A wound that might take weeks or months to heal will take days. They can also heal instantly by either borrowing healing light from another Mage or extracting a

drop of light from the sun. Both require practice and concentration, especially since the sun is powerful and can knock a person out if not kill them. Healing light in a Mage is separate from their main energy, so it has to be pulled out or given separately. They can't use their energy to heal any other Breed unless they're a Healer.

- **Sensing direction:** Most have the ability to sense direction due to the magnetic poles.
- **Sensing time:** Most have the ability to sense the time of day. However, if their energy is weak or someone has juiced from them, it would affect their ability the same as it would other common gifts. There has never been an explanation regarding time zones. It's magic!

RARE GIFTS

A Mage can have more than one rare gift, though it's less common. The gift name is also used as a way to label the Mage. A person who can charm is called a Charmer. Someone who can heal is called a Healer. One thing that intrigued me was the idea that every gift can also be a curse. They have their pros and cons, and they also have their limitations. Not all gifts have been explored, but here are the ones mentioned thus far. Individuals might choose to keep their gifts a secret from others; they are under no obligation to share that knowledge with anyone other than the Mageri. The gifts below are listed by the name given to the recipient:

- **Blockers** - They have a natural ability to block various Mage gifts. Some may be able to block all while others only specific gifts. For instance, a Charmer might have no effect on them, and a Stealer can't take their core light. This ability only works on Mage gifts. Blockers also exist in other Breeds where they can block certain Breed gifts, but they are extremely rare. Mage Blockers are still vulnerable to stunners.

- **Charmers** - Their sexual energy attracts the opposite sex (generally), regardless of Breed. They cannot control this gift; it's switched on all the time. For some it's a gift, but for others, it makes it difficult for them to trust anyone's true intentions. People are constantly drawn to and enamored of them, so genuine feelings are impossible to know.
- **Creators** - They can create a new Mage from either humans or Relics. Each Creator has their own unique mark that is passed down to their progeny. The exception is if one of their progeny is born a Creator. The first spark working on any other Breed would be almost unheard of, but crossbreeds in the Breed world do occur, usually by accident.
- **Feelers** - They can feel and understand complex emotions through touch and in the energy around them.
- *Glowing* - No official name, but sometimes they're referred to as Lanterns or Fireflies. They have the ability to emit light from their skin at will. Many don't respect their gift and call them glowworms as an insult.
- **Healers** - They can heal any Breed except humans. After placing their hands on the injury, there's a pop of electricity and a flash of light. This also works on another Mage, though there isn't much benefit to it since they can also heal a Mage with their healing light. Their gift has limits, like they're not able to heal those affected by poison, dehydration, or heat strokes since those conditions are too complex.
- **Infusers** - They can permanently fuse energy (including all gifts) from one Mage onto the core light of another. Their

gift is only useful when paired with a Stealer. When a Stealer steals the core light from another Mage, they can only hold on to that energy for a short time before it disappears. Their body knows that it's not theirs to keep. However, if they want to keep that Mage's gifts, they would need to pay an Infuser to seal that foreign energy onto their core light. Once that's done, the Stealer not only has their original gifts but will then possess the newly acquired ones. The infusion is permanent, and there is no way to undo it without another Stealer taking all their gifts, rendering them human again. That makes Infusers highly valuable to Stealers. This doesn't benefit Infusers in any way except that they can charge whatever they like. There are some Infusers who can seal energy onto objects.

- **Jumpers** - They move quickly from one spot to another. Jumpers can only jump short distances, like from the roof of one building to the next or from the ground onto a tree branch. The process is fast, similar to flashing.
- **Mentalists** - They have the ability to hear thoughts, send thoughts, or both—even across long distances. Some might be limited to only having this ability with their progeny or Creator.
- **Stealers** - They can pull core light from another Mage, rendering them mortal. Once this is done, they don't have the ability to return it. The energy and rare gifts are stored in their body for twenty-four hours before their body rejects it and the foreign energy is gone. During the short time they possess the energy, they can use the rare gifts, should they even know what they are. All gifts require knowledge of how to use them, so it might not benefit them in the narrow time frame that they have it. Stealers can permanently keep a gift but only if an Infuser seals it to their core light. Dark energy can sometimes make a Stealer

feel sick for the time that it stays in their body. Most Stealers are not stealing core light for gifts but to weaken their enemy and strip away their immortality. Once they do that, they can kill their opponent more easily.

- **Thermals** - They can control their body temperature. Others can feel the heat or cold coming off them if it's extreme enough. This rare gift allows them to tolerate frigid temperatures without freezing. Long periods of continual use are impractical since it creates a slow energy leak that will weaken them. A Thermal has to be conscious to use the gift, so they can't set their temperature and have it stay there while sleeping or if they're knocked out.
- **Touchers** - They can touch another person and form a mental link, allowing them to hear their thoughts. It doesn't necessarily work on everyone.
- **Wielders** - They're able to harness their energy and form a powerful energy ball of any size. When thrown, that energy causes destruction and even death. An experienced Wielder can manipulate the energy as its forming to produce specific results when the ball hits its target. In some cases, it might be small but powerful enough to incinerate whatever it comes in contact with. They might also be able to make a ball that breaks apart, killing more people around it like a grenade. They can also use it to break through doors or walls. These are destructive weapons that will kill any Breed, including Vampires, who are normally unaffected by Mage energy.

DEFECTS

As with any Breed, a Mage might have a defect when it comes to their abilities. One or more of their common gifts might be absent or have limitations, or their rare gift is not as powerful. There are Relics who specialize in helping those with impairments, but many may not seek help or realize help exists. It can also be dangerous to make one's defects known.

UNIQUES

And then we get to Uniques. You can learn much more about these in the Mageri series. Uniques are a super rare type of Mage who were once called Elementals since their power differed. Some might have thought they were a different Breed or a mutation. Uniques are created under specific circumstances that contribute to their excessive power. Most were hunted to extinction by their own kind, and those who weren't likely aren't identifying themselves. People fear power, and Uniques have formidable abilities. They have common Mage gifts and might also have a rare gift or two, but a Unique is a subset of Mage. Some even think they're urban legends since little is known about their abilities.

Lightning is speculated to play a role during their creation. Possibly even if it occurred prior to the first spark. For instance, maybe a severe lightning storm happened when they were young and struck them or their house. Perhaps that extra energy stored itself in their body or awakened dormant genes. Another possibility is they might have already had Breed DNA in their body. Often we never get an explanation for the miraculous.

Because Uniques are rare, it's difficult to list out their abilities and what is considered normal since it would require a larger pool of Uniques with the same abilities to compare with.

Uniques mentioned include:

- **Architects** - Thought to be able to shape energy into temporary weapons or walls.
- **Shiners** - Eyes turn silver when they lose control, hence their name. When a Mage handles an object, residual energy is left behind. A Shiner can manipulate the energy in those objects, allowing them to move the item. They can also harness lightning and use it as a weapon.
- **Shielders** - Able to create an energy shield or wall around them that works as a force field. Usually the only thing that can pass through the wall or dome is energy itself.
- **Summoners** - It's not entirely clear what they do. Some books suggest that they can raise the dead, like a person who evokes spirits. They can supposedly lift the veil between the living world and the dead, building doorways into other realms. Portals of light are mentioned in one book, but their energy isn't used to make walls or weapons like some of the others.

DISPELLING MYTHS

MAGIC

In the Mageriverse, a Mage cannot conjure magic or spells. They are not sorcerers as we know them. Human lore derived from a misinterpretation of the Breed's gifts.

A person is not born a Mage—not without a lot of intervention, special metals, and crossed fingers. Once a Creator selects a human or Relic, they will begin the process to make them immortal. Consent is not required. It's generally assumed that one cannot make a child into a Mage because their power is lesser and the transference would kill them.

Every Mage was formerly human or a Relic and became a Mage after their first spark. Once they receive the gift of immortality, there is no reversing it. Only a Stealer can remove their core light.

PART VIII

POTENTIALS

ABOUT

POTENTIAL
An original Breed created by Dannika Dark.

What is a Potential?

In the Mageriverse, a Potential is a human born with a special ability to become any Breed they choose through sex and will remain that Breed forever. Alternatively, they can choose to remain human. A birthmark that looks like a spade (like the suit of cards) identifies them as a Potential. The mark can be located anywhere on their body.

Potentials don't know what they are since they have no knowledge of the Breed world. If leadership in the Breed world becomes aware of a Potential's existence, they will likely make exceptions about revealing their world to them. Especially if that Potential does business with them or has Breed friends without realizing what they are. The more they associate with Breed, the greater the odds they could have sex with one of them. It's better if they know what they are so they can make an informed choice. But since they're born to humans, the odds of them finding out they're a Potential are slim. If leadership becomes aware of orphaned Potentials, they'll intervene to protect them.

When I first created the Mageriverse, humans could only become either a Vampire or a Mage. I liked the idea of a wild card, so I created Potentials. That opened the door for certain humans to unwittingly have the ability to become any Breed they want. But there's a catch: the Potential has to know what they are in order to make a conscious decision either way. Most immortals aren't aware of Potentials, and many who have heard of them think they're a myth. So not many could identify their special mark. That slims down the chances of a Potential being discovered. Not unless they accidentally had sex with an immortal, which might be an unfortunate one-night stand for some.

I love the power of choice. If a person knows they have the potential to become Breed, what would they do if they fell in love with another human? Stay mortal or succumb to the temptations of the Breed world despite the danger it holds? Wild cards are not only fun, they give the writer more freedom.

PHYSICAL CHARACTERISTICS

Potentials are born human and have no unique physical characteristics other than the birthmark. If they choose to become Breed, they retain the birthmark and their physical looks may change depending on which Breed they become.

POTENTIALS HISTORY

Potentials have existed for a long time, but they're not common. It's not a trait passed down from parent to child but more of a genetic lottery. It's speculated that somewhere in their ancestry, an unknown Breed species may have crossed over with their human ancestors. Not many Breed know about Potentials or believe it's possible. Some think they're an urban legend. The idea of a human choosing to become any Breed they desire seems far-fetched. A few know the truth of their existence, especially those who have witnessed it or met a former Potential and believed their story. For obvious reasons, Potentials who have chosen to become Breed don't make themselves known. They understand the real consequences of the Breed world finding out humans like them exist.

As long as a Potential remains human, they are always in danger. Not just from others who would discover them but also from the accidental and unwanted transference of Breed power. While Vampires would have no interest in Potentials since they can turn anyone, other Breeds might see Potentials as someone easily controlled. A Mage who isn't a Creator might want a Learner of their own for nefarious reasons. A Shifter might want someone they can train to be submissive since most Shifter women are dominant. Certain Breeds might like the idea of a "trainable" mate. Other Breeds might not have many females.

There are a number of reasons why someone might take advantage of a Potential. There may even be some who know about their existence—who hunt them to either sell, trade, or keep.

The higher authority is aware of their existence.

POTENTIAL FACTS

LIFESPAN

A Potential is born 100% human and has the lifespan of a human. They are susceptible to disease, viruses, and other sicknesses. If they become Breed, they will then acquire whatever lifespan is associated with that Breed along with all their traits. See *Family/Sex* for how they are turned.

BIRTHMARK

All Potentials are born with a mark that resembles a spade, like in a deck of cards. It has clearly defined edges and is located anywhere on the body. It's very distinct and doesn't look like a normal birthmark. No one yet knows the origin of Potentials. If they choose to become Breed, they still keep that mark.

HOW THEY ARE LOCATED

The higher authority knows about their existence and actively searches for them. They would rather find these individuals first before it's too late. If a Potential is not a trusted human, they could become Breed either by accident or by force. Either way, there's a risk of them exposing the Breed world.

Many Breed insiders work in the human world at hospitals or as pediatricians, holding positions where they can identify a Potential child. The goal is to identify and monitor them. It's possible that at some point the higher authority will bring them into the fold so they'll understand what they are. That's never been laid out in detail. More Potentials will slip by than not, but even if they do, the odds are they'll remain in the human world and never encounter Breed.

Child Potentials are never removed from their homes. Only orphans are taken to top secret locations, where they will remain until they're a legal adult. They'll learn about the Breed world and, as a result, become a trusted human. Whether they choose to become Breed or not will be up to them. It is not the higher authority's place to interfere with free will. Those who choose to remain human will know to conceal their birthmark and identity for their own safety.

FAMILY/SEX

A Potential becomes Breed through intercourse. If they only ever have sex with humans, they'll remain human. But if at any time in their life they have intercourse with Breed, they will become the same Breed as their partner and remain that way forever. Virginity has nothing to do with the transformation since it's not about their first sexual partner—only their first sexual encounter with Breed.

It's better for a Potential to know what they are. The wrong romantic encounter might result in unexpected trauma. They might not be able to handle the reality of the Breed world, and if they have a family or children, that would complicate matters. Most are likely never discovered or turned and live out their lives as humans.

HOW A POTENTIAL BECOMES BREED: When a Potential has sex with Breed, they become that Breed. Here is what we assume happens: For a woman, when sperm enters her sexual organs, her body will rapidly absorb and replicate that DNA. For a man, a woman's vaginal secretions enter the urethra and travel into their sexual organs. It's a magic that cannot be explained. A person will not become Breed through other fluid exchanges such as kissing, oral sex, and anal sex. Once the transition begins, it cannot be undone.

THE TRANSITION: The time it takes to transform from human to Breed will vary from person to person. It typically happens soon after sex or climaxing. The process is painful. It might begin with nausea or a funny feeling but quickly changes. They might experience the sensation of hot metal spears in the lower belly and other intense pain. It's only temporary until the change is complete. If they are transitioning to a Shifter, they might immediately shift to animal form during the process. There's not enough information at this time on whether as a Shifter, they'd have a separate animal spirit that inhabits the same body as them. Most likely they will, but there has to be more data to understand what the normal expectation is. There's one instance where a character doesn't have a separate animal spirit, but this person is also a Crossbreed, so it's unclear whether that condition is an anomaly. It would have to be further explored. With little known about Potentials, there could be a number of other unique traits that slightly differ from the Breed they become.

DEFECTS: Like everyone else in the Breed world, it's possible for a Potential to become Breed but with defects.

PART IX

RELICS

ABOUT

RELIC
An original Breed created by Dannika Dark.

What is a Relic?

In the Mageriverse, Relics are the most genetically similar to humans. They can catch viruses, infections, diseases, and so on. What sets them apart is that their gift allows them to absorb knowledge. I first considered writing Relics as an immortal Breed who inherits the knowledge of their ancestors. Then I realized they needed incentive to reproduce. Otherwise, what would stop them from getting a Mage or Vampire to turn them? This would create too much chaos, and they would likely become an extinct Breed.

I thought it would be wildly interesting if parents could not only pass on inherited knowledge but also keep adding to it. So with each child they have, that child will possess the knowledge of their ancestors but also the newly added knowledge of both parents. This would make each generation more knowledgeable than the last. They would have generational job security with many immortals. It encourages Relics to begin learning new information young and start building their careers before having children.

While immortality has its temptations, there is power in knowledge. Relics are wise enough to understand how beneficial they are by constantly learning and passing that on.

PHYSICAL CHARACTERISTICS

Relics have no special physical characteristics.

JOB PREFERENCES

Most Relic families are specialists. Based on their inherited knowledge, they will continue acquiring information in the area of their expertise. Many have long-term clients they've kept in the family, generation after generation. It's not only job security for their children, there's a level of trust that forms between the client and the family. For that reason, they will often stay where the majority of their important clients are. The more children they have, the better they are able to serve clients who move to other countries.

Relics have a number of job opportunities. They are healers, doctors, scientists, counselors, linguists, historians, teachers, and more. Some may specialize in extremely rare Breed gifts while others focus on helping those with defects. Some may possess knowledge about cures for obscure ailments. The knowledge they possess can be in any field, and it's far better for Relics to build upon their inherited specialties than diluting it with knowledge on unrelated topics. Older immortals might seek them out for therapy, and that's why Relics adhere to strict confidentiality rules.

Relics often pair up with a partner since the number of clients can be taxing and difficult to schedule. It's not uncommon for them to marry their partner.

LAWS

Relics are bound to the same laws set forth by the higher authority. Additionally, Relics who work with clients are bound to secrecy. Violation of that trust might be punishable by their leaders.

Relics have their own Councils within each city. The Councilmen change frequently due to their shorter lifespans.

RELIC HISTORY

Relics throughout history have always been a valuable asset to Breed. They are one of the most respected since everyone consults with them. They represent Breed history. Shifters hire Relics who specialize in conditions specific to their animal type and who also have experience delivering babies. Those who work with animal groups such as packs and prides will also counsel them. If someone seeks a Relic out for information and they're unable to help, the Relic has a network of contacts and might be able to put them in touch with someone with that skill set.

Many Relics live in the United Kingdom and Europe because they have established clientele. Over the years, Relics moved to the Americas and other countries to follow existing clients and acquire new ones. The only incentive for moving is if one of their wealthiest clients asked them to or if they lost business. But it can be hard to establish trust with a new individual or group.

In the Breed world, Relics are the doctors, mental health professionals, historians, and scientists. They each have a unique set of skills that differs from other Relic families. Immortals sometimes experience unusual events, injuries, defects, changes in power, et cetera that might require a professional opinion. Relics aren't limited to fields in health and science. Some retain knowledge of ancient languages, extinct Breeds, history, human genetics, and so much more.

It's not all sunshine and roses. Some Relics work for underground organizations or in labs conducting illegal science experiments. Some factions want biological weapons that will kill humans but not Breed, others may want something that will turn them all Breed. There are likely experiments going on with crossing genes and trying to create lab monsters. Because Relics have no gifts of protection, they are vulnerable to those who might want to use them, who would hold them against their will or threaten their family if they don't comply.

RELIC FACTS

LIFESPAN

Relics live the lifespan of a human.

HEALING

Relics do not have any special healing abilities.

INJURIES/SICKNESS

Because Relics are nearly identical to humans, they are prone to the same health issues. They can be born with genetic conditions, develop diseases, have high blood pressure, catch viruses, suffer strokes, and so on. They do not have any accelerated healing abilities like other Breeds do, so they could develop sepsis from a cut and die. Unlike other Breeds, human medicine is effective on them. It wouldn't be uncommon for Relics to seek treatment for various ailments among their own kind instead of in human hospitals. There are plenty of Relics who specialize in human/Relic biology and medicine.

DEFECTS

As with any Breed, Relics can have defects that impair their ability to store or recall knowledge. Some might struggle with infertility, thus preventing them from passing on their knowledge. Therefore, Relics are selective when it comes to whom they choose to marry. They will seek out a partner who doesn't have any known defects or fertility issues.

BECOMING IMMORTAL

Because Relics are the only Breed close to humans genetically, they are the only ones who can be turned by a Mage or Vampire. However, it's frowned upon in the Breed world. Elders would have to approve, and most Councils feel that switching Breeds to become immortal could make the Relic mentally unstable. Additionally, if they do become a Vampire or a Mage, they'll be considered a crossbreed. It's unlikely a younger Relic of childbearing age would be selected since they might grow to regret their decision.

If a Relic becomes a Mage or a Vampire, they will still possess their existing knowledge and be able to continue adding to it. They just won't be able to have any children to pass that on to. While creating an immortal with all this knowledge might seem sensible, if they were killed, all that knowledge would die with them. See more under *Family/Sex*.

FAMILY/SEX

RELATIONSHIPS AND PARTNERS: Relics often have work partners to manage clientele due to unpredictable schedules and the nature of the job. It's not uncommon for Relics to marry their partners. Their parents or even the Council may assist with the right partner assignment, so it could be viewed as a sort of arranged marriage. Relics see marriage as a more practical arrangement than a love match. Since partners spend so much time working together, marrying them can be a logical choice.

CHILDREN: Relics are family oriented. Having a child with another Relic is vital so they can pass down their knowledge. Producing offspring with a different Breed, if that were possible, would likely result in the gifts being canceled out. Because they're genetically close to humans, they are the only Breed who can have children with them. But because humans don't have Breed magic, the Relic's knowledge will not pass down to the children.

Relics will often seek out a life partner who has specific knowledge similar to or that complements their own, one that creates an ideal match in how their children could benefit.

Infertile men or women are considered undesirable and are not likely to find a Relic mate. If they don't have children, generations of knowledge will die with them.

BECOMING A MAGE OR VAMPIRE: Relics have the ability to become a Mage or Vampire because they're genetically close to humans. But it's not as easy as that. Aside from the strict approval process, most Relics prefer to stay mortal. Children are more valuable than time. Choosing immortality and outliving their children would create a moral dilemma. If the Mageri or elders approved, they likely wouldn't select a candidate who is young or already has children.

1. Once a Relic becomes immortal, they can no longer have children. If they have never had children, their knowledge will die with them. They might regret their decision if they were turned young or at an age where they could still conceive.
2. If a Relic already has children, becoming a Mage or Vampire would mean outliving their children and all their descendants. The mental anguish of watching their loved ones die could take an emotional toll that would have long-term effects that could make them unstable.

Most Relics believe in the natural order of things.

GIFTS

Relics are born with knowledge passed down by their ancestors. They can also build upon that knowledge and pass it on to their children. Most Relics only acquire new and valuable knowledge in their area of expertise that would benefit their children's careers.

Massive info dumps can be dangerous—meaning infusing more knowledge to one's DNA than needed. It will dilute their knowledge, and if they aren't careful, they might infuse incorrect or unverified information that is later debunked. For that reason, Relics are very selective of how, when, and what knowledge they choose to collect. Infusing knowledge from an entire book would be irresponsible without knowing if the source information was authenticated. Scientists and doctors understood the world very differently two hundred years ago. And when it comes to things like language, it requires time and effort to ensure that they are able to absorb that language correctly.

It's possible for a Relic to go through life and only have one or two things to add to their existing knowledge, and that's fine. Quality and reliability are far more important than quantity.

Relics don't always advertise their knowledge to those outside their network. They are more inclined to share what their specialties are with other Relics. When a Breed is seeking help or information, they can ask any Relic, who will then network with others to see what they can come up with, so Relics work as a referral system.

Relics can possess knowledge on more than one topic. This typically occurs when their parents each have a separate knowledge base. That's why Relics often marry someone who specializes in the same things, that way they can broaden their existing knowledge without too much extra. Two language experts might come together, but perhaps one has more information on ancient languages.

Marrying someone with an entirely different skill set is not unheard of, especially if they fell in love instead of it being more of an arranged partnership. A Relic might also have additional knowledge that's now obsolete, such as information about an extinct Breed. They no longer have use for the information, but they still retain it.

Relics might choose to keep some of their knowledge secret because of the dangers that would arise from others having that information. For instance, there might be a Relic who knows how to make a drink that will instantly kill a Vampire if consumed. They carry the weight of responsibility on their shoulders and realize that the world is a delicate balance.

They are the most reliable archive database since they know things from ancient times that have long since been forgotten or remembered incorrectly.

RELIC GIFTS

- **Inherent knowledge:** Relics are born with the knowledge of their ancestors. It is a permanent part of them. This doesn't include everything their ancestors ever learned— only knowledge that was specifically infused into their DNA. If a child is an orphan and doesn't know who their parents are, they might not know what their specialized knowledge is until they stumble upon it, such as the realization that they can understand Mandarin perfectly.

- **Infusing knowledge:** Relics can add newly learned information to their DNA by sheer will. The process requires concentration, and it's a deliberate act. They have the ability to seal it to their DNA so that they and their descendants born after the infusion will inherit that knowledge. Relics are extremely careful as to what they add, always fact-checking and making sure it's not something that might have an alternate explanation. They are selective as there's no way to undo information once it's added. They might only acquire one or two new things to their DNA, and that's fine. The gift inspires them to continue learning.

- **Erasing knowledge:** The act of erasing information added to their DNA cannot be done. Even if a Vampire did a full memory wipe, that knowledge is a part of who they are. They might still be able to access that information or recall it by accident. Even if they couldn't, that knowledge would pass on to any children if they have them.

PART X

SENSORS

ABOUT

SENSOR
A previously written supernatural reimagined by Dannika Dark.

What is a Sensor?

In the Mageriverse, Sensors are a Breed who are hypersensitive to emotions. They have the ability to not only take emotions and feelings from another person, they can also store them or even put them into others.

I haven't seen this depicted in many books, and often it's just referred to as "extrasensory" and not a supernatural species named Sensors. The concept is similar, where the characters usually have an uncanny ability to sense something others can't.

I wanted to create a Breed that isn't just sensitive to emotional imprints but also has the capability of manipulating them. Similar to a Mage, but instead of energy, they work with emotions. Not only can they detect emotions, they can store, sell, and weaponize them.

It's always important to consider the pros and cons of every Breed. For Sensors, the negative would be their constant exposure to emotions whether they like it or not. It's part of their job, but it's also something they experience whenever they're around people or in public. For that reason, it wouldn't be uncommon for Sensors to wear gloves.

Handshaking isn't customary in the Breed world, and Sensors may play a part in why that ritual doesn't exist. People would be exposed like an open book, and they also might receive unwanted emotions from a Sensor that could be used to manipulate them.

PHYSICAL CHARACTERISTICS

Sensors have no specific physical traits that set them apart from everyone else.

JOB PREFERENCES

Most Sensors will gravitate toward sensory exchange since the money is there and they have the natural skills for it. People sell emotional experiences to Sensors for money. Sensors are able to store any experience and sell it an unlimited number of times. This encourages some who are desperate for money to go out and do crazy acts—collecting emotional highs and selling them for money. Most immortals have lived dangerous lives and have many experiences to sell. But who buys them?

Sensory magic is recreational for some, but for others it's an addiction. They can experience things they never imagined, feel emotions they've never felt, and never have to leave the safety of a room. These sensory memories are as vivid as the moment it happened. There are certain experiences a reputable Sensor would never store, but some will sell taboo emotions for high dollar.

Sensors can also permanently extract emotions from memories. They can't remove the memory itself, only the feelings tied with it. Some people have trauma they want to let go of that's holding them back in life. Breed gather a lot of it over the years, especially the ancients. Once a Sensor extracts the emotions, they can either let them go or store them for the right buyer.

Sensors often work for law enforcement to aid in investigations. They're able to detect residual energy at crime scenes or on objects. They help investigators learn more about the victim, perpetrator, or the crime. Using them as lie detectors isn't reliable since people can manipulate or suppress their emotions.

Sensors can enhance human narcotics since they're not as potent for Breed unless taken in higher amounts. They might lace marijuana for a hallucinatory experience or even a calming effect.

Many Sensors advertise their wares by spiking candy or other treats with emotions (e.g., Sensor pops) and distributing them in bars or clubs with the permission of the owner. If their contact information isn't on the wrapper, the bartender will give it to anyone who asks. Not all businesses will allow it unless it's from a reputable seller who knows what they're doing. Sensors likely pay Breed establishments to distribute their candies, which are samplers. Clubs who agree see it as a harmless form of recreation since the emotions are innocuous and not likely to incite disruptive or violent behavior.

Sensors can also spike alcohol. They might work in a bar or club that has a specialty drink with a hint of sensory magic. Clubs don't sell spiked bottles. Aside from people stealing them, there's no way to regulate how much a person in a bar might consume of the product. For that reason, only individual drinks are spiked so that Sensor bartenders can better keep tabs on how much each person consumes. Usually they will put a limit to how many specialty drinks a customer is allowed.

Some Sensors run fortune teller businesses for humans. While they can't predict the future, they can touch a person's hands and pick up enough of their emotions through questioning that it will help guide them to what that person needs to hear. This wouldn't be considered a lucrative job, but Sensors can always find a side hustle.

SENSOR HISTORY

Over the years, Sensors have been viewed as a novelty in the Breed world. Their history is as such. They worked in the human world as palm readers, psychics, and even in the circus. Many of the jobs they once performed they still do.

Some leaders and powerful men hired them (or forced them) to work as spies posing as servants. When guests or business associates arrived, the Sensors could collect the glasses they were handling or brush by them to lift emotions, find out if they're trustworthy or giving off signs of deception.

One could imagine they were also used during an interrogation to determine if that person was telling the truth. They might have even participated in torture, inflicting unimaginable pain without causing physical harm.

Highly skilled Sensors were hired to manipulate emotions, which could easily be done with a spiked drink. Jobs like these were risky and could have gotten them killed.

SENSOR FACTS

LIFESPAN
Sensors are not immortal, but they have an extended lifespan that allows them to live for several hundred years. Once a Sensor reaches maturity, the aging process slows down.

HEALING
Like most Breeds, Sensors have accelerated healing. They're able to withstand serious injuries that would otherwise kill a human. They're not immortal, so they can die. Sensors have no additional healing abilities such as what Vampires can do after drinking blood.

There is a rare and special gift that some Sensors possess that allows them to heal a person by transferring strong emotions. Typically this can only be done with a person they deeply love, like a family member, because the power of love is what opens up the healing connection during the emotional exchange. It may only be possible when the emotions are strongest and the most pure, like what one feels when someone they love is dying. A serious injury alone might not be enough to initiate this exchange.

INJURIES/SICKNESS

A Sensor cannot develop human diseases or catch viruses. Because they don't have any gifts that expedite the healing process, they can die from bleeding out, serious head wounds, et cetera. If they're stabbed, they can patch it up and the wound will heal. But if someone sliced their jugular, they likely wouldn't survive because of the sudden and unstoppable blood loss. Not unless another Breed with healing abilities intervened.

SCARRING

Sensors can scar. While their body can withstand more trauma than a human's, they don't heal immediately, so scarring occurs.

TATTOO INK

Like all other Breeds, their body absorbs tattoo ink unless liquid fire is applied. If they don't seal it with liquid fire, the tattoo will disappear within a couple of days depending on the amount of ink used.

DEFECTS

All Breeds have those with defective gifts. Sensors are no different. You might have some dead receptors who can't pick up, transfer, or store emotions. Some might have muted abilities or be lacking in one. For that reason, Sensors will get to know their partner before they make a commitment to start a family. A parent with defective gifts could pass them on to the children. Any Breed with defective gifts is vulnerable. Additionally, they might suffer ridicule and have difficulty finding work—especially if their work revolves around their gifts.

GLOVES

Some Sensors prefer wearing gloves in public, especially those who are hypersensitive. Gloves protect them from dealing with emotional imprints left on surfaces or coming off people they touch. Some like to read the world around them. Others find it exhausting. Hypersensitives have difficulty tolerating powerful emotions and can feel even the slightest imprints left behind. It's a personal choice depending on what they can tolerate.

Children in particular wear gloves in public to protect them from unwanted emotions that are complex or corrupt. The young ones don't understand certain emotions and might be frightened or traumatized by them. Sensors prefer to wear Sensor gloves over regular gloves in retail stores since they're customizable. A skilled glovemaker can offer breathable fabrics that also offer 100% protection. They make all sizes from infants to those with large hands. Sensor gloves need to be practical, durable, and comfortable.

COMMONLY USED TERMS

There are Sensor-specific terms you'll see in the books. Refer to the glossary for definitions, or this section, which will elaborate on some of these.

- *dead receptor*
- *firebrand*
- *hypersensitive*
- *Sensor magic*
- *Sensor pops*
- *Sensorship*
- *sensory exchange*
- *sensory magic*

SENSOR LAWS

While the higher authority has laws that all Breeds must follow, every Breed has their own subset of laws created by their lawmakers. Sensors are less organized than most Breeds. They adhere to the laws set forth by the higher authority but also follow the guidance of their local Councils. This document may not list all the laws, but it provides the major ones that have been mentioned. Punishments vary.

COUNCILS

Most major cities have a Sensor Council that changes hands frequently. Councils help resolve issues within their territory, conduct investigations, determine punishment for crimes, and even help Sensors find the right work partners.

LAWS

- Killing humans is against the law.

- Exposing the Breed world to humans intentionally is against the law. This refers to deliberate acts on a higher scale.
- Treason is a high crime. This includes plotting to overthrow any leadership body or assassinate leaders.
- Stealing emotions without consent is illegal.
- Selling any emotional experience related to a nonconsensual sexual act or murder is illegal.
- Selling emotions that involve the exploitation of children is illegal.
- Manipulating a leader's emotions with spiked alcohol or otherwise is illegal. This doesn't exclude leaders from other Breeds or even higher authority representatives.

The reason *acquiring* the emotional experiences listed above isn't illegal is because some people survive an assault or trauma and pay a Sensor to remove the attached emotions. That way they don't have to constantly relive the pain, fear, and grief that might be consuming them. But a Sensor who does so should never keep those experiences to resell.

SENSORSHIP: A minority believe that all emotional experiences should be free to buy and sell. Those who do claim that the authorities are practicing Sensorship. Typically those who share these beliefs are either those addicted to illegal emotions or the Sensors who profit by selling them.

FAMILY/SEX

RELATIONSHIPS: Sensors with heightened or extra abilities are considered a catch. Those who want children will marry their own kind so their kids will also be Sensors. Even if they did manage to have a child with a Gravewalker or Chitah, for example, the child's gifts would likely cancel out or be weaker. Sensors cannot have children with humans.

SEX: Between consensual partners, sex can involve an emotional exchange. It allows partners to feel what the other is feeling, heightening the experience. The ideal way to do this is by clasping hands during the act.

PREGNANCY: Pregnant women can't use their sensory skills. They have issues harnessing emotional energy. If they work in sensory exchange, they'll take a hiatus from their job until the baby is born. Protecting the unborn child from unwanted emotions is important to them. Usually their body will suppress their abilities during pregnancy.

This is common with most Breeds who can have children. Sensors are born into their Breed. With the exception of Potentials, one cannot make another Sensor using magic.

CHILDREN: Like any Breed that can produce offspring, most Sensors will reject partners with known sensory defects. Otherwise, they might pass down to the children. Those can include the inability to lift or transfer emotions. Sensor children have to be taught how to use their gifts, and it's a gradual process. Most parents will not teach young children sensory exchange. They will often shield them from the outside world until they're old enough. How Sensors experience the world is significantly different, and too many complex emotions can have a negative effect on a child. It can also alter their perception of reality if they're unable to distinguish foreign emotions from their own. For that reason, Sensor gloves are commonplace with children.

GIFTS

During a sensory transfer, red light often glows in their palms. Transferring emotions or pulling them requires touch and cannot be done through gloves. The feeling during the exchange is warmth all over and a flood of mental images from the event. Sensors can't permanently remove memories, but the memories are tied in with the emotional experience. You can see, feel, hear, taste, and smell everything. Buying or selling emotional experiences is called a sensory exchange, but this term is sometimes used to describe any transferring of emotions, regardless if there's an exchange of money or favors.

Sensors feel every emotion they are collecting, so it can be an exhausting process for them if they make it their profession. When they're giving the emotion, they don't feel it but are aware of it.

Emotional transference: The chest is the preferred area to do the transfer on a recipient for the most intense experience, but it will work on other body parts.

SENSOR GIFTS

- **Pulling emotions:** Emotions can be permanently removed. The Sensor will either throw them away or store them to sell. Throwing them away simply involves choosing not to keep them. The emotional energy will leave their body very quickly. Some people pay Sensors to get rid of trauma that's preventing them from living a fulfilled life. Others sell emotional experiences for money. Sensors cannot erase memories. All they can do is remove the emotional experience—all the pain, grief, fear, exhilaration, joy, or whatever is associated with the memory.
- **Transferring emotions:** Sensory exchange can be addictive for buyers. Whether it's experiencing the thrill of skiing down a mountain, battling an army, jumping out of an airplane, or an intense sexual experience, people will pay good money for emotional highs. A person not only feels things from the perspective of the seller, they can also see, smell, taste, and hear the memories. A Sensor can sell a single experience an infinite number of times.
- **Easing pain:** Sensors can ease suffering through constant touch by pulling away some of that pain or replacing it with a stronger feeling. The effect ceases when contact is broken.
- **Food and drink:** Sensors can enhance alcohol, drugs, or anything edible. It requires skill since adding too much or polluted emotions can ruin their reputation. Most clubs will only buy spiked food and drink from reputable sellers. Sensor pops and spiked alcohol are a popular novelty at clubs and bars. The effects are temporary and harmless. They might feel aroused, relaxed, happy, or full of energy.

- **Weaponizing emotions:** If they're in a close-combat fight, Sensors can use their gifts to temporarily stun or stop their opponent. It largely depends on which emotions they have in their collection that could protect them in a dangerous situation. It would be to their benefit to have a few emotional experiences stored that aren't for sale to the public—ones where the seller experienced excruciating pain or death. This can have an immediate and extreme effect on anyone they touch, allowing them to fight back or escape. See *Firebrand*.
- **Firebrand:** This goes with the above on weaponizing emotions. This word is used to describe the emotional experience of burning alive. Receiving a firebrand can often sting for hours afterward.
- **Objects:** All objects carry residual emotional imprints. The stronger the emotion when the object was handled, the longer it lingers. The emotions aren't powerful since they're secondary, but if a Sensor is hypersensitive, they can feel intense. Some Sensors are more attuned to residual imprints than others. This is useful during investigations. They can touch a glass, chair, or murder weapon and gather information. Objects that hold emotions the longest are usually crystals and rocks. This can include natural metals.
- **Emotions in the air:** Occasionally a Sensor might sense emotions in the air if they're strong or the person is standing close. The larger the crowd and more heightened everyone's mood is, the harder it might be for a Sensor to tolerate.

LIMITATIONS

- Sensors are unable to lift emotions from objects and store them. Sensory exchange has to come directly from a person.
- Sensors can't erase memories of events. They can only remove the emotional memory, which creates disassociation.
- If a person is in pain, a Sensor can't remove the pain permanently by a single touch while they're currently experiencing it. They will need to maintain constant contact, either drawing out the pain (which can be a terrible experience for a Sensor) or replacing it with another sensation. However, they can remove the memory of the pain after the person has recovered.

REGARDING CHILDREN

It's not the Sensor way to remove emotional trauma from a Sensor child. They believe this form of memory manipulation can be more harmful to the child, especially given that Sensors need to understand and process difficult emotions better than any other Breed. In the long run, they believe it could do irreparable harm if a child remembers a trauma without any emotion surrounding it. They have likely seen how the child might grow up to be mentally unstable, which is problematic for anyone who buys and sells emotional experiences.

PART XI

SHIFTERS

ABOUT

SHIFTER
A previously written supernatural reimagined by Dannika Dark.

What is a Shifter?

In the Mageriverse, Shifters are a type of Breed who can shapeshift into an animal. Two spirits inhabit the same body; one of the human and one of the animal. Whichever one is in control, the body will shift accordingly. It's basically like two people driving the same car. Each Shifter is only one kind of animal. Many animal types exist, but apex predators or large mammals such as horses are more common than smaller mammals like rabbits and foxes. There are also avians, but a Shifter cannot be an insect. Tiny creatures such as mice are extremely rare. A number of Shifter animal types have gone extinct, such as the Tasmanian tigers. Sometimes creatures that have only been considered mythical exist among Shifters, such as phoenixes. Typically endangered animal types will stay in hiding.

Shifters are not werewolves. They do not turn into monsters, they do not shift because of a full moon, they don't die by silver or follow any of the werewolf lore. Shifters are not cursed but are born into their

Breed. While they have a dark history, they also have a rich culture with traditions and customs unique to different animal types, tribes, and countries. I wanted to explore how they are not necessarily united simply because of their Breed but also have division among themselves.

I took the concept of Shifters and added my own unique spin. While readers are familiar with books written about the man and animal being one, I enjoy adding limitations within each Breed in my universe. I was intrigued by the idea of the animal being its own spirit and wondered about the harmony and trust required between the human and animal. When they fall out of balance, the Shifter might take over and not allow the human out. Or perhaps the animal becomes unpredictable.

It's important to remember that while I've taken some facts from nature, Shifter behavior and biology in my books is fictional. Alphas exist among many animal types in my books, whether that actually occurs in nature or not. They typically only get pregnant during a heat cycle, whether that happens in nature or not. In looking at facts about the animals, I've kept some traits the same, added to, removed, embellished, and constructed a Breed with unique characteristics, history, and behavior for both the human side of them and their animal.

PHYSICAL CHARACTERISTICS

Shifters look like everyone else and do not have any physical traits that are unique to their Breed. Most of them will share the same eye color with their animal. Silver wolves are typically the rarest.

JOB PREFERENCES

Alpha and beta Shifters in particular seek out bounty hunter positions or other dangerous positions that not only build their income but establish their reputation as a person who supports the law and is able to work independently.

Because of their tumultuous history, there are not many Shifters who have acquired substantial generational wealth. After emancipation, many Shifters lacked skills and struggled. Some may work as trackers, but a vast majority are blue-collar workers or business owners. Many Shifters believe that owning a business is superior to working for someone because:

a.) establishes a solid reputation with local Shifters and other Breeds
b.) provides a steady and substantial income to the pack/family group
c.) family or packmates can fill positions and gain working experience
d.) they can branch out and expand with other locations
e.) the business can be passed on to children
f.) their business might have a trickle-down effect of providing jobs to others in the community. A club owner might hire outside entertainment or allow a Sensor to sell their wares.

Generally speaking, Shifters may even require less food in the house than one might assume because if they have good land, their animals can hunt or graze.

SHIFTER HISTORY

Shifters have a long history steeped in slavery. Other Breeds, especially the Mage and Vampire groups, saw them as inferior. Some immortals were concerned that the Shifter population had to be kept under control. Chitahs were less likely to believe that way since they are similar to Shifters in a number of ways, from the importance of family and social groups to having a primal instinct. Chitahs don't shift, but they often feel as if they have an "inner animal."

In some cases, slavery meant wearing a metal collar around their neck to prevent shifting if they were a particularly dangerous animal. For others, it was their animal who served other Breeds. Horse Shifters pulled carriages, wolf Shifters guarded property, and avian Shifters carried messages. There was also a dark period in time when Shifters were used in the circus. They were easier to control when separated and broken. This is why Shifters even today recognize that forming groups and living in numbers is the best protection.

Only in the past few hundred years have Shifters acquired freedom across the globe, though it varied by country. They are still considered lower-class citizens by many. Because most struggled to find jobs or a way of life, they have not yet achieved the same level of wealth as most immortals.

Emancipation and Land: In the United States, Colorado was the first state where Shifters established territories recognized by Breed laws. Once they were granted freedom, the Shifter Councils purchased a bunch of land to keep in reserve, knowing that packs and other groups of animals would require an abundance of space. The higher authority also provides additional land if approved. This has created friction between Shifters and other Breeds, who don't think it's fair. Given what the Shifters endured, it's more than fair.

Cage Fights: There is a dark history surrounding panther pits. For sport and money, immortals would arrange fights between panthers and other animal types. Often Shifters who were disobedient to their masters were fed to starving panthers. Modern cage fights still exist, often against the will of those fighting. A few strong ones may receive compensation, but it's now an illegal activity with dangerous consequences.

SHIFTER LAWS AND CUSTOMS

COUNCILS

Every territory has a Council made up of local leaders. The Council can vary in size, and they investigate matters within their own Breed. They also conduct mating ceremonies, hire private investigators to research matters, and enforce any established laws. They are less organized than other Breeds since not every Council may be on the up-and-up. In some cases, if there is a dispute among local packs or other family groups, they will let the leaders of those groups handle it.

If a crime is committed against someone in a group, such as sexual assault or murder, the Council allows the leader of that group to determine how he wants to be compensated: money, a life for a life, or even a challenge.

On challenges: Shifters can challenge another to the death for various reasons. If the victor allows his enemy to live, he has the authority to make specific demands that the loser has to abide by since his life was spared.

. . .

LAWS

Aside from following laws set forth by the higher authority, there are a few that pertain to Shifters or crimes against their Breed.

- Lying to the Council is considered a major offense.
- One group cannot attack another without provocation or unless they're defending their territory. If it is a land grab and the attacking group has killed the leader and taken over the property, they may be allowed to keep the land if there is no substantial proof of what occurred and who was in the wrong.
- Murdering a Packmaster or other group leader is against the law and punishable by death. The death penalty is more likely if they killed the leader while in human form. That one death can create chaos within the family since a beta cannot take over and a new alpha likely wouldn't be accepted by all.
- Cage fighting is illegal regardless of whether the fighters are willing and paid for their services.
- Killing humans is against the law.
- Revealing oneself to the human world is forbidden (this applies to all Breeds). There are exceptions when it's to an individual. This law is targeted toward those who are deliberate with their attempt to expose their identity and secrets to a large body of people or even the government.
- Plotting to overthrow the government is a high crime.
- Traitors against the higher authority can be executed.

SOCIAL BEHAVIORS THAT ARE NOT ILLEGAL BUT ARE FROWNED UPON

- Dating outside your Breed or animal type
- Tanning hides and using the fur of other Shifter animals when they are killed. Some may do it as a warning to others if that Shifter violated the law. There are old laws that permit it when there's a battle. Some may prefer to take a tooth or a claw as a souvenir over using their fur for blankets and rugs.
- Having human pets

CUSTOMS

Offering Food: It's considered polite to offer guests food when they enter your home as a show of trust. Some Shifters long ago used to poison their enemies. If the guest is a leader of another group and declines the offering, it will send a message that they don't trust the host, making any type of relationship between them difficult, especially if they are conducting business together.

Naming scheme for packs and other animal groups: Typically the group will be known by the last name of the leader. So if the leader's surname is Kline, they would be the Kline pack or Kline pride, et cetera. A leader can also choose a new name for a number of reasons. Otherwise the Council will assign them a name.

. . .

Joining a group: The leader will officially claim the new member. They meet with the local Council and sign an agreement. If the new member has a mate, this includes them as well.

New members of a group: This applies to wolves and even other animal groups. While their human forms may know one another, it's important that each individual of a family be introduced to the new member's animal and vice versa. To make sure there aren't any issues, the leader will supervise introductions.

Divorce: Divorcing is rare since most mate for life.

More than one mate: While it's not commonly accepted, it's not against the law. There are archaic traditions that some still practice, generally the wilder packs who live by their own rules.

Bitch: This term is sometimes used by some wolf Shifters when referring to a female. There was a time when, among Shifters, it didn't have a derogatory meaning any more than the word *alpha*. But times have changed, and some are drifting away from this terminology. Especially since some may still use it with reverence while others don't and it can be a fine line.

Owning wild and domestic animals: This doesn't appeal to most Shifters since they themselves are part animal and they may not believe you have a right to own any living thing. Some animals can sense Breed and may keep their distance.

SHIFTER FACTS

LIFESPAN
Once a Shifter reaches maturity, the aging process slows down. Shifters are not immortal and will not live forever. They have extended lifespans and age slowly. Life expectancy varies. They can live for hundreds of years or longer. Purebloods have a longer life expectancy. Someone several hundred years old can physically appear in their thirties. Alphas tend to live longer but also appear more mature-looking at a younger age.

FIRST CHANGE
When a Shifter reaches the age of maturity (usually late teens to early twenties), the first change is when they shift into animal form for the first time. It typically comes on with a fever, but an alpha can often sense it. Some Shifters may not know what their animal will be until their first change if their parents are two different animal types.

HEALING
Shifters are naturally resilient and heal quicker than humans. Shifting to their animal speeds up the healing process. The more times they

shift, the more they will heal. The process is exhausting, so too many shifts will make them sleep. If they are unable to shift for any reason and the injuries are grave, they can die. An alpha can force someone to shift by verbal command and a power in their voice, but the person has to be conscious.

INJURIES/SICKNESS:

- Foreign objects inside a Shifter need to be removed before they shift. Otherwise it can cause more damage by tearing the muscle, flesh, organs, et cetera. Foreign objects include knives, bullets, arrows, and other fragments.
- When a Shifter dies, they die in whatever form they were in at the time.
- Shifter children cannot shift until they go through their first change. Because of this, they are vulnerable during childhood to injuries, infections, or viruses. This is nature's way of controlling the population. Once they go through their first change, it triggers a natural Breed immunity to disease/viruses and aging slows down.
- Shifters aren't born with the same disabilities humans are, such as hearing/visual impairments, disease, hereditary conditions, and so on. So it is rare to see a Shifter who requires glasses, hearing aids, or the like. They also don't experience tooth decay or allergies. There are always exceptions to the rule, and some people consider those who have an unusual condition to be defective.
- Poison/Venom: Shifting won't neutralize poison or venom since it is a foreign substance inside the body or blood. Snakebites are particularly dangerous to all Shifters, especially those who live in a rural area.

- Shifters will scar if they don't shift after a severe injury or shift soon enough. That said, many Shifters proudly display battle scars and seal them with liquid fire. For women, scars aren't typically viewed as a badge of honor but are an indication they were abused. It's a double standard that exists, but not everyone judges so quickly.

SHIFTING

Some have described the sensation of shifting as similar to sliding down a dark tunnel into a pool of water. Shifters can change at will. Other times, it might happen when intense emotions occur. Their animal can force its way out, especially if they've been suppressed for too long.

A Shifter and their animal are two separate spirits inhabiting one form. Most people who shift cannot remember their shift—their animal takes over and they fall unconscious. Some remember the first few seconds, while others remember several minutes into the shift before it goes dark. Alphas are the exception and are powerful enough to stay conscious and even communicate with their animal. There are also outliers who have the ability to stay awake during their shift, but the animal is always in control. In human form, the animals are not entirely asleep but are dormant.

Shifters must form a relationship with their spirit animal. In order to establish trust, they allow their animal to come out regularly. It's good to keep to a schedule and keep the animal happy. And if they feel their animal growing restless, it's a good idea to make the time to shift as soon as possible. Prior to shifting, they can mentally convey to their animal what they need done, who to attack, or anything else. If they keep their animal caged and don't build trust, their animal might become aggressive or force their way out so there's zero control.

Shifting too many times consecutively will drain their energy. Alphas and betas can get through it easier, but most will weaken and require sleep—sometimes for a day or two.

CRAVINGS

This was a fun trait I added when developing the unique traits for this Breed. Each Shifter has one specific food craving when they come out of a shift, and it varies by person. If it's a food they've never had before, they might go years before identifying what it is. Generally in a group living together, it's a nice thing to leave food alone that is someone's craving.

PACKS AND OTHER SOCIAL GROUPS

Some animal types may live alone, but there is safety in numbers. Wolves live in a pack, bears in a sleuth, lions in a pride, et cetera. Animals that don't live in groups in the wild might still come together, though their house might be less structured and have more conflict.

For wolves, alphas lead a pack and they are called Packmasters. In a territory, the packs and other animal groups have a social status. Some are highly respected and others are untrustworthy. A good Shifter searching for a new home will seek out a reputable leader and hope they are accepted. When young alphas in an established group come of age, they are expected to move out. This applies to all kids once they've gone through their first change and are old enough, but alphas especially. Not only does it avoid potential conflict with the existing leader as they will naturally butt heads, but alphas are expected to go out in the world and prove their worth. When a young alpha starts a new pack or group, it's not uncommon for members from their former family to follow them. The new alpha would rather have their new core family be men and women he already trusts. It also opens up new spots in the old family for fresh blood. Read more about alphas under the *Alphas* section.

With wolves and other apex predators, once they acquire land, the animals will often regularly mark the territory borders. This is helpful when they live by neighboring packs or groups so animals don't cross territory lines, which could result in attacks or deaths. It's also a warning for rogues to keep out.

NUDITY
Outside of a sexual situation, Shifters are not self-conscious about their bodies since they shift all the time. Some families don't like animals in the house, so if they don't have their clothes waiting for them outside, they'll have to walk in naked. Shifters consider nudity to be natural and are less likely to be embarrassed. It really depends on the setting and individual.

STROBE LIGHTS
In the right sequence and speed, strobe lights can cause a Shifter to shift involuntarily. Most Breed bars do not allow strobe lights because of this. Those that do must have them set at an acceptable speed that is regulated.

BLOOD IN THEIR MOUTH
In animal form, predators who have blood in their mouth are harder to control and unpredictable. Once they get a taste of their enemy, the animal unleashes their fury. If an animal has blood in its mouth, most Shifters will back off.

FAMILY/SEX

COURTSHIP: Most Shifters mate with their own animal type. There is comfort and familiarity when they understand the nature of their partner's animal. In the Breed world, it's not socially acceptable to date outside your Breed, especially with Breeds who can't have children. Not everyone follows the norm. There are no courtship rituals unique to Shifters.

RELATIONSHIPS IN A PACK: It's a big no-no for single packmates in the same pack to fool around in secret. Packmasters keep the peace, and it's crucial for them to know about any developing relationships that could jeopardize the harmony in the pack. They will have to decide if the union can happen under their roof or if the couple needs to put in a transfer request to another pack. There might be two males vying for the same woman. This is another reason children move out once they come of age. A newly formed pack might be an exception. Though, in the beginning, a Packmaster would be more likely to select a larger number of single men and couples to prevent conflict. It will vary from house to house.

. . .

HUNTING FOR A MATE: Predators in particular might hunt for their mate in animal form and bring them a dead rabbit (or other prey) as an offering. This is typically only seen with life mates when both are in animal form. Rarely does the male animal bring the female the offering if she is in human form since the animals are bonded with each other, not the human.

GUARDING THE BED: It's an honor to have a wolf or other Shifter guard your bed while you sleep. It also conveys to the other Shifter that you trust them, since a Shifter in animal form can be dangerous.

SEXUAL BEHAVIOR: Most honorable Shifter men won't consider having sex with a woman until she's gone through the first change. It goes against their nature, so anyone who does is a lowlife. They don't consider her a grown woman until she's one with her animal, even if she's thirty. It's respectful.

GOING INTO HEAT:

- Going into heat is typically based on the woman's animal since not all animals experience a heat cycle. Because of Shifters' long lifespan, Mother Nature prefers to limit the window in which Shifters can get pregnant as a form of population control. Heat cycles typically occur once a year (or less) and can last from hours to days at a time.
- Women with a heat cycle only become pregnant when in heat, and it's almost always a sure thing. It doesn't mean it will happen the first time they have sex, only that when

a woman is in heat, they usually have sex a number of times before her cycle ends. There are always exceptions where a woman could become pregnant outside her cycle or not get pregnant during her cycle, but this is the general rule.

- Heat houses are a convenience that many Shifters build on their property. It allows the woman (single women in particular or mated women who don't want to get pregnant with their mate) to be separate from the house and have privacy when she's in heat. The males won't pick up her scent or hear her moaning. There's always a concern that unmated males will seduce them. Since the woman isn't in the right frame of mind, she might make an impulsive decision that leads to pregnancy. This can cause friction in the pack if neither of them are interested in mating but are forced to live under the same roof. It might be difficult for her later to find a mate. Couples might use this as a private retreat to get pregnant, especially if she tends to have a long cycle.

FUN SEX FACTS:

- Shifters get amorous after battle, especially when their mate fights alongside them.
- Many Shifter animal types prefer "doggy style" where the woman is on all fours since this feels more natural to them based on how their animal mates. This is why turning your back to a Shifter or backing up against him can be a social cue that you're interested.
- During sex, it sometimes feels as if they might shift and their animal will come out. They won't, but it makes the

act more intense as their animals are looking at each other through their human eyes.

- Males can scent a woman in heat. It's like an aphrodisiac that causes arousal. If it's not their mate or a single female, they will generally distance themselves since it's annoying and uncomfortable.

PREGNANCY/CHILDREN: Human pregnancy tests are not reliable. If the woman doesn't know, a Relic has a way to test her. Alpha males can often sense if a female is carrying an alpha. During pregnancy, a woman's animal goes dormant to allow the fetus to grow in the womb. Shifting is dangerous since the baby would remain in human form. The animal would have to be large enough, but even still, it's almost never done because of the risk. The animal inside will refuse to come out, always putting the baby first. Because the woman can't shift, she can't heal. This makes them vulnerable during pregnancy.

If two Shifters of different animal types have children, the child has a fifty-fifty chance of becoming either. The child will never be born a half-breed—part wolf and part lion, for instance. Parents won't usually know for certain what their child's animal is until they go through the first change, but they might exhibit common traits that are identified among certain animal groups. All Shifters except for purebloods have other animal types somewhere in their ancestry. Even if their parents were different animal types, if they mate with someone who is their same animal type, their child will only be that animal. Animal types do not skip generations and suddenly appear in children. That would be an anomaly.

ALPHAS

I was going to include this under *Family/Sex* and then realized I need to just have a whole section on alphas.

First off, when it comes to animal behavior, Shifters in my world are a mixture of fact and fiction. *Alpha* typically refers to a certain type of behavior and may not exist with all animal species. In my world, an alpha describes a person born with additional Shifter magic. It's not about being macho or physically stronger; it's about having innate abilities and the potential to lead.

It's important to raise an alpha the right way or they'll never reach their true potential. Others may not follow them and they'll wind up a rogue. Most Shifters don't trust rogue alphas. Being rogue implies they have a bad reputation or are incapable of leading others.

The alpha son of a Packmaster (or other animal group leader) is in a better position to become a great leader. They receive advice and positive influence from their father, learning by example how to run a house. A good leader will mentor other alphas in the house or advise their parents. Shifters looking for a pack always seek out leaders who have a solid reputation and/or reputable family history. Young alphas eventually leave home to gain leadership and fighting experience. Some may join the human military; others become bounty hunters or private investigators. They will generally put themselves in positions of hardship or danger to test themselves and gain experience. They will also work at generating an income to help them acquire a home and land when the time comes. It's important for them to create a name for themselves so that when deciding who will join their group, they have only the best to choose from.

Betas and omegas exist in my world as well, usually more so in a wolf pack. Betas exude a lot of power and authority, something alphas can sense. Sometimes they are the firstborn child where the alpha power skipped over them. Betas support alphas as the second-in-command in a pack. Many work as bounty hunters or in similar jobs after leaving their first pack, the same way an alpha does, to gain experience.

Omega is just a term for the lowest-ranking wolf in the pack. It's not a status a Shifter is born into but one they acquired by letting the pack down or being the weakest link. Most wolves at the bottom will work hard or even deceive to keep off that bottom rung. It means they are the least trusted, might receive the least benefits in the house, and are the most likely to be cut or traded.

ALPHA POWER

- Alphas can force other Shifters to shift on command. They have an innate power within them, and it's especially beneficial when there's an injured Shifter who is barely conscious and unable to make themselves shift to heal.

- Alphas have more Shifter magic in them than everyone else. They can usually make lower-ranking Shifters submit to their command, especially when those Shifters are in animal form. The alpha will push power into his voice, but generally it only works on obedient or weak Shifters. If the other Shifters have their alpha present, they will only obey their leader.

- Alphas can sense other alphas since their power is stronger. They can walk by a complete stranger and know whether they're an alpha.

ALPHA FACTS

- It's very common for Packmasters of wolf packs to get a visible tattoo that will make them easily identifiable. Local Shifters will know who the alphas are by their markings even if they've never met them. That allows everyone to know who runs which pack/family group so they know not to cross them.
- Alphas are not specific to wolves. Any animal type that is a predator can have an alpha child with that extra Shifter magic. They are best suited for leading a group.

ALPHA BABIES

- Alphas are born alphas. It's not a status they can achieve.
- Strong alpha babies rarely cry at birth.
- Alphas can usually sense if an unborn child is an alpha. The baby's power is stronger.
- Alphas are more likely to produce an alpha child, especially if their mate is an alpha female.
- Most couples can only have one alpha, if any at all, and typically it's the first child. Chances after that become slim, and for that reason, many couples may only have one or

two children. There are always exceptions, but nature prefers the oldest to be the strongest since the brothers will grow up behind him. This natural order will reduce friction.

- Unborn Shifter babies sense the world around them. Alpha babies in particular. If they sense the mother is constantly afraid, they might decide it's safer on the outside where the mother wolf can protect them. This accounts for some premature births. While some consider it an old wives' tale, there is some truth to it.
- Redheads are not common in the Breed world in general. Among Shifters, they are thought to have a higher likelihood of producing alphas because redheaded alphas are often more powerful than most other alphas. For that reason, redheads are desirable among Shifters. Some men ridiculously assume that single female redheads are more likely to sleep around since every male would pursue them.

ALPHA FEMALES

A woman can be born alpha, but she doesn't possess the same Shifter magic as a male that would allow her to push power into her voice and command others to shift. For that reason, they typically don't lead family groups (packs especially) since others might challenge them. It really depends on the animal type.

Many alpha females are naturally drawn to alpha males. If that alpha leads a group, they will be a power couple. She is a strong influence in the house, and others will be obedient to her commands.

Alpha males in particular can usually sense an alpha female.

PART XII

VAMPIRES

ABOUT

VAMPIRE
A previously written supernatural reimagined by Dannika Dark.

What is a Vampire?

In the Mageriverse, Vampires have unique traits, different from what we've read about or seen in movies. I wanted to take a known supernatural and strip down all the myths and take a closer look at how they came to be. If Vampires were once seen as monsters, wouldn't it benefit them to create falsities about their strengths and weaknesses? Why give humans all the ammunition they need for mass extermination?

Once I created a list of abilities and limitations, I considered how a human would interpret what they'd seen and what assumptions they would make. For instance, people believe you can kill a Vampire by staking them. I created the concept of impalement wood, which only paralyzes Vampires. But to a human, they would look very dead—especially if the stake were driven through the heart.

I didn't want to portray Vampires as creatures at the mercy of their blood addiction. While they *can* suffer bloodlust, Vampires don't need blood to survive. The magic within them keeps them immortal. For that reason, I find them far more interesting to write. They're not hindered by an impulsive need for blood. I don't have to worry about a woman cutting her finger and her Vampire lover turning into a feral animal.

I also didn't want to create a Breed whose existence came at the expense of other people's lives. One thing to consider was how would it be possible for a large Vampire population to regularly feed without being discovered in this day and age? Not only that, but we might run out of victims if their numbers grew. So I separated blood as a desire and not a need. If a human saw a Vampire in bloodlust, they would assume these creatures fed on blood to survive.

Breed laws didn't always exist, so many Vampires gave in to their impulses. The smart ones realized how feeding on humans could catch up with them, especially if they were trying to fly under the radar. So it was in a Vampire's best interest to not indulge in blood recreationally. This likely started the process of makers forming close relationships with their younglings to help them through the bloodlust period so they wouldn't get tangled up in their progenies' mistakes. But there were likely others who made Vampires without regard, and I'm certain that it eventually came back to bite them.

No pun intended.

Blood addiction aside, I took every common myth and compared it with my Vampires to come up with logical explanations. In many cases, it's likely that Vampires created the rumors to throw people off.

PHYSICAL CHARACTERISTICS

Eyes: Inky black irises that never vary in color. It's the darkest black with a glassy look. Their pupils are fully dilated, and the eye color they were born with disappears. At a distance it might pass for a dark

THE CROSSBREED SERIES COMPANION: AN INSIDER'S G... 413

brown, but in certain lighting and up close, the color is a black onyx that can be unnerving to look at, especially because of the power behind their gaze. See more under *Gifts*.

Skin: Vampires have flawless skin that's free of wrinkles caused by sun damage. It gives them a more youthful appearance. Upon their making, their skin is restored to the condition they were born with. So if they were born with any moles or birthmarks, those will remain. Anything resulting from sun damage will not. Over the years, they can acquire lines from repeated facial gestures such as frowning or smiling.

Teeth: Vampires have upper fangs that aren't visible unless they push down (punch out). A Vampire can control it by will, though sometimes it happens reflexively when they're angry or aroused. They can retract them and appear normal again. Fangs are used to penetrate skin, to puncture veins and arteries, and make the victim bleed.

JOB PREFERENCES

Most Breeds work in trades related to their abilities. Vampires are known as secret sellers. Some are in it for the money, while others prefer collecting favors. Vampires will sit in public places and listen to private conversations. They can use that information as blackmail or sell it to interested parties. For that reason, some hire them as spies. *Note:* Many people don't like conducting business in their home, so they choose a public location. Most Breed clubs and bars have at least one soundproof room where people can talk business without fear of a Vampire listening in. It's a profitable investment since the rooms are rented by the hour.

Vampires are the obvious choice as guards. They're strong, have heightened senses, aren't easily detected by other Breeds, and don't require food or sleep.

Some Vampires work for the higher authority, but they have strict rules around charming people for the truth. The higher authority prefers hard evidence since a person's mind can be easily manipulated.

Vampires are needed for their ability to erase memories and charm humans. They can easily infiltrate a hospital, morgue, police station, hotel, or anywhere that they're summoned. They work diligently to protect the Breed world from discovery by charming people to erase evidence and then scrubbing their memories. They can also get into places that others can't because of their talent.

VAMPIRE HISTORY

Throughout history, Vampires were viewed as monsters—the undead who feed on humans. Out of fear, they were staked, buried, and burned alive. Before sunglasses were invented, they weren't able to conceal their black eyes. Going out in the daytime is uncomfortable since they have sensitive eyes. Over the centuries, most people didn't work at night. Blending in with society was a challenge for Vampires— one that forced some to retreat and live in covens. Caves were popular dwellings.

Vampires once traveled long distances in coffins. Humans aren't likely to tamper with corpses, so Vampires could travel in peace on ships and trains. They wouldn't have to worry about shielding their eyes from the sun or people getting unnerved by their black eyes.

Vampires made younglings to create an extra layer of protection since strength lay in numbers. Because there weren't any Breed laws in those days to control the population, it was difficult to manage rogues or stop Vampires from turning whomever they liked.

Vampires are labeled as secret stealers due to their ability to charm people for information. Most Breeds don't trust them since they can erase memories, extract information against someone's will, and influence choices. It can be difficult for a Vampire to gain someone's favor, and often they might lower their gaze to put others at ease.

There's a dark history surrounding Vampires. Some with blood addictions kept bloodslaves. Humans die too easily, and the more you kill, the greater your chances of being caught. So they would hold another Breed or Vampire captive, consuming their blood whenever they liked. Some might have created younglings for that sole purpose.

Additionally, Vampire blood has healing properties for all Breeds. Some used to impale Vampires and keep them around like a first aid kit, drinking their blood whenever they needed to heal. Vampires were treated as cattle, and that's one reason they consider their blood sacred and don't give it up freely.

VAMPIRE FACTS

LIFESPAN

Immortal. In theory, they can live forever. However, all things created can be destroyed. See farther down under *Death* for more on how a Vampire can die.

HEALING

Like most Breeds, Vampires have accelerated healing abilities. However, the more blood they lose, the slower they heal. They also have a healing agent in their saliva similar to Chitahs where they can lick a small scratch or wound and heal it. Not large areas or to the same degree that Chitahs can heal. The vast majority will not use this for any other purpose than sealing up puncture wounds left by fangs. It's something that happens by willing it; otherwise, the wound would inadvertently seal while they're still drinking.

Drinking blood will quicken the healing process, and this can be blood from anyone. Vampire blood is the strongest. Humans have the weakest blood in terms of healing.

Vampire blood is powerful and can heal any Breed and even humans. However, most Vampires don't give it freely as they consider their blood sacred.

INJURIES/SICKNESS

- A Vampire cannot catch viruses, develop diseases, or get infections.
- **Broken bones and cuts:** These take several minutes to heal on their own—healing time varies. If they've lost blood, it'll take longer. Drinking blood will speed up healing.
- **Bullets or foreign objects:** If the object is still inside their body, it'll get pushed out during the healing process before the wound seals. Impalement wood is the exception and will always need to be manually extracted.
- **Burns:** Severe burns that take off the flesh require more time to heal, especially without another Vampire's blood to expedite the healing process. Healing is painful and can take days, especially if organs are re-forming.
- **Severed limbs:** If the bones separate from the body, they're not likely to grow back. It may depend on the strength of a Vampire, but generally speaking, no. It's possible if the limb is held to the wound and they ingest Vampire blood it might reattach, but they can't grow a new one.

DEATH

Examples of how a Vampire can die:

- Beheading

- Fire. But it's important to burn them down to the bones. Any partial remains have the potential to regenerate, though it would be slow, agonizing, and uncertain.
- Wolves and other apex predators who hunt in groups can tear them apart and consume them. Bones that are removed won't regenerate. They still need to be beheaded, but Shifters will always finish the job.

IMPALEMENT WOOD

Impalement wood is illegal to sell on the open market but not illegal to own, especially since wood is ubiquitous. These are weapons used against Vampires to paralyze them. They don't kill Vampires.

Certain woods, such as cedar and beech, can effectively paralyze a Vampire when left inside their body. Bamboo is one that cannot. Once removed, the Vampire will be able to move again, and their wound will heal. If it's driven through the heart, the heart will stop, making them appear dead. It's not uncommon for their spirit to jump outside their body for as long as the heart is stopped. Once the wood is removed, they'll return to their body and the heart will resume beating. Grave-walkers can see their spirits, which is how some staked Vampires were able to lead them to their grave.

When a Vampire is impaled, they can still feel, hear, and see, but they cannot move or speak. In theory, the wood required to paralyze can be small, but there's a greater risk using something smaller than a pencil since wood can easily break. One would have to get dangerously close to the Vampire, and it might not even be enough to fully paralyze them. The black market has a number of creative weapons, some which are explosive and send numerous pieces of impalement wood into their victim. Some are fashioned into arrows, but wooden bullets or other weapons that fire at high speed aren't commonly used. Because of the velocity the wood can either split apart or punch right through the Vampire.

TATTOOS

Tattoos only last a few days before the body absorbs the ink and it's gone. Like other Breeds, if they want a permanent tattoo, they'll need to seal it with liquid fire.

BLOOD FACTS

Vampire blood is often described as a dark flavor like the spices in merlot mixed with a sweet undercurrent. Most Vampires don't give it freely. When they do, it's called blood sharing. They don't need blood to survive or stay youthful. All Vampires indulge in a drop or two now and again. If they go years without consuming a drop, they'll likely become gaunt—such as what happens when a Vampire is buried alive for a long period of time. Many refer to their blood as lifeblood because it has the ability to give immortality and heal.

Human blood: To a Vampire, the taste of human blood is often described as spirited and pure, which makes them more desirable to drink. Even though human blood tastes delicious, it's the weakest in terms of healing. It's also illegal to drink from humans. There's no law regarding bagged blood.

Breed blood: While it's not as tasty as human blood, consuming blood from any Breed will satisfy a Vampire with bloodlust. Breed blood will also heal a Vampire faster than a human's. It's not illegal to feed on another Breed so long as it's consensual.

Vampire blood is powerful. When a Vampire feeds another their blood, it can create an imbalance of power where they have influence over that person. Those susceptible are younglings and the opposite sex. A number of elements factor in, such as the age of the Vampire feeding, the quantity of blood consumed, and if they already had a relationship built from trust. Vampire blood will heal any Breed and also humans. Additionally, a Vampire who drinks Vampire blood will heal from injuries almost immediately.

Drinking your maker's blood is considered taboo. The first exchange when turning a youngling is acceptable. After that, it's not done unless it's for healing purposes. Makers and their younglings share the same blood, so some consider it incestuous. But more importantly, the older a Vampire, the more powerful their blood. Repeated feedings will exert control and influence over young Vampires. It's especially problematic if they're the opposite sex.

AB negative is rare and considered the most delicious blood type. It's a delicacy among Vampires since it's hard to come by. It can get them drunk. Blood processed through a blood bank can also have an intoxicating effect on a Vampire if too much is consumed. *See more below.*

A female Vampire's blood is typically more addictive than a male's. This could be why there are fewer female Vampires. If their blood is like ambrosia, men might fall under their influence and women could control them.

Blood can be an addiction. Newly made Vampires go through a period of bloodlust. Their makers help them learn to control their impulsive urges. Blood is an important element in their world, so it's crucial that they know how to prevent an addiction so they can perform tasks that require them to drink it, such as reading blood to gather information. Infrequent consumption or sampling small amounts isn't considered problematic for most. The more frequently they consume it, the greater the chances of going into bloodlust again.

Never drink from a corpse. There's a general belief among Vampires

that one should never drink from a dead body. Dead blood is unpredictable and could make a Vampire sick or go mad, especially if it's
consumed in large quantities or regularly.

Blood banks. The blood extracted and preserved from a living person
is different than blood from a corpse. It won't harm Vampires and is
not considered dead blood. Donated blood goes through a process
where parts of it are separated, so it can have a powerfully intoxicating
effect on a Vampire, especially AB negative. It wouldn't be uncommon
for a Vampire to have a bag of this in their fridge for special occasions.

BLOODLUST

Younglings go through a bloodlust phase. For some, it might last
months; for others, years. After the first taste of Vampire blood, they
want more and don't know how to control their desire. The sight or
smell of blood could make them react like a hungry animal. Worst-case
scenario, they attack the person bleeding. A youngling with more
control might lick drops of blood off the floor but refrain from
violence. The job of a maker is to teach them how to control those
desires until they reach a point when the sight or smell doesn't affect
them at all. Most will limit their exposure to blood in the early months
or years. They must learn how to read blood, but if they consume too
much early on, they could go mad and become impossible to control.
Younglings need to learn how to drink without being consumed by the
power.

A human can also experience bloodlust if given too much Vampire
blood for healing, but that doesn't mean they've been turned. As
long as they remain human, their bloodlust will last on and off
between a few hours and a few days. Older Vampires can succumb to
bloodlust if they consume blood in large quantities regularly. When

they stop, it can create a withdrawal. The effects aren't lasting since they're older.

Vampires who surrender to bloodlust by stealing it from others in violent attacks are often called feeders.

SONIC WEAPON

A sonic device exists that can be used to block Vampire hearing. The soundwaves are not detected by other Breeds, but to a Vampire, it's loud and bothersome, like feedback from a sound system. It'll force the Vampire to either leave the premises or mute their hearing. Many may not realize where the sound is coming from or that it's being used intentionally. This is not a practical device nor one that's readily available.

COMMONLY USED TERMS

There are Vampire-specific terms you'll see in the books. Refer to the glossary for definitions, or this section, which will elaborate on some terms from the list below.

- *bloodlust*
- *blood sharing*
- *bloodslave*
- *charming*
- *coven*
- *fang*
- *fangdaddy*
- *fanghole*
- *feeder*
- *impalement wood*
- *lifeblood*
- *maker*
- *memory wipe*

- *scrubbing*
- *shadow walking*
- *Vamp*
- *youngling*

DEROGATORY TERMS FOR VAMPIRES
fang
fangdaddy (referring to maker)
fanghole
Vamp

Vampires might sometimes refer to humans as bloodbags, cocktails, or juice boxes, just to name a few. They can be such fangholes.

VAMPIRE LAWS

While the higher authority has a set of laws that applies to all Breeds, such as it being illegal to kill humans, each Breed has their own separate laws created by their lawmakers. This document may not encompass all laws but lists the ones mentioned to date. Vampires aren't as organized as some Breeds.

ELDERS
Most major cities and some small towns are led by Vampire elders. They are older or ancient Vampires who also work with other Breeds to resolve conflict. When laws are broken or Vampires have run amok, they will determine the appropriate punishment or course of action.

LAWS
Most Breeds have laws that protect humans. Vampires are no exception.

- Feeding humans Vampire blood for any reason is forbidden unless they're being turned.

- Drinking from humans, even consensually, is forbidden. They're considered more delicious and thus easier to kill.
- Killing humans is against the law.
- Revealing oneself to the human world is forbidden (this applies to all Breeds). There are exceptions when it's to an individual. This law is targeted toward those who are deliberate with their attempt to expose their identity and secrets to a large body of people or even the government.
- Drinking from other Breeds is not illegal so long as it's consensual.
- Vampires are supposed to obtain permission from the elders when they want to turn someone. The process helps with population control and allows the elders to track younglings. It's not illegal to do it without permission, but if the youngling goes rogue or commits murder, the maker could also be punished. Turning someone in secret might also raise suspicion that the maker is up to something or using the youngling as a bloodslave.
- Makers shouldn't feed their younglings their blood aside from healing them.

Since not every crime warrants the death penalty and there isn't enough room in Breed jails, punishments vary. They could involve financial restitution, servitude, memory scrubbing, or even acting as a maker to a youngling.

Regarding killing one's maker: they could suffer punishment, but it always depends on the scenario. Since every single Vampire can create another Vampire, there is no special protection afforded them like there is with Mage Creators.

FAMILY/SEX

Only humans can be turned by a Vampire. Relics are the exception since their DNA is closest to a human's, but other Breeds cannot be changed. Flukes could happen, but generally there's something in a person's Breed magic that will not allow it.

Vampires prefer to turn humans who don't have family ties to the human world. It will make the transition more difficult if they have a spouse or children, especially since they will often fake their death. It's a cleaner process to choose someone who won't have incentive to turn their back on the Breed world or betray their secrets.

In today's world, most Vampires have no need to make progeny as a form of protection. Since they're responsible for them as a parent is to a child, having a youngling in the home can be a time-consuming responsibility. With laws in place, makers are now accountable for the actions of their progeny.

MAKING A VAMPIRE: Any Vampire can make another Vampire, but some may not have the skills or learned to master it. The process involves a blood exchange. First from the human to the Vampire and then from the Vampire to the human. It's not just about the blood, it also requires the Vampire willing it to happen, which likely activates something in the blood that initiates the change. Because it is a deliberate process, it prevents anyone from accidentally being turned. The Vampire will drink enough to slow the human's heart close to death. Because of the blood exchange, they appear temporarily dead with only the Vampire's blood magic keeping them alive. It's not uncommon for the Vampire to stage the human's death so the police don't start a search.

YOUNGLINGS: This is the term used for newly made Vampires. Younglings live with their makers while learning about Vampires, their gifts, the Breed world, and how to control bloodlust. Some might live with their maker for a year, but others have more issues adapting and require longer. It's not mandatory they leave if they get along with their maker, but most prefer independence at some point. Because their maker's blood is a part of them, they have a special connection with them. Even if their maker is a bad person, they still want to trust them, believe in them, and forgive them. The loyalty they feel can prevent them from making common-sense choices about their maker. It could be nature's way of preventing younglings from murdering their makers.

MAKERS: Any Vampire can turn someone, provided they know how and the candidate is not a defect. Elders have set forth rules to prevent Vampires from turning people and abandoning them. Makers are responsible for teaching their younglings how to control their impulses as well as how to use their new abilities. They teach them history, the laws, and how to adapt socially in the Breed world. Younglings live with their makers for as long as it takes for them to become independent, and makers are fully responsible for their actions while caring for them. That's one reason Vampires choose not to turn just anyone. Their youngling is a reflection of them. Not only could it ruin their reputation if their progeny act out, they could also suffer a penalty for any crimes committed.

FAMILY/SEX:

- **Vampires cannot reproduce.** Their magic doesn't allow them to impregnate or conceive.
- **Most are loners.** Vampires typically don't marry or mate since their lifespans are incredibly long and people can fall out of love. If they do choose a partner, they prefer another Vampire for a variety of compatibility and safety reasons.
- **Sex with non-Vampires is dangerous.** If they lose control for even a second, whether out of lust or anger, they could crush or kill a non-Vampire partner.
- **Erogenous zones.** Vampires are highly aroused when someone strokes or licks their main arteries. This isn't something a non-Vampire would know, but it comes instinctually to a Vampire to arouse their Vampire partner in this way.
- **Female Vampires don't menstruate.**
- **Female Vampires are less common.** Many are beautiful because their looks were why they were chosen. Because of the population imbalance, they're coveted by males. Should the woman entertain the idea of a mate, she has the power to be especially selective and only seek out intelligent males who are trustworthy and loyal. Because of how most female Vampires entered the Breed world, they aren't very trusting of people's intentions or ulterior motives.

Like most other Breeds, Vampires prefer to be with their own kind if it's a permanent match. There aren't as many female Vampires as there are male, so this isn't a reality for most. There are downsides to pairing up with a non-Vampire, one being that most have no desire to be with a Vampire. They fear their strength and their ability to manipulate one's mind and memories. Because of a Vampire's incredible hearing and ability to charm, a person may never feel like they have privacy. Unless their partner is a Mage or another Vampire, they will likely outlive them, which would be incredibly difficult. There are a number of reasons that factor into why most Vampires are loners, but it doesn't mean they can't form good friendships or have casual relationships.

EYE CONTACT: Most people don't look Vampires in the eye. Vampires have the ability to charm, so for that reason, gazes will always avert. It can negatively affect a Vampire to never have someone trust them or look into their eyes. It likely contributes to their solitary life.

Vampires have a bad reputation as secret stealers. For that reason, when a Vampire turns his gaze down, it's a nonthreatening gesture. They are conveying to the other party that they can be trusted since their gaze is considered dangerous.

VAMPIRE GIFTS

Vampires possess a number of natural gifts. They can control and manipulate others, extract information from blood, and more. Regarding blood powers, this section covers their abilities beyond healing.

Vampires instinctually know the best places to bite to access the most blood. An artery produces more blood but can be messy if the intention is not to kill. Veins are generally the target during sex or when blood reading. Once the Vampire penetrates the skin, they'll retract their fangs so they can consume blood without their teeth getting in the way. When they're reading someone's blood, they only require a few drops.

BLOOD READING

Vampires can detect information by tasting blood, such as what a person is feeling, whether they're lying, and much more. Some hear whispers as if the blood is alive and telling secrets. The flavor in combination with the knowledge produces a rush—one a Vampire learns to control. Vampires are secretive about what they can read, and every Vampire's ability differs.

HEIGHTENED VISION

Vampires can see extremely well in dim and pitch-black conditions and don't require a light source. They notice things others don't, like the capillaries on someone's face reddening or the veins in the eyes. They're perceptive regarding visual cues, which makes it easy for them to tell when a person is nervous, angry, embarrassed, or even lying.

HEIGHTENED HEARING

Vampires have amplified hearing abilities. Skill sets vary for each Vampire. Within close proximity, they can focus on a person's heart-beat or breathing. Because they can hear conversations and sounds that are normally out of range, they are able to mute out specific sounds so they won't go mad listening to everything. This form of selective hearing is useful in noisy clubs when they want to mute out the music or conversations beyond a certain range. This is something that requires practice to master.

Thick walls and distance make sounds quieter or undetectable. For instance, they can't hear the heartbeat of a Vampire buried in a grave-yard. There's too much earth between them.

Unexpected loud noises don't usually bother them since they have an internal defense mechanism that suppresses any sudden amplified sounds such as gunfire or a car engine revving. Fireworks are difficult to selectively mute out since the decibels are extremely loud, continually changing, and the explosions sporadic. Most will just mute everything until the fireworks have ended.

CHARMING

Direct eye contact required. While being charmed, the victim's face goes blank and they'll answer any questions the Vampire asks. In most cases, they'll only respond to the Vampire and not anyone else who might be questioning them. There might also be a special magic in the Vampire's voice during this process that draws their subject in. Charming is a deliberate act and doesn't work just through eye contact—the Vampire has to be initiating their power. In most cases it's obvious when they're doing it, but some Vampires have finessed their skills so that people are completely unaware the Vampire is turning on their power in casual conversation. Below are examples of how they can use this ability.

- **Truth serum:** Vampires have the ability to look into someone's eyes and put them in a trance. It works like a truth serum, allowing them to get information out of a person.
- **Influencing behavior:** Vampires can influence others to do things, but that varies based on the request and the level of power a Vampire has. It works better if the person is willing or it wouldn't go against their core beliefs. The Vampire can ask them to walk inside a restaurant and order a salad and make them believe they want a salad. If the Vampire erases their memory of the charming, they won't remember the Vampire suggested it. They'll believe it is their true desire. It's more difficult to get a person to do something in the future, like asking them to fly to Chicago next week. They will have time to think about that implanted desire and change their mind. After a Vampire charms information out of someone, if they don't want them to remember the event, they'll remove the memory of the conversation. It works better if they send them away to do something like order a drink or go to the bathroom. The secondary act is a form of mental distraction so the person won't wonder what they're doing sitting in a vacant parking lot or an abandoned stairwell.

- **Influencing beliefs:** A Vampire can make someone believe things through charming, but unless it includes a memory wipe, it'll only be temporary. Like they might suggest to a man that he wants to dance. The man will begin to dance but will stop when the charming spell wears off.
- **The person will remember being charmed unless the Vampire takes steps to prevent it.** If it was a subtle suggestion, they won't make the connection. But if it was an obvious extraction of information, they'll remember the entire conversation. Some Vampires don't care to go the extra step of scrubbing a person's memory. It might be important for the person to remember the conversation so they know the Vampire has what they want.
- **A skilled Vampire can charm a person without their realizing it.** Some of them can work their magic in a casual conversation without arousing any suspicion. It takes practice, and it also requires the Vampire to have gained the person's trust enough to hold eye contact with them on a more frequent basis. They will put just enough power into their gaze to extract the truth and make it seem like the person wanted to answer their question. This would be too obvious to pull off regarding secrets since people would never divulge those casually.

SCRUBBING/MEMORY WIPE
Direct eye contact required.

- **Scrubbing:** The act of erasing memories. Subjects will go into a trancelike state while the Vampire plucks out specific memories to permanently erase. Many Vampires do this immediately after charming someone for information if they don't want the victim to remember them or the conversation. The older the memory or the more there are, the trickier it is to remove. It creates too many gaps in time, and if too much is taken, the person could wind up with swiss cheese for a brain.

- **Memory wipe:** The act of erasing a person's entire life memories. Usually they will replace those memories with a new identity. This is done if the Vampire doesn't want to kill the person but they have too many memories to extract. Whether new memories are given or not, most individuals won't be mentally sound afterward. They will struggle with too many dark spots where they don't have specific memories.

- **Headaches during memory recall:** When someone has had a memory removed, often they'll experience a headache or piercing pain in their temple if they try to recall that gap in time. Not everyone will associate this with being scrubbed unless they have reason to believe so.

- **Scrubbing and memory wipes can be reversed.** There's a fail-safe Vampires can use that will restore erased memories. During the process, a special phrase or word is implanted in the person's mind. If that word is spoken to the victim again, it will undo the erasure. Only the Vampire who took the memories can unlock the memories—no one else can speak the words and get the same result.

STRENGTH

Vampires are extraordinarily strong and don't tire easily. After a long run, they're not likely to be sweating or panting. Their body exhibits control during strenuous activities. The exception might be during sex. A lot of emotions are wrapped up in the act, so they could lose control and may sweat and be out of breath like a normal person.

Vampires can break stone and crush bones. There are limits to their strength. For instance, a Vampire can turn a car over but not a bus or other large vehicle. They have to exercise restraint when touching others. Because they can lose control during sex, intercourse is dangerous with a non-Vampire. Those who engage in interbreeding might prefer certain sexual positions that will avoid injury to their partner.

SHADOW WALKING
In dark spaces, Vampires can move fluidly within the shadows, allowing them to scale walls and move fast. They can't shadow walk in the daytime unless it's in a dark building, absent of windows and light. Additionally, they can't shadow walk in artificial light. So if they're on a brightly lit street, they'll have to move into a dark alleyway. The speed in which they can move through shadows is similar to how fast a Mage can flash. Typically it's just for short distances, especially when going upward. They can't float, but they can grab surfaces and move without gravity hindering them. The skill varies by Vampire, and some may not have fully mastered it.

FOOD/DRINK
Vampires do not require food or drink to survive. They have no appetite, and their body doesn't need it. Their digestive system still works if food or drink is introduced, and for obvious reasons, some Vampires prefer not having to use the toilet. Those who do eat or drink do so for either the enjoyment or to avoid drawing negative attention to themself in social settings. Not having to eat or drink is beneficial for Vampires who work as guards twenty-four hours a day. Their ability to sustain immortality without wasting away is unknown. That said, they may become gaunt over the years if they never consume a drop of blood, as what often occurs with Vampires buried alive for long periods.

COLD/HEAT

Vampires are impervious to extreme temperatures. They are aware of heat and cold, but their core temperature regulates and their body is unaffected. The exception would be if they were burned by fire. Temperature regulation allows them to stand outside in the freezing cold all night while on guard. They also won't break a sweat in sweltering heat. Because of this gift, they don't depend on weather-appropriate clothing. Most will still wear jackets or T-shirts, depending on the season, to blend in.

SLEEP

Vampires don't sleep the way everyone else does where they fall unconscious and dream. Most are awake twenty-four hours a day. To keep from going mad, many will have occasional periods of rest in the dark where they lie quietly and shut off their brain. That might explain why some Vampires once slept in coffins—a way to block out the world and enter a trancelike state.

DETECTION/IMMUNITY

- **Chitahs:** They have no personal scent for a Chitah to detect. A Chitah might smell their cologne or body wash, but the unique scent that makes people trackable isn't there. They are also unaffected by Chitah venom.
- **Mage:** A Mage is unable to detect Vampire energy. Additionally, Vampires are unaffected by Mage energy. If a Mage blasted them, they would feel nothing. This isn't to be confused with being a Blocker. A Vampire is not immune to all Mage gifts. For instance, they can be killed by energy balls from a Wielder.
- **Sensors:** Vampires are not immune to Sensor gifts. Sensors can also pick up their emotional imprints just fine.

. . .

LIMITATIONS

- **Vampires are sensitive to sunlight.** It hurts their eyes. Older Vampires have built up a tolerance to it, but it's common for Vampires to wear sunglasses in the daytime while outside.
- **Sunglasses:** Wearing these will hinder a Vampire's ability to charm someone, regardless of who is wearing them. Mirrored shades are the most effective, but an extremely dark pair that conceals the eyes completely may also work. It's not uncommon for some Breeds to wear them in a Vampire's presence since not everyone trusts Vampires.

DEFECTS: As with any Breed, some Vampires have defects when it comes to their abilities. That might include an inability to see well in the dark, if at all. They might lack fangs, be unable to turn a human into a Vampire, or even require food and drink. Defects aren't common and will vary in severity and type. Their own kind would judge them more harshly than any other Breed. Since Vampires can't have children, a defect wouldn't be as big of an issue in finding a mate as it would for Breeds that procreate. There are Relics out there who specialize in helping those with impairments, but many Vampires may not seek help or realize it exists. Revealing one's defects can be dangerous as it's never good to let anyone know your weaknesses.

DISPELLING MYTHS

Human lore derives from a misinterpretation of Breed gifts. When a Vampire is staked with impalement wood, they're paralyzed. It would be easy to assume they're dead, thus coming to the conclusion that staking a Vampire is how you kill them. Vampires avoiding sunlight might lead one to believe that they can also be killed by it.

However, Vampires created a lot of untruths about their kind as a way to prove to humans that they *aren't* a Vampire. People once believed them to be devils or monsters, and towns would burn them at the stake without a fair trial. By creating lies, it threw off suspicion. People would see them eating garlic, casting a reflection in a mirror, or wearing silver and breathe a sigh of relief, deciding maybe they're just eccentric. This was especially important around the time the church got involved, so Vampires threw in a few extra myths about holy water and crosses.

If humans had known the truth about how to identify Vampires, it would have been devastating. This was a time when beheadings and burnings were common methods of execution, which would lead to certain death if a Vampire was captured. The less humans knew, the better. Vampire lore also varies by region, so the combination of human ignorance with Vampire lies created different stories in places like South America, Germany, and Africa.

This section contains the most commonly known myths we associate with Vampires.

DRINKING BLOOD

Vampires do not need to feed on blood to survive. Blood *can* be an addiction, especially for a youngling, so seeing a Vampire feeding could lead one to believe that they need blood to survive.

CASTING A REFLECTION

Vampires cast a reflection like everyone else. This was a myth fabricated by Vampires so they could easily prove they weren't the undead. Some Vampires might have kept large mirrors in the foyer of their home to put guests at ease but also to make it appear that they too were on the lookout for Vampires.

COFFINS

Resting or traveling in coffins might have been a necessity at one time. Stumbling across a man in a coffin and seeing him rise might have fueled the rumors about Vampires being the undead. Especially if that coffin was in their home.

CROSSES

No effect. The rumor that crosses harm them is likely how they got the church off their back.

DEAD

Vampires are not dead. Their heart beats, and their skin is warm. Because some drank blood and slept in coffins, that combined with flawless skin might have led some to believe they were the undead. It's also likely that someone who was turned was recognized by their family, who either assumed they died or couldn't figure out why they hadn't aged in fifty years.

GARLIC
No effect unless they simply dislike garlic. Some Vampires on the run or traveling might have an aversion to pungent smells since it would make it easier for a Chitah to track them.

HOLY WATER
No effect.

PERMISSION TO ENTER A HOME
Many believe that Vampires cannot enter unless they are invited in. This is a myth with the origin unknown.

SILVER
No effect.

THE SUN
Sunlight doesn't harm or burn Vampires. Most dislike the daylight or sunny days because their pupils are fully dilated, making them more sensitive to sunlight. Modern sunglasses make it more comfortable for them to move around in the day. Some of the older ones have simply learned to tolerate it better after centuries of practice. It still hurts, but their threshold for pain increases with time.

TURNING INTO A BAT
Just... no. Technically, that would make them a Shifter. Stumbling upon a coven in a cave filled with bats might have led some to believe it.

WOODEN STAKES
These do not kill Vampires. There are certain types of wood, such as

cedar and beech, that fall under the category of "impalement wood."
All the wood types haven't yet been named, but there are even articles
written about how some cultures used specific types of wood. When a
Vampire is staked with impalement wood, it causes paralysis for as long
as it remains in them. This would make them appear dead. It was
necessary to allow humans to believe in this untruth so they would do
nothing further to the Vampire before burying them. It gave the
Vampire a chance of surviving. But this is also how a lot of Vampires
wound up buried over the years and why Gravewalkers were called
upon to find them.

If impalement wood is driven through the heart, the heart will stop.
But the Vampire remains in a paralyzed state, fully aware of what's
happening around them. Most humans and even Breed assumed that
staking a Vampire through the heart killed them since they weren't
moving and the heartbeat stopped. See *Facts* in the *Vampires* section
for more on impalement wood.

BONUS SHORT STORY 1

THE HUNTER

A HUNTER MOON SHORT STORY

CHAPTER 1

With a full belly from a hearty dinner of lasagna and cheesecake, Hunter sluggishly followed Harley around the foyer. Crush had popped in for a minute to drop off Raven and Christian from a trip they'd gone on to a faraway place. Hunter was so glad he brought Harley. He giggled and got down on all fours, pretending to be a dog. Harley just gave him a sloppy kiss, which made Hunter squeal before throwing his arms around him. Having a dog around was so much fun. Sometimes all the big people forgot what it was like to be small. But Harley knew even though he wasn't people.

"Thanks for picking us up at the airport," Raven said, giving her dad a hug. "Maybe next time Christian can sit in the front."

"Someone needed to guard all your luggage," Crush replied, patting her back. "Plus I got the dog. Maybe next time I'll just bring the bike."

"Over my rotting corpse," Christian said under his breath.

Hunter peered over Harley's back and watched Christian. He was nice but mysterious. Hunter sometimes saw him gliding through the shadows of the house at night, but everyone said that's what Vampires do.

Hunter knew all about Breed. The bad man who raised him told him all kinds of things, but now a lot of it didn't make sense. Patrick had warned him that Vampires were malicious devils, but Christian didn't seem like a bad man. Hunter wasn't close with him, but he was starting to figure out that Patrick had lied about a lot of things.

"You should have gone to Africa with us," Christian remarked, arms folded while he leaned against the wall by the door.

Crush gave him the side-eye. "Damn lions would have eaten me."

"A hearty meal, to be sure."

Raven moved her suitcase away from the door. "I'll call you tomorrow, Daddy, and tell you everything. Go home before you get too sleepy to drive."

When Crush whistled, Harley stood to attention, tail wagging.

Hunter pouted. Goodbyes weren't easy for him. Sometimes he got scared that when he said goodbye to his daddy, it meant he wouldn't come back. Goodbye felt like such a forever word, and he didn't want to say it to people he loved. Hunter hugged Harley extra tight and gave him a kiss on the neck.

Crush ambled over and rumpled Hunter's hair. "Maybe you can ask your old man if it's okay to come over and visit. I know my buddy Harley is looking for someone to play ball with him in the yard, and I'm getting too damn old."

Hunter beamed at the invitation. Crush was a funny man, but he always gave him a coin from his pocket. Hunter signed his reply, but Crush didn't understand.

But then he winked at Hunter, so maybe he did.

"I know what you mean, kid," he said, giving Harley a pat on the side.

Raven ran her fingers through her black hair and yawned. "If you ever want to go on vacation, I think you know who will dog-sit for you."

Crush strutted back to the door, coins jingling in his pocket. "And leave my sidekick behind?"

"Jaysus," Christian muttered. "Does he not have enough room in the new castle?"

Hunter giggled. Sometimes he didn't understand all the grown-up jokes, but he liked the looks they would give each other.

As Hunter stood, Harley gave him another lick before trotting behind his human.

Hunter gasped when his feet lifted off the ground and he soared up in the air, landing on Switch's shoulders.

"Ah, so *here* you are," he scolded. But when Hunter touched his forehead, he could tell Switch was only teasing.

Hunter gathered up Switch's long hair and shaped it into a ponytail on top of his head.

Switch turned around and marched toward the hallway in the east wing. "Tomorrow after signing lessons, we're going on a field trip."

Hunter frowned. What was so special about that? He played outside in the field all the time. Even flew a kite shaped like an octopus the other day.

"A field trip," Switch continued, "is when you go to a really cool place to learn something new. I got your dad's permission to take you to the planetarium."

Hunter blew at a candle on a wall sconce, the flame flickering but not going out.

"A planetarium is where you learn about all the planets and stars up in the sky. They have this really neat room where you can watch the universe."

Hunter kicked his legs back excitedly. That sounded like so much fun. He liked it when everyone would sit outside sometimes and stare up at the sky.

"But you need your sleep." Switch made a loud growl as he bent forward, lifted Hunter off his shoulders, and set him on the floor. "You're getting too big for shoulder rides. I think the cutoff age is six."

Hunter held up seven fingers, deciding he wanted another year of riding on shoulders. What was the rule? Was he going to be too big at seven? Hunter felt so small around grown-ups, but sometimes he didn't mind. It meant going on shoulder rides or getting tossed in the pool. Sometimes at night when he fell asleep in a chair, his daddy would carry him to bed. He thought about how nice it felt and wished he was strong enough to do the same for someone else.

Hunter dashed off as fast as he could down the long hall with the pretty blue windows. He waved at Switch before turning left down his private hallway. At the far end, his door was ajar and his daddy was waiting for him.

Instead of jumping into his bed, Hunter ran right into his father's arms. One of his most favorite things in the world was having a daddy. It made him feel safe and protected, and he loved it when the man others called Shepherd would put his strong arms around him. He was like a stone man covered with soft skin. Though not so soft in some places. Scars marked up his hands, arms, and even chest. Sometimes Hunter traced his finger over them, wondering how he got hurt so bad. They reminded him of the scar he had on his own face. Patrick once told him that the fates had cursed him—that he was born with a scar on his face because he was a bad apple.

That couldn't be true. Not when his daddy was so nice and gave him hugs. Sometimes he would even buy Hunter toys for no reason, and he had more scars than anyone Hunter had ever met. So that meant Patrick had lied.

Shepherd rummaged through the drawers before helping him change clothes. Hunter was big enough to dress himself, but he liked the help. It made him feel loved and taken care of. After putting on the green pajamas with the dinosaur on the T-shirt, he picked up his favorite stuffed bear from the foot of the bed and clutched it tight.

"You want the lights on or off, little man?"

Hunter looked at the dark window. Tiny twinkle lights were strung all around it, and sometimes they turned them on at night so he wasn't left in the dark. Especially when he had nightmares. But Hunter didn't want his daddy to think he wasn't brave, so he held up his hands and closed his fingers together.

"Off it is." After pulling back the covers, Shepherd patted the pillow. "I heard you've got a big day tomorrow with Switch. Planetarium, huh? I've never been to a sciencey place like that, but it sounds pretty great."

Hunter bounced onto the bed, his grin wide as he wondered what a planetarium looked like. How in the heck could they see stars in the daytime? It didn't seem possible unless they somehow turned the sunlight off. Maybe they could do that. Hunter had so many questions but hadn't learned enough in sign language to ask. He could write, but it took time to get all his letters to look nice.

His daddy recently stopped encouraging him to talk, which he was glad about. Hunter didn't like talking. Whenever Patrick caught him talking loudly or to anyone, he would grab Hunter and send a thunderbolt of pain inside his body. Patrick was a Mage, so he could do all sorts of stuff to make it hurt.

And it hurt so bad that Hunter would run and hide beneath the covers, tears in his eyes. Another time, he wet his pants and it got on the floor. Patrick said that a dog was better house-trained than him. Now he would never have to see that man again.

Shepherd wagged his finger at him. "Stay in bed tonight. Got it? No sneaking off."

Hunter gave a closed-lipped smile. Sneaking around at night was his favorite thing. He liked spying on everyone to see what they were doing. They had different conversations at night than they did when he was around, but he also liked exploring rooms and pretending he was a ninja. Niko had taught him how to see things differently—how to pretend the swimming pool was the ocean or that the hallways were secret passageways through unknown lands. Blue sometimes did the same, but only when she wanted to get him to run an errand or leave a room. Neither of them were silly like Wyatt. Sometimes people called him Spooky, and Hunter really liked that name.

Shepherd brushed his hair back and then kissed him on the forehead. "Love you, little man. Have good dreams."

Hunter took a deep breath. His daddy smelled a little like sweat, but he didn't mind. Patrick had never hugged or kissed him or even said he loved him. Hunter wasn't even sure what those words meant until people in this house started saying it to him. Not everyone, but a few had.

None said it like his daddy. Hunter knew how to read emotions through touch. Sometimes the way people looked wasn't how they were feeling. He had felt the love feeling before when he brushed by people at some of Patrick's parties, but those feelings were between other people.

This was different. It was a love that was all his to keep. He made the sign with his hand and put it on his daddy's chest.

Love you. Love you. Love you.

"Good night." The strong man reached over and switched off the electric lantern. "Get some sleep if you want to look at the stars tomorrow."

When the door closed, all Hunter could think about was the words *field trip.* Now *that* sounded like a thrilling adventure! How did they expect him to sleep?

He flung back the covers and leaped to his dresser. After putting on the striped pink socks that had the sticky treads on the bottom, he quietly opened the door and peered into the hallway. He knew his daddy hadn't gone to bed. It was too early for that, so he had to be careful not to run into him or he'd get in big trouble.

Big trouble in this house wasn't the same as his previous home. It meant someone would have a serious talk with him. If it was something really bad, sometimes he would get a toy taken away for a short time. That happened once when he got mad and threw a fork across the table. He didn't mean to hurt anyone, but since his daddy wasn't there, Niko took him aside and explained how if we don't learn to control our temper, those bad feelings can hurt the people we love. Hunter had a hard time understanding. He knew it wasn't nice to hurt people, and he'd never do it on purpose. But sometimes he just didn't know what to do with all the anger.

Breaking things didn't get him in trouble unless it was on purpose. He learned quickly that whenever he did something, he would be asked if it was on purpose or an accident. An accident meant he wouldn't get in trouble. Sometimes he wanted to lie so he wouldn't get scolded, but it was impossible to lie around his daddy, Claude, or Niko. Even Wyatt sometimes knew. Wyatt said he had tells, but Hunter didn't understand what that meant. It was always better to be honest. Someday he would learn more words and be able to explain his side of the story.

He tiptoed quietly down the hallway, which was drenched in darkness. His daddy usually kept a single lantern lit in case Hunter had to use the bathroom at night, but tonight he'd forgotten. After Hunter reached the end and looked both ways, he sprinted to the left. There weren't any lights on in the back hall, so he ran as if there were monsters nipping at his heels. Once he reached the center hall, he caught his breath and peered around the corner. Hunter never got to explore the last house he lived in. He was locked inside his room every night so he wouldn't wander. But it wasn't half as big as this place, and there was so much here to explore!

He tested a few doorknobs, but they wouldn't turn.

"Son of a ghost!" Wyatt exclaimed from up ahead.

Hunter pressed himself against the cold wall.

Wyatt's voice grew louder. "I already looked! Swear to the specters. Call everyone in the gathering room. Family meeting."

A bright light came into view from Wyatt's phone as he briskly crossed the hall, his boot heels knocking against the stone floor at a desperate pace.

Curious, Hunter slinked along the wall until he found a chair to hide behind. He often pretended to be a cat that nobody could hear. Cats were so clever, and no one ever noticed them. When Gem flashed by, Hunter's eyes rounded.

So cool! It would be so much fun to run as fast as Gem. Claude and Raven could also run fast, but they didn't do it as often. Once he'd wanted Gem to carry him and run, but he couldn't ask using his voice. She probably wouldn't have since she didn't seem strong enough to lift him.

Hunter concealed his emotions and pretended to be a piece of furniture. If Claudie walked by, he might smell him.

Hunter smiled, wondering what Claude might think about the nickname. Hunter liked the way the name Claudie rolled around in his head like a silly joke. Maybe one day he would paint a picture of him and put his nickname at the bottom.

"Hell if I know," Raven said as she crossed the room with Christian. "I've got jet lag, so this better be life or death."

"Shall I carry you, Precious? Are your hooves all tuckered out?"

She elbowed Christian in the ribs as they walked toward the dining hall. Just after they passed by, Christian glanced over his shoulder and winked at him.

How does he know I'm here?

Hunter had held his breath and everything because he knew how Vampires could hear a pin drop. Christian wouldn't tell anyone—of that he was certain. Christian once said that snitches get stitches. Hunter didn't exactly understand what that meant, but he knew that Christian could keep super special secrets. He kept promises for Viktor, and once he swore not to tell anyone that Gem accidentally chipped one of the statues when she was flashing too fast and ran into it.

After everyone passed through the foyer and the chatter overlapped in the distance, Hunter crept quietly into the dining room. Kira had already snuffed out the candles on the round iron chandelier that hung over the table. Even though it was dark, he knew some people could see good in the dark, so he got down on his hands and knees and crawled on all fours beneath one of the booths up ahead. Everyone was inside the gathering room, their voices carrying through the open archways. He listened to them talking about things like Africa and a submarine.

What's a submarine? he wondered.

Someone clapped their hands together.

"All right," Wyatt boomed. "I have a situation."

"Your whole life is a situation," Shepherd grumbled.

A few people chuckled.

"I'm missing a flash drive with some important information on it," Wyatt continued.

"I didn't take it," Gem piped in.

"Did anyone come across a red flash drive?" Wyatt asked calmly. There was something in the way he spoke that was different—like he was only pretending to be calm. "There's sensitive data on it, and I don't have any other copies."

"Perhaps you'll find it in your arse," Christian remarked.

Shepherd cursed. "Spooky, we don't have time for this shit. None of us swiped your flash drive."

"I'm not saying you did," Wyatt retorted. "But sometimes people find things and just assume they don't belong to anyone."

"So what you're *really* saying is that you misplaced it," Gem countered. "No one stole your flash drive; you lost it. And you think one of us accidentally found it."

It got real quiet, and Hunter froze, wondering if they could hear him.

"Maybe Kira swept it up," Niko offered. "You don't exactly keep a tidy room."

Wyatt made a raspberry sound that almost made Hunter giggle. "Hold your ponies. I keep it plenty tidy. I've got a trash can in there, but I clean up my own mess and not everyone here does. I'm not pointing fingers." It was quiet for a beat, and Hunter wondered if he was pointing at someone. "Anyhow, I already had Viktor ask her, and she hasn't seen it. Switch doesn't know either."

"What about Hunter?" Niko proposed, making Hunter tense up.

What's a flash drive? Did I take it? Maybe I did. No, they said it was something red. I don't remember finding anything red.

"Hunter wouldn't steal."

That was his daddy speaking up for him.

"*No*," Wyatt began, stretching out the vowel. "But maybe the little monkey thought it was a toy and put it into the garbage disposal."

"Let's not be dramatic," Viktor said.

Hunter wanted to see more, so he quietly made his way to the entryway and stayed in the shadows. Peering inside, he could see everyone a little better. Not much since they only had a few candles lit.

Claude was standing by the hearth next to a lantern. Hunter had his cheek pressed to the floor, so the only thing he could see beneath the leather chairs was Claude's big feet. He recognized the sneakers.

Niko walked into view and stood behind one of the chairs, facing away from Hunter. "I'm not implying Hunter would knowingly steal. But children are curious, and if he didn't know what the object is, he might have thought it was a treasure." Niko turned his head and looked directly at Hunter.

Hunter's chest hurt, and his lip quivered. He hadn't done anything wrong.

Niko turned his gaze back to the group. "Perhaps you're right, Shepherd. If the boy had found anything, he would have certainly brought it to our attention. Wyatt, have you left the house since you last had it?"

Wyatt paced and snapped the black beanie off his head. He twirled it around his finger. "No. I haven't been out in a week. Some of us have to work day and night."

A pillow flew at his head, and Blue leaned forward from the leather couch on the right. "Don't pull that shit with us. We offer to help all the time and you send us away."

Wyatt tucked some of his hat in his back pocket. "Not everyone here knows how to code," he said, using that silly gesture he did with his pointing and middle fingers.

"Stop with the air quotes." Blue shook her head. "Half the time you're not even working. Unless you count watching food reviews on the internet as work."

"Look, buttercup—"

Viktor cleared his throat, which silenced everyone. "Wyatt has informed me of what is on this device, and it is critical we locate it. We cannot waste time on petty arguments. If he has not left the house, it is somewhere here."

Hunter liked the way Viktor talked. His consonants were so different from how everyone else said them. Hunter picked at a loose piece of stone in the wall.

Field trip.

If they thought he stole that red thing, they might not let him go on the field trip.

I'll find it. Then they can't make me stay home. I'll be a hero!

"What's it look like?" Raven asked.

Wyatt folded all his fingers down except the middle one and held his hand out. "It's about yea big."

Hunter studied the size of Wyatt's finger.

Christian stood. "You keep aiming that at my wife and I'll drain you."

Blue chuckled and patted Raven's knee. "Hear that? You're a wife now."

Raven frowned. "I like the sound of *lover* a lot better. *Wife* sounds like I'm supposed to be doing dishes and picking up after him."

"You mean you don't do that already?" Blue asked, reclining out of view.

Raven grinned up at Christian. "I didn't even pick up the dignity he left behind when he ran from the charging rhino."

Christian whirled around. "Are you daft? I saved your arse by leading him away from the vehicle. *Nighttime tour*," he grumbled. "Why don't you tell them about our tour guide with a sense of humor?"

Raven sat back and snickered. "The tour guide didn't know he was booking a Vampire. They didn't ask our Breed when I paid. Azi doesn't like Vampires. We didn't find that out until we were in the middle of nowhere and he suggested that Christian get out of the Jeep and take pictures of me."

Christian stroked his dark beard and turned away.

"The best part was what happened in our tent that night." Raven got up and faced him. "I always joke about spiders in his bedroom, but I've never seen anything that big."

"Haven't you now?" Christian asked, turning toward her.

She smiled up at him. "He was unpacking our blankets while I was outside peeing. The next thing I know, I hear this loud scream—"

Christian covered her mouth. "What you know about the king baboon spider could fill a thimble. Thought I told you never to repeat that story?" He suddenly snapped his hand away from her mouth.

Raven smiled, her fangs showing.

He cocked his head to the side. "Then perhaps I should tell them all about what happened on the submarine." Christian waggled his eyebrows.

She covered his mouth. "Don't you *dare*."

He kissed her hand and backed up a step. "All's fair in love and war."

Wyatt put his hat back on. "Can we catch up on the last episode of *The Love Boat* later? I'm all booked up on crazy, and if I don't find this flash drive, people will die."

It got real quiet, and everyone blanched. *Die* wasn't a nice word. Hunter knew it meant a forever goodbye, but sometimes Spooky saw people who died, so maybe it wasn't forever.

Shepherd stood up and ran his hand over his short hair. "What rooms have you been moving between?"

Wyatt scratched his chin. "Lately? All over. Game rooms, dining, kitchen, hallways, libraries, office, bedroom, bathrooms, courtyard..."

"Jesus. This is a clusterfuck." Shepherd swung his gaze up to the ceiling. "How many square feet in this place?"

"Why would you leave your room with something that important?" Gem asked. "It has to be in your office or bedroom."

Wyatt shook his head. "I share information with Viktor all the time. Sometimes he wants to see me in his office, and other times we'll go to a soundproof room. I also put things in my pocket when I'm working and then go do other stuff. I take breaks and walk around to clear my head. I don't know, Rollergirl. I'm just missing a red flash drive."

Blue stood up and took off her feather earrings. "I'll search all his pockets. As much as I don't want to dig through your dirty laundry, something tells me you didn't bother. While I'm at it, I'll check the laundry basket and dryer. It might have tumbled out."

When Hunter caught Blue heading his way, he scrambled back and then ducked beneath one of the booths again. It was nice and dark in the dining room, so all he saw were the faint shadows of their legs shuffling by. They were forming search plans, and Hunter listened carefully.

He wanted to help because that's what big boys were supposed to do. Six meant he was almost seven, and seven was practically ten.

When it finally got quiet, he crawled out from beneath the table. As soon as he popped to his feet, he noticed Niko standing in the gathering room entryway.

"Apologies. I didn't mean to accuse you of something you didn't do," Niko said.

Hunter shrugged.

"But when things go missing, it's always important to ask everyone if they might have found it. That's why Wyatt summoned us in here. None of us would have purposefully stolen his belongings, but we might have found it. That's why it's important when you find things that don't belong to you that you return them. Taking things without payment or trade is bad karma." Niko's hand touched Hunter's back as they walked into the hallway. "You needn't worry. Your secret is safe with me. You're a clever one. Always hiding, always watching—even when we don't know. I bet you might have some ideas of where to find what we're looking for."

Hunter nodded, eager to start the hunt.

Niko suddenly knelt down before him but didn't look at him in the eye. He never did. "Just be sure your father doesn't know what you're up to. Sometimes it's okay to break the rules a little bit if you're doing it for the right reasons. Helping people is always the right reason. Can you make me a promise?"

Hunter remembered that Niko couldn't see him nod, so he patted his shoulder.

Niko's lips twitched. "There are two places you mustn't go: outside or downstairs. Not even the courtyard or the gym. If the door leads outside or to a staircase going down, you turn away no matter how tempted you might be to follow. Those are dangerous places at night, and you should never go alone. You heard what Wyatt said about not having left the house. That means the flash drive is somewhere inside. I'm afraid I can't learn sign language like the others to better understand you, but I can read your light. Energy has a language all its own. So if you think you've found something but it's somewhere you're not supposed to go, come find me. I'll understand. Do you agree?"

Hunter patted his shoulder again. Niko had a kind face, and his emotions always felt stronger than what he showed in his expression.

Niko looked at him for a moment before rising to his feet. "Good luck, Hunter Moon."

CHAPTER 2

Hunter could have squealed with excitement as he darted down the hall. The sticky things on the bottom of his socks kept him from sliding around on the floor. He liked sliding, but once he fell and hit the back of his head, so he was more careful now.

Wyatt had a few places he liked to go. When he smoked his funny-smelling cigarettes, he would pace the halls and fall asleep in strange places. He also got forgetful whenever he was in a silly mood. Once he spent an hour trying to find a pair of headphones that were on his head.

Hunter skipped across the foyer and then jogged up the stairs. His daddy had volunteered to search Wyatt's special garden before checking the kitchen. That would keep him busy for a while.

Up, up, up!

Hunter was out of breath by the time he reached the second floor. He zigzagged down the main hallway that led to Spooky's office, trying to hide in the dark spots along the wall.

This is so much fun!

He peered inside the office and saw a huge mess of papers littered on the floor.

"I looked three times." Wyatt laced his fingers on top of his head. "Unless it grew legs, it's not in here."

Blue tied up her long pretty hair. She had on a white shirt without sleeves that showed her scars. Hunter used to feel bad about the scar on his face until he moved here. Now he was around so many cool people with scars that it seemed normal.

"Well, before I start digging through your dirty underwear, we're checking this room one more time. This is where you keep all your shit." She lifted up one of the beanbag chairs and looked beneath it. "Start on that side of the room. Look in the couch cushions. And I mean pull them all out. After that, you'll need to drag the couch away from the wall and look underneath. It's probably long overdue for a cleaning anyhow."

He crossed the room. "Sure. Leave all the heavy stuff to me."

Blue stacked a beanbag on top of another. "File a complaint."

Turning away, Hunter steered his gaze to the floor. Sometimes things fell out of people's pockets and got kicked around. He opened the door next to Wyatt's office and entered a room with a large table. After turning on the light, he searched all the chairs and on the floor.

Nothing but a dust bunny and a pen.

He shut the door and ambled down the hall. Hunter scanned the floor where it met with the walls, and at each locked door he would stick his fingers beneath the crack to feel around. When he reached the last door, he frowned.

Where could you be, little flash drive?

Hunter spun on his heel and veered right. He stared at his middle finger, trying to imagine the size. What did it look like? Was it round like a straw? Square like a brick? Did it flash like his lighted sneakers? Maybe it had wheels like a car. Flash drive could mean it flashed like a police car.

"I wager you're supposed to be in bed."

Hunter glanced up at the very tall Mr. Claude. He wasn't Claudie right now—not with that serious look on his face.

Claude had nice hair that was kind of long but it curled up. Hunter's hair just twisted in all different directions, and Claude said it was because he was related to Peter Pan. He could be silly sometimes, but not now. Not with his hands on his hips.

Hunter stood very still.

Claude knelt down, and his nostrils twitched. "It's late, little one. What adventures are you up to at this hour?"

Hunter shrugged a little. Even kneeling, Claude was so very tall. Like a skyscraper with feet. Sometimes it hurt to tilt his neck back and look up at him.

"Should I carry you back to your room?"

Hunter adamantly shook his head. Not now. Not while it was just starting to get fun. Hunter didn't know the sign for flash drive, but he wanted to tell Claude what he was doing. So he showed Claude his middle finger.

Claude belted out a laugh. "I'll take that as a no. You slay me." He pinched his nose before standing up. "I'm looking for something. Care to join me?"

Hunter nodded excitedly.

Claude narrowed his eyes. "Ah. So you know what's going on. Well, in that case, let's check out the game room."

Hunter tugged on the back of Claude's shirt. Then he used his fingers to make a running motion—a really fast one. Not everyone in the house had picked up the words he used with his hands, but he signed "carry" anyhow, just in case Claude might understand.

The nice Chitah frowned. "Are you asking me to run with you on my back?" He pinched his chin. "That might be dangerous."

Realizing he understood, Hunter practically tore the back of Claude's shirt until the neckline strangled him.

"You're gonna choke me doing that. Okay, but don't tell your dad. I'll get in big trouble." He bent forward and looked Hunter straight in the eyes. "Promise?"

Hunter was mesmerized by his golden eyes, but they were scary to look right into. It made Hunter shiver all over, so he nodded quickly before walking behind Claude and hopping onto his back.

Claude stood, holding Hunter's legs against his sides while Hunter got a strong grip around Claude's neck.

"I want you to hold on tight," he said, hunching down just a little bit. "This will be fast, so don't let go."

Hunter felt dizzy with excitement. The back hall was dark except for ambient light from connecting hallways. As soon as Claude sprinted forward, Hunter squeaked like a mouse.

They flew like the wind! Claude's feet pounded against the floor like a windup toy, and the walls blurred. Hunter felt like a bird soaring through the sky and wanted to reach out with his arms, but he knew better.

When they reached the end and stopped, Hunter gasped for breath. Claude set him down on his feet, but Hunter teetered when it felt like they were still running.

"All right, little one. We've got work to do."

Hunter waved goodbye, deciding he wanted to search all by himself. Heart still pounding, he left Claude and made his way in the opposite direction in search of the library where Wyatt sometimes liked to sleep. When he approached the open doorway, he noticed a lantern flickering inside the room. Kira was probably still walking the halls, lighting candles as she usually did late at night. Sometimes she caught Hunter wandering and would shoo him back to bed. She didn't talk much either, but Hunter really liked her a lot. Kira was serious like his daddy, but she made time for him. She even let him help her work, but that was okay. He liked being helpful.

After a brief stroll, the soft glow of lights drew him to the end of a hallway. He poked his head through the open door and gawked at Gem's room. It was magical—all the colorful fabrics covering the walls and glittering lights that made him want to snuggle up in there forever.

Hunter wasted no time checking out the awesome rock collection by the windows. Tiny white lights were strung around the walls and windows like fireflies. A candle flickered in a blue jar on the shelf, and all the lights sparkled against the pretty rocks. Hunter knew he'd get in trouble for touching them, but he couldn't resist lifting the big one. Maybe someday he'd be strong like his daddy and could lift heavy things without his arms shaking. He gently put it back on the shelf.

"Jiminy Christmas! What are you doing in here?"

Hunter jumped at the sound of Gem's voice.

She entered the room, her purple skirt shimmering. It almost matched her colorful hair. "It's past your bedtime. Were you looking for your daddy?"

He shook his head.

Gem neared the shelf and ran her slender fingers over a big pointy rock that looked like glass. "Aren't they beautiful? These rocks are older than any of us. They've been around for a long time." She picked up a round dirty-looking one. Gem was closer to his height, so Hunter didn't feel so small around her. She let him touch the bumpy stone. "The earth made this a long time ago. Some of them are thousands of years old, and some are millions. When there's a pocket of air in a rock, it makes a geode. It's kind of ugly-looking, isn't it?"

He smiled.

"Can you lift off the top? It's a little heavy, so be careful."

Hunter gripped the top of the rock with his fingers curling into the edge and carefully lifted it up. When he did, his eyes filled with amazement. Purple crystals sparkled inside the rock, glittering like the makeup Gem sometimes wore on her eyelids. When he turned his stone over, he saw more tiny crystals.

"Behold! It's like magic, isn't it? I love all kinds of stones, but crystals are my favorite. You wouldn't know to look at that ugly rock how pretty it really is."

He stared at the purple stones. Every time he moved his hand just a little bit, it sparkled like the mirrored silver ball at the roller-skating rink that Gem had once taken him to. Once he got a long look, he carefully put the top back on so Gem could set it on her shelf.

She patted it. "I like to imagine how lonely he was for all those years until someone found him and took the time to see what was on the inside. And now he's here, where someone can love and admire him."

Gem picked up a small blue stone and handed it to him. "This is a blue apatite. Every stone has energy. If you're ever feeling blue, just hold it in your hand and try to feel all the good energy. That's why I wear this one around my neck." She showed him her long crystal. "That one's yours, if you want it. You can come look at my rocks anytime, just don't pick any of them up. If they break, they can't be fixed. We can't go around breaking the things we love."

Hunter was used to rules. He grew up with lots of them. But these made sense to him. He sure didn't want to break any of the pretty stones. Then he wouldn't be able to come and look at them, and Gem would be sad.

"You should be in bed," she said, leading him to the door. "I think maybe Shepherd—"

Before she could finish her sentence, Hunter ran like the wind. Not as fast as Claude, but he turned the corner like a race car driver and jogged upstairs. Then he slowed down, remembering to look for the mysterious red flash drive.

A beam of light streaked over the ceiling and then back down. Hunter tiptoed behind Raven as she plodded down the hall, twirling the flashlight in her hand. Her yawn was so loud it made him giggle.

Raven spun around and blinded him with the light. "You scared the heck out of me, kiddo."

Hunter's lips thinned as he waited for her to bring up how he should be in bed. Grown-ups spent an awful lot of time pointing out what he was supposed to be doing when they weren't doing it themselves. They stayed up all hours, ate when they wanted to, slept when they wanted to. Sometimes they got up on the roof.

Hunter couldn't wait to grow up. He was going to stay up all night long and eat nothing but pizza and mint chocolate ice cream.

She shined her light behind him and looked around. "I could use some help. Wanna hold the flashlight?"

He eagerly took it from her and led the way, brightening the dark path ahead of them. Hunter suddenly felt like a protector, and if a bad man jumped out of the shadows, he might hit him with the flashlight and save Raven. He didn't spend a whole lot of time with her, but he sure liked the way she talked to people. She didn't seem scared of anyone.

"I guess I'm behind on ASL because of my trip. Is that what you call the sign language Switch is teaching?" she asked. "Why don't you teach me a new word?"

Hunter was learning lots of words, but he hadn't figured out how to make full sentences. He could put some words together, but Switch told him it would take time and he might need help from an expert in the future. It didn't seem that hard, but he was frustrated with all the thoughts in his head that he couldn't get out.

Switch had asked him what words he wanted to learn, and Hunter asked for a sign for each of the Breeds. Switch didn't know all of them —said that some Breeds didn't have words in sign language so they would have to spell them out or make one up. But Vampire was pretty easy to learn.

Hunter tapped two fingers shaped like a *V* against his neck.

Raven studied him for a minute as they walked. "I think I know what that means," she said, trying to hide her smile. "I'll have to show that one to Christian. So I bet you're wondering what I'm doing walking around with a flashlight. I'm looking for a little gizmo that belongs to Wyatt. It's a red plastic thing about this big," she said, holding her fingers a distance apart.

Hunter showed her his middle finger to correct the size.

Raven chortled. "You really take after your father."

They entered a room Hunter had never seen before. He shined the light on a giant couch in the middle that was shaped like a big square bed. The wall around the door was painted black with bright yellow dots and colorful ghosts. A round yellow thing that looked like a face with its mouth open was eating one of the dots. He swung the light to a bookshelf filled with cats and scary monsters.

"This is Wyatt's room." Raven tossed pillows from the couch onto the floor. "I won't tell if you accidentally break all those hideous gargoyles on the shelf." She grunted while shoving her hand between the cushions. "This is gonna take forever. I don't think I can stay awake for another hour. This wasn't in the brochure."

Hunter didn't want to break anything, even the ugly monsters. So he played detective and investigated all the places where Wyatt might have put a flash drive. He sure had a strange room. Messy. Junk everywhere. Empty chip bags, socks on the floor, and a bowl filled with coins. It made Hunter think of the quarter his daddy had once given him to ride a mechanical horse. Hunter still had that quarter and would never ever give it away. It made him remember how nice his daddy was even before he loved him.

"Can I see the flashlight?" Raven reached out, and he handed it to her. She got down on her knees and put her head against the floor, the light shining beneath the sofa. "I swear that man needs a babysitter. All I wanted to do was get off the plane and go to bed. I haven't slept in five days. I couldn't even sleep on the plane because of some lunatic who was yelling at the flight attendants."

While she kept talking to herself, Hunter decided to look elsewhere. Sometimes grown-ups looked for things in all the wrong places. Usually Hunter put something down when he got distracted, and grown-ups were the same way but they didn't have such a great memory. They would set things down on purpose and forget all about it.

The rock from Gem bounced around in his pocket as he hurried down the dark hallway. Shadows moved at night and threatened to chase after him if he didn't run fast enough. But he knew nothing would hurt him. Not here. This was the safe place, and that made him feel brave.

Shadows slithered across the arched ceiling as he headed toward the central stairs. When he first moved to Keystone, the house felt like a maze that would swallow him up. But each time he explored, every corner and every window became more and more familiar. A lot of the rooms remained locked, but he knew his way around better than anyone.

I have to find it. I just have to! If I don't and they catch me, I'll get in trouble. Then they won't know how hard I tried, and I won't get to go on the field trip.

Hunter's inside voice was loud, and he used it with confidence. No one could hear it but him, but that inside voice helped him think better and gave him direction.

When he reached the wide stairs, he checked every step on his way down since all the lanterns were lit on the wall around the curve. People sat on the steps all the time and sometimes set things down. Hunter enjoyed sitting on the wide landing and letting marbles tumble to the bottom, one at a time. He liked the clicking sound they made, especially when there were a whole bunch of them.

Having to turn around and look at the step behind him became tiresome, so Hunter started walking backward so he could inspect each step, one at a time. Another step. One more step...

Hunter missed his footing and flew backward.

Strong hands caught him, and he stared up at black eyes gazing down from above. Christian's face was upside down, and Hunter noticed all the whiskers growing underneath his chin and neck.

"Be a good lad and don't crack your skull." Christian lifted him and set him down on the ground floor. "Helping your da, are we?" He gave him another wink. "Aye. Your secret is safe with me. Just remember you're a wee lad, so watch your step."

Hunter thought about the rock in Gem's room and how she said it couldn't be fixed if it broke. That wasn't entirely true when it came to people. His daddy was kind of a doctor, and Christian could do magic.

One time Hunter skinned his knee real bad when he jumped out of a tree and landed on the concrete pathway in the courtyard. Niko touched his knee, and after a warm jolt, the pain vanished! When they washed off the blood, there wasn't even a scratch. Hunter never told his daddy about that. He was afraid if he did, he wouldn't be allowed to climb trees anymore.

Hunter smiled at the Vampire, deciding to heed his advice.

Christian chuckled darkly before pulling a peppermint from his pocket. He tossed it to Hunter, who caught it like a professional baseball player.

Hunter stuffed the candy in his pajama bottom pocket and bolted toward the dining room, leaving Christian behind.

The kitchen had bright overhead lights, so as soon as he walked in, he reached up for the switch. But when his finger grazed the panel, he worried his father might see the light and catch him. Wyatt spent a lot of time in the kitchen, and sometimes he demonstrated to Hunter how to make weird snacks. Like the time he drizzled chocolate on his onion rings. Or another time they made ice cream with pretzels, but Hunter really liked that experiment.

Hunter opened up the fridge and took out a juice bottle. After removing the cap, he gulped down several swallows and gasped for air. Juice always tasted better late at night after an adventure. He put the cap back on and left the fridge door open so he could see. Hunter opened the pantry door and then pulled out a step stool from beneath the shelf. Kira sometimes used it to reach things way up high. He stepped up and searched all the shelves he could reach. Kira didn't like a lot of snacks that came in packages. She always gave Hunter treats like apples or grapes. Wyatt had a snack machine upstairs, but he also kept a few larger bags down here. They were actually for everyone, so they were in a separate spot from all the regular food. Hunter felt along the shelves, behind the bags and on top of cans. After completing his search, he shut the door and folded his arms.

It was time to put on his thinking cap. That was the expression he heard the others use sometimes when they had to get serious. It couldn't be on any of the countertops or Kira would have seen it when she was cooking that yummy lasagna. Hunter snorted at the idea of it being in the oven. Maybe Viktor's wolf got really hungry and gobbled it up. Or maybe it got sucked down the drain and washed away to the ocean.

Hunter noticed the deep freezer across the room. He scurried toward it and carefully pushed open the heavy lid. It didn't have a light, so he couldn't see very well. Some of the light from the nearby fridge helped but not much. He hoisted himself onto the edge and teetered for a minute before resting his hands on cold bags of peas and meat. Wyatt was always reaching on the bottom right, so that must be where he kept all his french fries. Still, Hunter couldn't see the pictures on the bags in the corner.

Especially when the lid slammed down against his butt.

Oww, he thought, more annoyed than hurt. *Stupid door.*

He kept feeling around, his little fingers numb as he tossed one of the bags over to the left. One ripped open, and he heard tiny objects spill out everywhere like his marbles tumbling down the stairs. Determined, he kept searching. His fingers touched the cold, smooth edge of the freezer while he hung upside down. Just beneath another bag, he felt a hard object that didn't seem to belong. Hunter wrapped his fingers around it, his muscles trembling as the freezer edge dug into his belly.

He was about to collapse inside the frosty compartment when the door suddenly flung open and someone gripped the back of his shirt, yanking him up. Smoky air poured out of the freezer and trailed his movement.

His daddy gave him a stern look with those dark brown eyes. "I thought we had an agreement. And here I find you getting your ass locked in a freezer. What if that door had slammed shut and you couldn't get it open? I thought you were in bed. I wouldn't have heard you screaming." He put his hand over his face, which was turning red.

Hunter had learned things about his father. Sometimes when he got a mean face, he wasn't actually mad. It was fear, and Hunter only knew that when he touched his hand.

Like now.

Hunter gripped Shepherd's pointing finger and let him know through touch that he was okay. And he was sorry. And all the things he couldn't say in words that his father somehow understood. He just wanted his daddy to be proud of him, but sometimes he couldn't help doing things he wasn't supposed to do. Like sneaking out.

After a minute, Shepherd knelt down in front of him and wiped some of the ice out of his tousled hair. "If you get hungry at night, I can put snacks in your room. Get you a tiny little refrigerator with drinks. I know that's probably not how other people raise their kids, but we're not like other people. It's a long walk to the kitchen, so maybe it's not fair that you can't get a midnight snack without it becoming a fiasco." His gaze flicked down. "What's that in your hand?"

Hunter wasn't sure yet. He held it out and splayed his fingers, revealing a red plastic thingamajig.

All of a sudden, he got scared.

He'll think I stole it. But I didn't steal it! I don't know how to make the word for steal. Now they'll think I was hiding it all along. No field trip. No more hugs. I'll have to give the special rock back to Gem. I was just trying to help.

Shepherd picked up the plastic rectangle and looked at it closely. "I'll be damned. You found the flash drive. We've been looking all over for this. Where did you find it?"

He believes me!

Elated, Hunter tapped his hand on the freezer lid. He puffed out his chest and widened his smile.

His daddy chuckled and shook his head. "One of these days, Spooks is gonna lose his brain in there. Let me guess—by the fries, right?"

Hunter nodded, smiling back as if they shared a funny secret. Spooky could be so crazy with all his snacking.

And he left it in the freezer of all places! So silly.

Shepherd stood up, still looking at the flash drive. "There's a lot of important stuff on here. You found this all by yourself?"

Hunter made sure to nod slowly so his daddy would know it wasn't by accident. He signed the words for "I look." Someday he would learn more words and he would be able to tell the full story, but for now it seemed like enough.

"I'm proud of you even though you disobeyed me. I guess I know where you get that from." Shepherd stared at him for a long moment and got that sad look in his eyes. "You're a bright kid. Sometimes I can't believe you're mine. But I think I can guess who you get all those smarts from. Someday I'll tell you all about her." Shepherd tucked the little plastic thing in his pocket before lifting Hunter off the ground. Hunter put his hands on his shoulder, always amazed at how tough his daddy was. Nobody could ever hurt him. He was the strongest and most bravest man in the world, and Hunter wanted to grow up to be just like him.

A hero.

He cupped his hands on his daddy's face. Shepherd didn't smile much with his mouth but he did with his eyes. Like now. Hunter used his thumbs to force a smile on his daddy's face, and it made him giggle.

"Tell you what, little man. I know tomorrow you're doing that field trip thing, but do you think Switch would let me come too? Work can wait. Maybe afterward, we can grab some hot dogs and practice talking without words. But only if you want me to go."

Hunter nodded excitedly. Switch would do almost anything asked of him. This was so much better! Hunter wouldn't have to come home and wonder how to tell his father about all the amazing things he saw. He wouldn't have to draw pictures to show him. They could share the memory.

Together.

BONUS SHORT STORY 2

A BLEAK DECEMBER

A CROSSBREED SERIES SHORT STORY

CHAPTER 1

Cognito, 1935

Christian rubbed his smooth jaw as he studied the crowded room. A bevy of young, aristocratic lasses eagerly surveyed the party in search of men worth their time. Masquerade balls had fallen out of fashion in recent years—until this season. In the midst of the Great Depression, dressing like Hollywood starlets was all the rage. Immortals had hardly suffered any financial loss, and many were scooping up businesses and homes, turning human districts into Breed ones.

Most of the men in the room had skinny mustaches and enough pomade in their hair to grease a wheel. Women styled their short hair in waves or curls. They powdered their faces and wore dark lipstick, which was left behind on glasses and napkins. Some had masks secured around their heads while others held them up to their eyes with a slender stick. Christian wore a black one that only framed his eyes.

The live band in a nearby room played lively music that filled the halls of the mansion. He wasn't even sure whose place this was. After a while, all the parties ran together. Christian leaned against the wall and watched two men light up their Chesterfield cigarettes while blathering about real estate.

"Christian Poe. How the hell are you, man?"

He met eyes with the numpty in a top hat who made a point to tell bad jokes at every party and slap everyone on the back. Tom was an alcoholic with a penchant for beautiful women. He wasn't much to look at with his splotchy complexion and pug nose, but he had enough money that everyone overlooked his obnoxious personality.

Christian inclined his head. "Grand. I see you're not partaking in the mask wearing."

Tom chuckled and clapped his shoulder. "I'm not a fan. I like people to see who they're talking to. I spotted you holding up the wall over here. Say, where's that dame you're always with?"

Christian bristled. Tom knew full well her name was Lenore Parrish. And if his beady little eyes so much as steered in her direction...

"Never mind that," Tom said. "We've got all night. Why don't we find some booze?"

"I'll pass," Christian said with a mirthless smile.

"An Irishman who turns down a drink. Never thought I'd see the day." He cackled and then grabbed another man's attention. "Elliot Robinson! As I live and breathe. You still carry those good cigars on you?"

Once free of the eejit, Christian took a breath. He normally had a smashing time at these gatherings. Laughter, alcohol, dancing. But tonight something else was on his mind. He held his right hand over the breast of his suit jacket, feeling the lump beneath of an object hidden inside an inner pocket.

A Burmese ruby, to be exact. One he'd purchased at auction three years ago for Lenore, only for her to call his expenditure foolish. He'd promised to get his money back, but that was a lie. Lenore had set her eyes on that necklace and wanted it, so Christian never fully understood why she had rejected his gift. Was it because he'd spent every dime of his money or because he had outbid everyone, including her?

Lenore was a beautiful creature—one no man could attain. Christian understood her as no one else could. Especially during those intimate times when she allowed him to drink her sacred blood. He had sampled her strength and resilience like a fine wine. Lenore was a master at concealing her true feelings. She carried on entire conversations with people she despised, and they would think she adored them. But when her blood crossed his lips, there were moments when he could sense a feeling that came across as ownership. That somehow he belonged to her, and he liked that feeling.

Christian had carried that ruby in his pocket ever since, hoping enough time would pass that she'd appreciate the gift and what it meant. She deserved the best of everything. No one had ever given him as many opportunities as Lenore had.

It was hard to shake the thoughts he had of her. He clasped his hands together, watching the crowd gather in pockets. He was always introduced as her trusted advisor, but tonight was different. She had asked him to accompany her as a companion. That word had rolled around in his noggin for the past twenty-four hours. *Companion.* What did that mean? While they hadn't arrived together, he knew it meant she wouldn't separate from him. Companion implied they would be at each other's side for the whole of the evening.

Christian had changed so much in these past years. He served her the way no other loyal employee ever could. She had taken him under her wing, and in return, he made sure that all her threats were eliminated. Every person in that room was just another face and meant nothing to him if they were Lenore's enemy. And if they were her ally, they would be his as well.

"Chrissy, darling. Why are you hiding yourself away?"

His breath caught as Lenore approached him. Her body shimmered in a strappy gold dress that reached her ankles. Despite its length, it revealed everything. She held a gold fan up to her eyes, shielding her face. Lenore loved her fans and found them a suitable compromise to masks.

She closed her fan and playfully thumped him on the head. "I told you I wouldn't be long. My driver had an errand that took us a little longer than expected. Dear oh dear. Have you been standing here by yourself all evening?"

While her words were innocuous, her eyes were filled with judgment. Lenore knew how to work a room, and she was grooming him to be better in social situations. He struggled because this wasn't his crowd. Christian had grown up poor, and that was the only life he'd ever known. Lenore opened a whole new world to him, but acclimating still took time.

"I fear it's not possible to have a good time without your company," he admitted.

Her radiant smile lit up the room. She clutched his arm and stood beside him as they watched attractive blondes who looked like pinup models handing out champagne. "Has anyone asked about me?"

"I wager you already know about that one," he said, jerking his chin toward Tom.

Lenore made a quiet sound of disapproval that only he could hear. "If that vile man comes anywhere near me—"

"Then I'll take care of him," he finished.

Lenore squeezed his arm and then led him into another room. The crystal chandeliers overhead twinkled. Tonight felt magical and dreamlike. Lenore held his arm as they strolled past some of the most influential immortals in the city. He glanced at her slender neck, bewitched by the way she wore her hair differently than every other woman of their time. Her blond locks were braided into a crown around her head, delicate tendrils floating against her face on either side.

She carried herself like royalty, her back straight and head high. His chest tightened the more she held on. Normally they conversed in groups while Lenore made new connections and he told jokes. He wondered if they would leave together. Would she invite him to her place? Could he be so bold as to invite her to his?

They had never been intimate. Lenore had never promised her

heart to him—only wealth and status. In fact, she had grown distant since that incident with the necklace a few years ago. As a result, he'd worked harder to get back in her good graces and did anything she asked of him.

"How long have we known each other now?" she pondered. "Was it 1917 when we first met?"

"Twenty-one."

"Feels like so much longer," she purred.

Why was she being so affectionate? He couldn't get over her very public display of parading him through the room arm in arm as if they were a couple. Lenore hadn't shown him this much tenderness in a long time. So long that her touch made his fangs elongate. He felt hungry for her, and that hunger kindled a desire in him to protect. Why else would she entrust him with all her secrets? He killed for her like a wild animal kills for its mate.

A tall Chitah cast his gaze on Lenore, his golden eyes sliding up and down the length of her lithe body. Lenore was a seductress. While she didn't have an abundance of curves, she knew how to be provocative without crossing the line. She wasn't low-hanging fruit. Lenore Parrish was the perfect specimen of a woman that even other Breeds coveted.

They finally reached a grand room where the band was playing so loud that he grimaced. The song quickly ended and changed to "Cheek to Cheek."

"Dance with me," she said, turning to face him.

When she clasped her hand in his, he placed his free hand around her waist and she clutched his shoulder. As the singer crooned, "Heaven," Lenore gazed ardently in his eyes. In that moment, he felt her disapproval melt away.

He felt forgiven.

"You look handsome tonight." She leaned in until their cheeks touched. "There's something I want to discuss with you," she whispered.

He adjusted his Vampire hearing so that the music was turned way down. Performing a quick scan, he didn't notice any other Vampires in the immediate vicinity. It wasn't hard to spot their eyes through the masks. In any case, most Vampires avoided the noisiest rooms. Some parties had bans on Vampires, but Lenore was part of that change in society's attitude toward their kind.

His heart pounded when she pressed her body against his. "Aye. What do you desire?"

"You've been alone for a long time, Chrissy. I think it's time that we do something about that."

He closed his eyes, his mask obtrusively in the way. She smelled different tonight—like jasmine.

"And what do you suggest we do?"

"I'm so glad you asked. There's someone I want you to meet."

He jerked his head back as their feet continued to move. "I don't understand."

Her lips quirked. "Sometimes I barely understand your Irish accent. You should consider dropping it. People don't like the Irish, and the accent holds you back."

"They also don't like Vampires, but here we are."

She leaned in close again. "Everything I do is for your own good. You know that. You know that I always have your best interests at heart. Do you think I was born with this silly American accent? No. I've learned that you can be the most talented, the most beautiful, and the most intelligent, but none of it matters if you're an outsider. It always comes back to that one thing."

"Would you rather I speak like an American?" He slipped into a heavy Southern drawl. "Would that make you right happy, little girl?"

Lenore gripped his hand so tight that it stressed his bones. "Don't do that again."

She wasn't a fan of his jokes.

Lenore stepped back and did a twirl before they came back together. "There's an important Mage with influence in this city. She's the one everyone goes to for real estate and loans. She's expressed an interest in matching with a wealthy man, but someone protective who isn't out for himself. She doesn't trust many people, but that's to be expected with notoriety. Together, you two could be a real power-house. It just so happens she's interested in meeting you."

"You can't be serious," he said flatly.

Her lips drew close to his ear, her voice a breath. "I want you to seduce her. Become her partner in every way. This is what you've worked for, and you might not have an opportunity like this again. She has a fetish for Vampires. I think she had a bad experience binding with another Mage, and we're the only other Breed that isn't affected by their light. I could work a little womanly magic as her friend and get inside information on what her heart desires. All you have to do is become that fantasy."

The music suddenly filled his ears like a nightmare, making the room spin. Christian hadn't had a wink of sleep in decades, and yet this felt so much like a fever dream.

He pulled back, and the dancing stopped. "I can't. I won't."

She gripped his arm as he turned away. "You're letting your emotions tell you what to do. What have I said about that?"

Lenore had always warned him that emotions brought every man to ruin. They were the Achilles' heel for immortals. Yet he couldn't dismiss the rejection he felt. In that moment, Christian realized he would never have her.

Not unless...

He reached inside his jacket and pulled out the ruby pendant. It swung at the end of a silver chain as if he were hypnotizing her, and Lenore's black eyes followed it back and forth. She blanched, and before she could say a word, he leaned in and seized the moment.

"You're everything I desire. If I were a mortal, I wouldn't get a wink of sleep thinking about you. I crave your affection. Do you think I could just let go of your heart that easily?"

Lenore leaned close as if to say something but then looked off to the side, aware of the music dying down and the size of the room.

Instead, she took a deep breath and cut through the crowd toward the doorway.

"You insolent fool," she whispered under her breath.

She met eyes with a masked man off to the left. They looked at each other longer than normal, the white-haired man nodding at her as she disappeared around the corner.

Christian ripped off his mask and tossed it to the floor while he followed behind her. He glimpsed her collecting her mink coat before hustling out the front door.

He inclined his head at familiar faces, playing it cool while the tapping of his shoes against the marble floor sounded like a death march. Once outside, he listened for the click of her heels since she was nowhere in sight. Instead of waiting for her personal driver to get the car, Lenore was halfway down the driveway.

Once away from the lights, Christian shadow walked to catch up. Tiny flecks of snow fell from the bleak December sky, but not enough to dust the ground.

"Don't walk away from me," he said, lightly gripping her arm.

She spun around. "Why must you ruin *everything*?"

"Fecking hell. There's nothing I haven't done for you, and you need not ask."

She shook her head. "Crass language bores me. You're better than that."

"Am I?" He cocked his head to the side. "Something tells me I'll never be good enough. But apparently I'm absolute perfection for a random stranger I don't even know."

Her lips pressed tightly, and it made her lovely features less beguiling. "Three years, Christian. Three years and I thought you were over that silly infatuation of turning this into a love match. I knew I shouldn't have fed you so much blood."

"It's not the blood."

Lenore tried in vain to suppress a grin. "It was so easy in the beginning. We had a good time, and I saw potential in you. But you turned your affections into something dark and twisted. I barely recognize you anymore."

"I'll *not* have you blame everything on me."

Her hand slapped over his mouth so fast that it split his lip. "All you had to do tonight was entertain a beautiful woman and you would have had everything I promised you."

Lenore's driver, who had jogged past them, rolled up in her white Rolls-Royce limousine. She lowered her hand and pushed the mink coat into his arms. "Ride with me. We'll talk and iron all this out." She opened the back door.

Christian gave the driver a cursory glance before getting in. The glass divider between the front and back seat hardly offered any privacy. The driver didn't have a roof over his head nor windows on either side. The car was styled like a horse-drawn carriage. When Lenore purchased her first car, he asked why she didn't hire a deaf driver. She didn't seem fazed at all at having private conversations around her chauffeurs. And that's when she admitted to scrubbing their memories of the drive each and every time. Christian couldn't imagine what it was like for a man to willingly accept a job that would turn his memory into a pincushion.

Lenore was sitting beside him on the brown bench seat. They had plenty of legroom, so he stretched his legs as much as he could and folded his arms. The car turned around and bounced over a few holes in the driveway before they merged onto the street.

He didn't care for these infernal contraptions. All of these inventions were happening so quickly, and most of them weren't safe. Not that he could die, but he certainly had no desire to sail through the windshield and land in a tree like so many others had. At least with a motorbike, he could control the speed and direction.

"Won't you at least consider the match?" she pressed. "I promise she isn't unattractive."

"Looks mean nothing," he admitted.

And that was true. While Lenore was stunning, Christian found himself drawn to women with a sharp tongue who looked at him with desire in their eyes, not disdain. It wasn't supple breasts and a firm backside that made his cock harden as much as a tenacious spirit. A confident woman exuded beauty in all forms.

Christian had misread the look in her eyes this evening. It was desire all right, but a desire to move him around a chessboard. He found himself still clutching the pendant in his hand. After tucking it in his breast pocket, he raked his hands through his hair.

"Perhaps I should have discussed it with you earlier, but I wanted you to meet her." Lenore moved the mink coat to her left and scooted closer. She stroked his jaw with her slender fingers. "You missed a spot."

"Perhaps I'll let it grow out."

"Perhaps you will," she said obliquely.

Christian never saw it coming. Lenore reached behind her with her left arm and swung it around so fast that it was a blur. The impalement wood ripped through his chest, the pain instantaneous. It wasn't until her fist met with his chest that he realized what was happening.

Lenore had staked him.

CHAPTER 2

Christian's head fell back, and he slumped down the seat. The agony! Not the worst injury he'd ever sustained, but other injuries always healed. The impalement wood was trapped inside his body like an unwelcome invader. All he could do was sit there and endure the unrelenting pain that gripped him with every bump in the road. Somehow it had missed his heart, but the wheezing in his chest told him that blood was filling up a lung. He would eventually stop leaking internally, but not soon enough.

Lenore's voice was muffled and distant. Christian focused hard on blocking out the pain, enduring it. He had practiced many times inflicting pain on himself, leaving daggers in his leg for lengths of time.

Lenore had buried the weapon deep. Even if he fell over, there was no chance of knocking it out. The stake wasn't big around. Impalement wood only needed to be strong enough to pierce skin and potentially move past bone. He wondered if it was an arrow since the wood seemed narrow and pale.

Her voice finally came in crystal clear. "You had too many unrealistic expectations. Emotions cloud judgment, and this will not do." She slid open the glass divider. "Take us to the old cemetery north of Township Road."

The glass slid closed again, but Christian could only see the ceiling above. Even in the back of a dark car, absent of any light but the ambient glow of the headlights, he noticed a tiny stain that looked like blood. Was it his or someone else's?

Lenore turned toward him and rested her palm on his chest. "Don't worry, Chrissy. I don't believe in murder. But you already know that."

Of course you don't believe in murder. You just have other people do it for you.

It was the longest ride of his life. He felt every bump, and Lenore merely held him up so he didn't fall onto the floor. She didn't say another word—just gave a few disapproving sighs.

Had she planned this all along? Was this a consequence of refusing her suggested match? Or was it an impulsive decision because of the necklace?

No, Lenore had never struck him as impulsive. She was quite meticulous. He had never seen her as angry as she was when he bought that necklace. He could only surmise that she'd decided if he ever crossed the line again, she would do away with him.

The car slowed down, and his heart hammered against his chest when the driver got out. Lenore was strong enough to carry him, but she had the driver do it. Christian's view was an upside-down graveyard. They passed tombstones and decrepit bushes that had rotted away. Christian liked to sit in cemeteries. It was the only quiet place he could relax and get away from the noise of the city. But he had never been to this one. It was ancient—filled with headstones, tombs, and broken pathways. Dead vines gripped statues like varicose veins.

"Set him down here," Lenore instructed her driver.

Christian's body straightened when he felt the tall grass cushioning his back. Lenore gave her driver a look, and he strolled out of sight.

She gathered up the bottom of her sparkling gown and lifted it a little before kneeling at his feet. While stroking his face, she gave him a pitying stare. As if she'd found a suffering animal on the side of the road.

As if she had a heart.

"You should have never held on to the notion that we could be a match. You have to think with your head and not with your heart. Love is a weakness, and it's not in our nature to be weak. That's why you're here. The only way to survive in this world is to be rid of those juvenile emotions. A good match works. I'm not in a position where I'm ready to pair off with someone, but you are. This could have been a big move for us."

Christian wondered how the hell it would benefit him to marry a woman he didn't love. All because she sold real estate? Money didn't interest him, and he didn't see how that situation would make his life any better.

Lenore glanced up and sighed. "You couldn't even pretend to be contrite. Why on earth do you think a woman could love you? Respect and admire? Certainly. But only once you attain wealth and social status. Love is an unrealistic expectation for a man like you, Christian. You're uncouth, and your deadpan humor is atrocious. I've warned you repeatedly about speaking your mind; that'll get you nowhere. Sometimes I forget how young you really are. Emotions are for humans. You foolishly believe what you feel is love."

She chuckled and stared down at him. "Look where that got you. I've been around long enough to know how to play the game. That's why I'll never be in your shoes. You must be wondering when the sword will appear. I'm not a killer. You are. So burying you is my only option." Lenore looked off to the side. "I'd rather be burned a thousand times than be shut away in a coffin. But no matter. Think of it as a gift."

All he could think about was the stake in his chest and how close it was to the heart in his pocket. As always, Lenore was right. Was it love that he felt for her or infatuation?

Obsession was a better word.

While none of it mattered now, who was she to tell him that what he'd felt wasn't real?

Lenore swept a lock of his hair back. "It's your own fault you're in this predicament. If you still have that necklace, it means you're still broke. What kind of match is that for a woman if you can't even afford a car? I spent weeks building you up in her mind. Do you realize what it would have done to my reputation if she'd found out you were a fraud? That you had no fortune and were pining over me?" Lenore slapped him. "After everything I've done for you."

His heart clenched.

Lenore touched the tip of the stake, and her tone changed. "Now I have to contrive a story, and I can't even tell her you're dead since you might find your way out of here someday. Such a mess."

Christian had somehow adjusted to the pain in his chest. As long as he remained still, it became an afterthought compared to the pain of betrayal. The things he wanted to say—the things he wanted to ask.

Why does it have to be this way? Can't you let me go? I've done everything for you. I've slain your enemies and buried your secrets. I've given you everything I have, and all you've given in return is a place in a coffin. Do you feel nothing for me? Surely you must. You hired me. You mentored me. You fed me that ancient blood that still courses in my veins. And yet there you stand like an executioner. For what? Because I refused to mate with another woman? Because I dared to give you my heart? Because I don't have enough money? Is that it?

The open grave was already waiting for him, so it had to be because of his refusal of the Mage. Or maybe she'd always had a box waiting for him, just in case.

She searched his eyes. "For all your faults, you were the most loyal. You must desperately want to air your grievances. Do you not see the position you put me in? Rejection makes a man bitter, so what's to stop you from betraying me? We won't be able to resolve this, and I can't spend every day looking over my shoulder. None of the deeds you did were my doing. That was all you, Chrissy."

Lenore had always pitched ideas to him about perceived enemies. Even though he couldn't understand why anyone would seek to ruin her, the threat festered in his mind. Some of her targets were people she had private business dealings with, but what about the downtrodden ones? Never once had he questioned her. Lenore's fear and worry was enough. She did so many good things for others, and yet there were those who didn't respect her either because she was a woman or a Vampire. Her charitable contributions weren't enough, and like Tom at the party, there were those who just saw her as something to conquer.

She had always introduced him to others as her trusted advisor, and that made him feel valued and important. But it had been a façade. As he lay there on the grass, staring up at her lovely face and golden hair, he realized he was nothing more than a pawn. Maybe a knight, at best.

"You never set goals," she went on. "You didn't put in the bare minimum to improve yourself or else you wouldn't have foolishly kept that necklace. I thought maybe there was a chance, but now I can see it was all for naught. You only ever put in half the effort." She brushed her fingers over the small patch of whiskers on his neck, attempting to drive home her point.

Lenore leaned in close, and for a moment, he thought she would kiss him. Instead, she pressed her cheek against his, just as she'd done on the dance floor while that song played.

"No hard feelings?" she asked in a whispered voice. "I suppose this is goodbye. In the end, I think you'll realize that I had no choice."

Jasmine filled his nose, clouding his thoughts. It had been such a perfect evening, and there was no going back. No talking it out. Her silky tendrils of hair tickled his forehead before she pulled away and stood. Lenore didn't speak another word to him. She simply vanished out of his life as if she'd never existed.

The driver struggled to lift him up. He was strong but not a Vampire. Lenore trusted few Breeds, and while they never spoke about it, Christian suspected this guy was a human who probably assumed she would one day turn him if he was loyal enough. The man paused for a moment before letting go.

Christian became weightless.

A second later, his back and head slammed against wood. The driver stood at the edge of the shallow grave and looked in. Christian could tell he wasn't six feet under, but that hardly mattered. With the impalement wood, he wasn't going anywhere. The man lowered a shovel and stabbed at Christian's arm a few times until it flipped inside the coffin.

Hardly a coffin. He felt like a matchstick in a wooden box. She couldn't even spring for a nice one with padding. The smell of pine replaced the jasmine.

Lenore's driver slanted the lid inside and carefully let go until it clapped shut. Christian stared at the darkness, but even in the pitch black he could see the grain in the wood. It creaked when the man eased himself into the hole and started nailing the edges shut. Each hammered nail felt like it was driving into his heart, and rage consumed him. Not fear. Not even regret or sadness for his slow demise.

Just pure, unhinged fury.

This was how it would end? Not in battle, not while performing a heroic act. Not even in a freak accident by flying through a car windshield and having his head severed. No, it was at the hands of a woman he'd devoted his life to. A woman who had cradled his neck while he tasted her blood, who made promises that they would be the most powerful people in the city one day. A woman who made him feel like he could be someone. Every choice he'd made was his own, including the decision to dream that she could one day look at him with admiration and love.

Clumps of mud and dirt loudly shook the coffin as the driver began covering up Lenore's mistake.

Love. He scoffed in his mind. *I'll never make that mistake again.*

If I ever get out of here.

As time passed, the air grew hot and thick. Lenore's words repeated in his head like a curse. No woman could ever love him. He didn't make an effort to improve himself. He spoke his mind too freely.

But what nestled in his thoughts were all the people he'd slain. In that dark coffin, their screams turned into laughter. He was a monster. In the end, Lenore couldn't appreciate all he had done for her. Why? Because he wasn't good enough. Aye, she could trust him. But what improvements had he shown in the past decade? He hadn't made enough personal connections, and he'd certainly put no effort into rebuilding his meager fortune. His feelings for Lenore were mixing like oil and water—his soul was divided as if an axe had split him in half. Part of him still wanted to be a worthy man, but the other half was dark and wicked, yearning for revenge.

He'd never done so much self-reflecting in all his life. What purpose did his life serve? What would his family have thought of the man he'd become? His brothers had all gone their separate ways, probably taken wives and bought land in some distant part of the country where they had talked about traveling. They were old men by now, and when they died, they would be surrounded by those they loved.

Christian would waste away for centuries with his thoughts until nothing remained but bones. How would he survive that long? It had only been a few hours and all he could fantasize about was pounding his fists against the wood and screaming for mercy.

This is what demons deserve.

When the oxygen ran out, Christian made a silent vow that if he were ever freed, he would do something valuable with his life. What that was, he didn't know. But he sure as shite would never make the same mistakes again.

CHAPTER 3

Ten years later

Christian floated in a sea of infinite darkness, the tides of time lapping at his thoughts, returning memories to shore like messages in a bottle. Occasionally he forgot who he was, so he made an effort in the darkness to remember his life. Every conversation, every joke, every kiss, every deed, every mistake. He missed the company of women.

Jaysus, did he miss them.

He fantasized about finding a lass and making her cry out with need. But the darkness was lonely, so he often filled those fantasies with people watching them.

He missed people. For all their frivolities and insufferable traits, there was comfort in the company of others. He had imaginary conversations to pass the time, and he remembered as many interactions as he could from his life. The world was alive and spinning all above him while he simply existed in silence. He couldn't even whistle or hum.

Christian often wondered about the passage of time.

How long have I been in here? A year? Five years? What will a century feel like? Perhaps I never existed.

What changes had transpired above? To stave off madness, Christian played imaginary games. He recalled as many animal facts as he could. They were the smarter species on the planet. Hunt and be hunted. So simple. Mortals and immortals alike played far too many games. He wished he had ventured to places like Africa to witness all the beauty he'd only read about in books. The world was vast and filled with wonders—none of which he'd ever see.

What he wouldn't give for a sweet. There was no oxygen to fill his lungs, but he could still detect smells. The odors enveloping him were unthinkable. Not decay so much as the stench of neglect and rotting wood. A soothing rhythm filled his mind, growing louder and louder until it shook the walls around him.

Shook him right awake. His weak heart, which had never stopped beating, fluttered for a moment when something hard struck the wood, cracking it in the middle.

"Son of a ghost!" he heard a man exclaim. "That hurt my shoulder."

The scraping and shoveling continued as boots walked over his grave. The wood squeaked when someone tried to pry open the lid.

"I can't get it open. There's not enough room," the man complained.

"Step to the side." That voice was different. Deeper and slightly more distant.

"Last time I did that, I got my foot wedged in the mud. No, thanks. Toss down the rope. I'll tie it on the handles, and we'll hoist it up. I want extra for this. Manual labor isn't in my repertoire."

Another voice grumbled obscenities.

Was he dreaming? Had he finally reached a new stage in hallucination? Christian often wondered if he even existed. Maybe his whole life had been nothing but a dream within a dream.

The walls around him rattled each time someone shouted, "Lift!"

Christian suddenly rolled to the right when something split.

"Don't let go!" the first man shouted. "Lift!"

Christian was on his back again after it felt like they were dragging around his coffin. Something else occurred to him: he could breathe. He hadn't taken a breath in a long time, and as a result, his chest tightened as if a giant were sitting on it. After a while, he had blocked out the pain. Other times it was a comfort—a reminder that he was alive and not just a stream of consciousness. Now his chest expanded, and he sputtered a few involuntary coughs. Blood rushed to his head, making him dizzy.

The wood creaked from both sides, and moments later, the lid flew away. Cool night air touched his skin, and for the first time in longer than he could remember, he could breathe in fresh air.

Sweet relief.

One man covered his nose and stepped back.

A second on his right leaned down for a closer look. "That's not him."

The third fella on the left furrowed his brow. He had a newsboy hat on top of his wavy brown hair, and his olive-green eyes zeroed in on Christian. "What do you mean, that's not him?"

"I mean it's not him," the other man fired back.

Newsboy Hat Guy wiped his muddy hands. "You *specifically* said your brother was buried in *this* cemetery. This is the only living soul I picked up. This is it. Look closer beneath all that beard."

"I don't appreciate your tone, Gravewalker. I'm only paying for you to find my brother. If you can't find him, I'm not paying for this."

Newsboy threw up his hands. "This is *exactly* why I hate this job. I don't get any respect from fleshwalkers like you."

The man on the right pointed his finger. "I'll make sure this is the end of your career if you keep flapping those gums, Mr. Blessing. I took a chance on you because of your rates, but now I see you get what you pay for."

Newsboy made a raspberry sound, and with that, the other two men stalked off.

After kicking a clump of mud, the young man stared down at Christian, hands on his hips. "So how long have you been lying around in that eternity box?" He worried his lip, a tuft of hair on his chin. "My mother warned me about setting free an unclaimed Vampire. No one can vouch for you, and I don't know what the blazes you did to get in there. On the other hand, I once met a fellow who said if you free an unclaimed person, it's good luck—that your lives intersected for a reason. He also said it's a great way to collect favors, and it just so happens I'm short on dough."

Does this gobshite ever put a cork in it? Of all the people to find me...

The man reached down and searched Christian's trouser pockets. He tossed aside a folding comb before locating the billfold. When he opened it, he pinched a decayed bill between his fingers. "I can't read the year. Doesn't matter. That all you got?" The money floated onto Christian's chest. "Swell. I dig up the poorest man in Cognito. You're probably in cahoots with the Emerson brothers who sold all that bad moonshine. They went missing last spring, you know. So did a lot of their distributors. That's what they get for spiking alcohol with bad sensory magic." He dropped the billfold into Christian's coffin.

Christian couldn't even remember what he'd put in his wallet, but it was usually just a few bills for tipping.

The man canted his head. "Nice suit. That party must have been a gas." He adjusted his hat. "There's an unwritten code that we have to return unclaimed souls. But I could use a little padding in my pocket, if you catch my drift. I got diddly-squat on this job, so what if we cut a deal?"

Christian blinked.

The man narrowed his eyes. "Is that a yes? Because if you flip your wig when I pull that stake out, I'll make sure you're sorry. Agreed?"

Christian blinked again. Blinking was mostly involuntary, but it was the one small thing he could control.

The man knelt. "Wyatt Blessing, at your service. Remember that name and be sure to throw some business my way, will you? I just moved here, and I need work. It's tough starting over in a new city, and everyone here has connections. I can do the same work but cheaper. This isn't exactly my dream job, but it pays the bills." He gripped his hands around the stake. "Remember your promise. Blinks count. One... Two—"

He yanked out the stake before he hit three.

Christian felt the wound slowly sealing, but not fast enough. He curled his fingers in, and the bones creaked from years of inactivity.

Wyatt peered over the coffin. "What's your name?"

"Christian Poe," he croaked. His last name came out in a whisper. His throat was so dry.

Wyatt tipped his hat. "You're lucky I found you out here. The road's blocked off, and they don't allow visitors here no more. Private cemetery. We had to sneak in."

Christian was still trying to process all the smells and sounds. He hadn't heard crickets in forever. The earth above his coffin had been too thick for him to enjoy the noises of the living world. Sometimes he'd faintly heard a dog howling, but he couldn't be certain if it had just been his imagination.

The man hooked his arm beneath Christian's and helped him sit up. "There ya go. How long have you been in there?"

"What year is it?" Christian rasped before coughing to clear out his lungs.

Wyatt's eyebrows quirked. "Nineteen forty-five."

Jaysus.

He'd been underground for a decade. A whole decade. Glancing down, he saw that his beard had grown obscenely long. While his nails were also long, they hadn't grown to the length he would expect. Perhaps at some point, the body goes into self-preservation mode and stops getting rid of dead cells. His nice suit was tattered from something eating away at it. Perhaps insects, or time. Heavy rains had soaked through the cracks in the wood, leaving stains on his clothing. He recalled feeling insects crawling on him every so often, but they avoided Vampire blood. It didn't make them immortal since merely drinking a Vampire's blood wasn't enough. It likely made them sick if it didn't kill them. They were too tiny to process that kind of magic. At least he was spared that fate.

Before his thoughts wandered any farther, he sharpened his attention on the Gravewalker. "What did I miss?"

Wyatt tipped his hat. "Well, the war just ended."

"What war?" Christian gripped the edge of the coffin, deciding what he needed to perk him right up. "Can you spare a pint?"

Wyatt backed up. "I hope you mean beer."

Christian's fangs punched out.

"Remember your promise. It doesn't include sucking on my neck."

"I'll pay extra."

"I'll pass."

If he didn't get a few drops of blood in him soon, he'd go mad. Then a hot bath, a change of clothes, and a place to stay. He didn't own property in town and only rented. All his things would be gone. Perhaps for the better. Maybe he could build a small place in the woods, somewhere to hide out for a while.

"Bring me someone. I'll erase their memories afterward."

"That's a therapy session I ain't got time for. Look, if you sit tight for a little while, I can hunt down a squirrel."

"Over my rotting corpse."

Wyatt shrugged. "Suit yourself." He flicked a business card to the ground. "Send me a decent cut for saving your life. I don't care who you are or why you were down there. Not my business. Just send me a little dough and we'll be even-steven. If you can't do that, send a few customers my way on referral."

Christian reflexively reached up and caught something else the Gravewalker threw at him. He held the package of spearmint gum beneath his nose and drew in a deep breath. His mouth watered, and when he licked his lips, they were as cracked as the mud beneath a dried-up lake.

The man gave him a lopsided grin as he unwrapped a piece. "Thought you could use a breath freshener. See you round, Christian Poe. Don't make me regret digging you up." Then he flicked the gum wrapper to the ground and strolled off, whistling an unfamiliar tune.

Christian rubbed his hand over the rip in his coat where the stake had gone through. A thought occurred to him, and he reached inside his jacket and fished out the ruby necklace. Though the chain had broken, the stone was whole and perfectly intact. His blood had dried around it, creating a thin shell. No matter. Now it was nothing more than a trinket.

"Weren't you a heap of trouble?" he muttered. He checked his other pocket to make sure there weren't any holes and dropped the large stone inside.

It still held monetary value but not sentimental. Now his heart had grown just as stony and cold. Anger no longer consumed him. He wanted to make good on the vow he'd made himself many years ago that he'd do something worthwhile with his life—take a job that would make up for all the innocent lives he'd taken. Maybe a guard.

Christian got up and stepped out of the coffin. The laces on his shoes were still tied. Once he worked out all the kinks in his joints, he gave the coffin a solid kick, splitting the rotted wood. "I'm doing it all different this time. Feck all the games. I'll not change for anyone. If people can't handle a healthy dose of humor and rugged good looks, they can kiss my petrified arse."

It felt good to hear his voice again. Somehow it validated his existence. He picked up the gum wrapper the Gravewalker had discarded and tucked it inside his pocket. "Manners like a pig," he muttered under his breath.

Christian staggered through the graveyard, squinting from the brilliant moonlight. Had it always been this bright? At least they hadn't dug him up in the daytime. Walking felt wonderful and awful all at once, like he was a rusty machine forced to move without any oil.

Once he located the dirt road, he followed it while singing as loudly as a drunken fool. The intoxicating beauty of the night awakened his soul. The sound of his footsteps and his breath, the feel of warm drizzle on his face, night creatures fleeing at the sight of him.

Ten long years. Had the world changed much? Fashion hadn't made any significant strides by the looks of the men.

As a Vampire, Christian didn't fret over his situation. Once he got a pint of the red to fully heal, he would charm a fool for a place to stay and pocket cash—enough to get on his feet. Then he could find a job and sort out his life. Start over.

When he reached another road, he turned right, uncertain if it led toward or away from Cognito. Was Lenore still there, or had she moved on? She'd once told him it wasn't good to remain in one place for more than fifty years. Would she recognize him? Did he even care anymore?

No. He sure as shite didn't.

A car horn blared from behind. Christian pivoted around and shielded his eyes from the blinding headlights. When the large vehicle rolled to a stop, he approached the driver's side.

A man with piercing blue eyes gave him an appraising look. He had a stern expression, and by the size of his broad shoulders looked like a man who could take care of himself. Christian assessed the stranger as quickly as he could. The fedora covered his hair, and he was nicely dressed. No wedding ring. A second later, he felt it—the energy. It flared off the Mage as he must have been testing Christian to find out if he was Breed. Energy didn't affect him, but it made his hair stand on end.

"Where did you crawl out of?" the driver asked, his voice a pleasant baritone.

Christian rested his hand on the hood and grinned, revealing his fangs. "Nineteen thirty-five." He gave the car a light tap. "She's a dandy."

The man frowned. "It's a Chevrolet. The war put a wrench in car production. I might take a trip to Europe soon and see what's going on over there. I want something smaller and flashier. This thing is too big for me."

Christian gave a crooked smile. "I wager that's what my ex said. You wouldn't happen to have any room in there for a passenger now, would you? Promise I won't bite."

The man raised his eyebrow but kept his gaze low. "I only pulled over because I thought you were a human. I don't make a point of picking up strays."

"If I wanted you dead, we wouldn't be having this conversation. But seeing as you've generously donated your time to hear my plight, I've spent ten years in a pine box, and I think there's still a beetle in my beard. I have no idea where I am and no idea where I'm going. I'd feel more myself again if I had a pint of the red, but instead of ripping your throat out, I'm standing in the rain, asking for a lift."

"We're thirty minutes out of town. That's a long drive. Vampires don't have self-control," he replied matter-of-factly.

"What you know about Vampires could fill a thimble." Christian dusted off his damp jacket. "For your information, I've been exercising self-control for the past decade."

"By choice?" The man tapped his fingers on the side of the car. "Get in. But let me warn you: I have friends in high places. If anything happens, they'll track you down. I've also got a stake, and if you so much as look at me funny, I'll bury it so deep that even archaeologists won't find it."

"Nothing warms the cockles of my heart like a threat." Christian strolled around to the other side and got in. The interior smelled like expensive cologne. "What brings you out this way?"

The Mage chuckled. "Destiny. Where are you headed?"

"Wherever the fates allow." Christian opened a piece of gum, and the moment he put the stick in his mouth, he nearly died from the flavor bursting on his tongue. He moaned and then offered the pack to the stranger. "Gum?"

The man wrinkled his nose. "How long has that been in your pocket?"

Christian laughed darkly. "Is alcohol still legal, or did they take it off the market again? I could use a bottle or two of good whiskey."

"You could use a bath. And if your toenails look anything like your fingernails, you might want to give them a trim. No broad will talk to you with a beard like that."

Christian stroked his long beard. "I don't know. It's kind of growing on me."

"Literally." The man belted out a laugh as he put the car in drive. "What kind of work do you do?"

Christian gave it a thought. "A personal guard would be up my alley, but I'll work in a Breed jail if I have to."

"Do you have any experience?"

Christian thought about the list of people he'd killed. Protecting a man couldn't be anywhere near as difficult as killing one. Given his experience, he'd do whatever was necessary without hesitation. His days of pretending to be an aristocrat were over. "I've got more experience than I'd care to admit. If you know anyone looking, I'd appreciate the favor."

The man stared pensively at the road. "It just so happens I might be in the market for a personal guard. I've been having trouble with a local gang, and now they're trying to take me down."

"Then I'm your man."

The Mage gave a tight-lipped smile and inclined his head. "I'm Justus De Gradi."

"Christian. Christian Poe."

Explore more by Dannika Dark

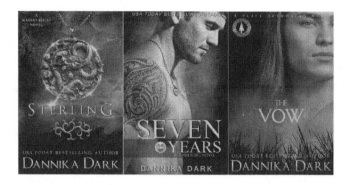

THE MAGERI SERIES:

Urban fantasy. When a young woman unwittingly receives the gift of immortality from a Mage, she must leave everything behind. But her conviction is put to the ultimate test when she falls for her mortal enemy. Passionate, dark, and full of unpredictable twists, the Mageri series will take you on an unforgettable journey of love, friendship, and the hidden power within us all. Cliff-hanger-free.

THE SEVEN SERIES:

Paranormal romance. Austin Cole and his brothers are forming a pack, and the last thing on their minds is getting tethered to a mate. But the more they resist, the harder they fall. A series about brotherhood, family, second chances, and finding that person who completes you. Cliff-hanger-free. HEA in each book.

THE BLACK ARROWHEAD SERIES:

Paranormal romance. Some of the kids from the Seven series are all grown up. New friends and old unite, overcoming all odds to leave their mark in this world. Brave women, fiercely loyal men, and plenty of twists will leave you on the edge of your seat in this action-packed series destined to become a top-shelf favorite.

Note: While all of Dannika's books are written in the same universe, each series can be read independently from the rest. Dannika Dark owns the intellectual property rights to some of the original Breeds depicted within these books. Use of these creations is strictly prohibited.

If you would like to experience each twist and crossover as it was intended, suggested reading order can be found at dannikadark.net

Immortals live among us.

Made in the USA
Columbia, SC
26 December 2024

50639858R00312